EMERGING
PRACTICES
IN
MATHEMATICS
EDUCATION

EMERGING
PRACTICES

IN

MATHEMATICS
EDUCATION

Twenty-Second Yearbook

THE NATIONAL COUNCIL OF TEACHERS
OF MATHEMATICS

WASHINGTON, D. C.   1954

Manufactured in the United States of America

Preface

IN DECEMBER 1951 the Yearbook Planning Committee of the National Council of Teachers of Mathematics met with 20-some selected members of the National Council in New York City to discuss long-term planning of yearbooks. Among other proposed themes for yearbooks was that of this Twenty-Second Yearbook, EMERGING PRACTICES IN MATHEMATICS EDUCATION. In April 1952 the Yearbook Planning Committee of the Council published in *The Mathematics Teacher* the following announcement of its plan for the Twenty-Second Yearbook:

Upon recommendation by the Yearbook Planning Committee, the Board of Directors of the National Council of Teachers of Mathematics has voted to publish a yearbook on the subject of EMERGING PRACTICES IN MATHEMATICS EDUCATION. In the preparation of the Yearbook, the Committee will be assisted by John R. Clark of Teachers College, Columbia University, a former editor of *The Mathematics Teacher*.

Emerging practices, whether in the elementary school, secondary school, or teacher education, are innovations which challenge the so-called standard, conventional approved practices. Emerging practices may or may not obtain wide acceptance in the near future. The Committee believes, however, that teachers generally are vitally interested in knowing about the work of those teachers who are experimenting with new subject matter, new organizations of old subject matter, new teaching procedures, new techniques of evaluation, new approaches in teacher education (preservice or inservice), new aids to learning, or new theories of learning.

We invite you to help us find teachers who are employing new, promising approaches to problems in mathematics education.

The following is a partial list of practices or areas of experimentation which have been suggested to the Yearbook Planning Committee as being appropriate for the Yearbook: (a) Mathematics in the core program; (b) A four-year nonacademic curriculum for the high school; (c) Approximate computation in Grades VII and VIII; (d) A background course in arithmetic for teachers in elementary schools; (e) New approaches to long division (f) Nongeometric originals in demonstrative geometry—more or fewer?; (g) A concept approach to algebra; (h) Mental arithmetic in the elementary school; (i) An arithmetic clinic; (j) Subgrouping within a class; (k) The mathematics curriculum of a small high school; (l) Teacher and pupil-made learning aids; (m) New

v

proposals for organizing the content of academic courses in mathematics; (n) Experience with concept tests in arithmetic; (o) Using "Group-process" in teaching mathematics; (p) A self-selected curriculum in arithmetic; (q) A workshop institute for teachers of mathematics; (r) A high-school course in arithmetic; (s) Using history of mathematics in teaching secondary-school mathematics; (t) Statistics needed by the high school pupils; (u) Using films and filmstrips in teaching; (v) Teaching space-perception—a new approach; (w) Choosing applications to fit pupil needs.

This list of topics is included to suggest the wide range and variety of the aspects of mathematics education. To date, no topics or contributors have been selected.

The Yearbook Planning Committee urges the members of the Council to co-operate in identifying potential contributors to the Yearbook. On a 2-cent postcard, addressed to John R. Clark, Teachers College, Columbia University, New York 27, N. Y., comment upon any practice (giving the name and address of the practitioner) which you think worthy of consideration for inclusion in the Yearbook. PLEASE DO IT NOW.

Shortly thereafter the Board of Directors of the National Council asked the writer to become the Editor, and to choose a Planning Committee to co-operate with him in the preparation of this Yearbook. The writer fortunately was able to enlist the co-operation of John Kinsella, Joy E. Mahachek, Philip Peak, and Veryl Schult who have actively and efficiently worked with him in the planning and publication of this volume.

The Planning Committee of the Twenty-Second Yearbook has had the able assistance of three members of the Yearbook Committee of the National Council, Frank Lankford, D. W. Snader, and F. L. Wren. Throughout its work the Planning Committee has enjoyed the co-operation of John R. Mayor, the President of the National Council.

The response of members of the National Council to the announcement in *The Mathematics Teacher* was encouraging. Many persons volunteered to contribute. Others expressed their belief in the timeliness of the theme. At its first meeting, in Philadelphia in 1952, the Planning Committee realized that it would be unable to organize a yearbook using only the titles proposed by volunteer contributors. The Committee then agreed that the Yearbook should be built around or organized about the following categories of emerging practices:

PART ONE. Various Provisions for Differentiated Mathematics Curriculums

PART TWO. Laboratory Teaching in Mathematics

PART THREE. Teacher Education

PART FOUR. New Emphases in Subject Matter

PART FIVE. The Evaluation of Mathematical Learning.

The Planning Committee then sought a group of contributors who, together with the volunteer group, would undertake contributions to implement the above plan. This, then, is a sketch of the evolution of the Twenty-Second Yearbook.

From the beginning the Planning Committee has been enthusiastic about the value to the profession of descriptions of these emerging practices. It confidently hopes that the reader of this Yearbook will be stimulated to search for better procedures for attaining the objectives which our profession holds to be valid.

JOHN R. CLARK, *Editor*

Contents

PART ONE

VARIOUS PROVISIONS FOR DIFFERENTIATED MATHEMATICS
CURRICULUMS

PART TWO

LABORATORY TEACHING IN MATHEMATICS

CONTENTS

PART THREE

TEACHER EDUCATION

CONTENTS

PART FOUR

New Emphases in Subject Matter

CONTENTS

PART FIVE

THE EVALUATION OF MATHEMATICAL LEARNING

PART SIX

BIBLIOGRAPHY OF "WHAT IS GOING ON IN YOUR SCHOOLS?"—
1950–1953

J. A. Brown, Wisconsin High School, Madison, Wisconsin and J. R. Mayor, University of Wisconsin, Madison, Wisconsin

SELECTED REFERENCES

PART ONE

Various Provisions for Differentiated Mathematics Curriculums

Introduction

FROM time immemorial man has known that individuals differ, and yet many of the activities of our society have been patterned with the expressed purpose of making these differences as insignificant as possible. At one time it was felt this could best be accomplished by providing exactly the same experiences for all. However, after some time it was realized that this method involved the impossible assumption that all organisms start out with equal characteristics; consequently, the more recent approach is to tailor the experiences so they may more nearly fit the inherent characteristics of the individual.

This section of the Yearbook concerns itself with some of the methods which are now in use to provide that wide variety of experience which is required to fit the needs of all the pupils. You will find in the following pages practices which range in adaptability from the small high school of less than 100 pupils to the large high school of several thousand students. The material presented is not intended to exhaust the practices which may be in use, but it is presented only because such practices are in use and have been found to operate successfully in the various situations.

The contributions have been classified into five sections. This arrangement places before the reader an organized body of information he can use more efficiently. By the very nature of the teaching profession there is certain to be some overlapping between the sections. The five sections are:

SECTION 1. Providing differentiated curriculums through a new organization of content.

SECTION 2. Providing differentiated curriculums in schools where homogeneous grouping is feasible.

SECTION 3. Providing differentiated curriculums in schools where homogeneous grouping is not feasible.

SECTION 4. Differentiated curriculums resulting from pupil, parent, teacher, and community planning.
SECTION 5. Guidance for the optimum use of differentiated curriculums.

The contributors to each of the five sections have related the practices which they are using or with which they are familiar, consequently the total story must be told in each case even though part of it may represent a topic which rightly should appear in a different section.

As you read these articles you will find in them a picture of emerging practices as they pertain to the mathematics curriculums in our public schools. You will also find many suggestions and ideas you may wish to try out along with those you are already using successfully in your own classes.

P. P.

1

Providing a Differentiated Curriculum Through a New Organization of Content

An Emerging Mathematics Curriculum

CHARLOTTE CARLTON

BECAUSE of the many changes continually taking place in the economic, political, industrial, and social life of our nation, our educational program cannot remain static. Our schools must accept the challenge of growth and progress by providing the curriculums which will aid the students in adjusting to the changes affecting their lives.

The leaders in the teaching of mathematics have not failed to consider the need for change in the offerings of courses in their field. At the turn of the 20th Century, possibly earlier, some of the leaders recognized that the secondary curriculum composed only of the traditional courses of algebra, geometry, and trigonometry was far separated from the mathematical needs of many of the pupils. In E. H. Moore's famous presidential address given before The American Mathematical Society in 1902 he argued that the traditional compartmental organization of mathematics should be abandoned; he advocated a closer correlation between the different branches of mathematics.

In an effort to put into practice the ideas which Dr. Moore presented and to meet the needs of more of the pupils a course, general mathematics for Grade IX, was added to the then existing curriculum. The idea of general mathematics was excellent but the course has not proved as successful as hoped, partly for the following reasons:

1. Oversocialization of content to the extent of neglecting the emphasis on basic mathematical concepts and principles.
2. Overcrowding the course with ideas, in the belief that this would be the terminal mathematics course for many boys and girls.
3. Labeling the course as one for weak students.
4. Lack of preparation and poor attitude of those required to teach the course.

During the past decade the fact that further change in the mathematics curriculum was necessary was made very clear in the following circumstances:

1. The small fraction of the student body continuing mathematics beyond Grade IX.
2. The large number of boys entering the service during World War II with lack of understanding of mathematics.
3. The many young employees of business and industry who were found to be weak in the basic fundamentals of mathematics.

Many of the boys and girls going from high school into business, industry, and the armed forces had not studied any mathematics since they had completed the general mathematics course in the ninth grade. Possibly the only other courses being offered were algebra, geometry, and trigonometry which, as they were being taught, did not satisfy the needs and receive the interest of the majority of the pupils.

The mathematics teachers of Florida not only recognized this important problem but they worked together to find a solution. The Florida State Department of Education made it possible for a group of 36 carefully selected teachers to meet for a workshop at the University of Florida in the summers of 1948 and 1949. The participants brought ideas gathered from experiences in many different counties of the state, from both the large and the small high schools. Under the able and enthusiastic leadership of William A. Gager these teachers revised the secondary-mathematics curriculum of the state and prepared materials in line with the revision. The program which they developed was adopted by the State Department of Education and published in Bulletin No. 36, *Functional Mathematics in the Secondary Schools.*

The revised mathematics curriculum of the state includes, in addition to the traditional courses, a sequence of mathematically sound and functionally worthwhile courses for Grade VII through Grade XII. Functional mathematics for Grade VII through Grade XII comprises the main track of the curriculum, with a sidetrack of traditional courses, Algebra 1, Plane Geometry, Algebra 2, Trigonometry and Solid Geometry, from Grade IX through Grade XII.

All of the boys and girls of Grade VII and Grade VIII take the courses in functional mathematics. At the beginning of the ninth grade the students choose the course, functional Mathematics 9 or Algebra 1, on the basis of their need for mathematics. Those students who plan to enter the field of engineering or some scientific work for which extensive drill in mathematical techniques is necessary might choose the traditional courses. The majority of the students, those who need mathematics for general education, will elect the functional mathematics courses. It must be emphasized that both of these tracks are mathematically strong, and the choice should be based entirely on the *purpose* for which the student is taking mathematics.

The teachers who revised the curriculum recommended that students who elect functional mathematics be encouraged to take at least two years—Mathematics 9 and 10. These courses should prove so interesting and valuable to the students that many will choose to continue them through Grade XII. However, if a student should select only one course after Mathematics 9 and 10, he should be advised to take Mathematics 11. If after two years of functional mathematics the student should change his plans for the future and should feel the need for some traditional courses in preparation for specialized work, he should be allowed to take Algebra 2, Trigonometry, and Solid Geometry.

For the small high school where the number of students taking mathematics does not warrant a double-track program the workshop group recommended the functional mathematics courses. They felt these would better serve the majority of the boys and girls than would the traditional courses. At the same time the functional courses could provide adequate training for the few who wished to continue in specialized fields.

These functional courses of the main track offer mathematics which has meaning for the student, which meets his present needs, and which he can be made to realize will meet some future need. They are courses designed to provide experiences which are mathematically sound, functionally worthwhile, personally satisfying, and socially significant. They are courses planned toward the goal of making the student mathematically competent so that he may successfully take his place in society and make a worthwhile contribution as a citizen.

The entire functional program centers around the development of an understanding of the basic mathematical concepts and principles. Since these concepts and principles form the thread which runs through all branches of mathematics, they are the force which is used to unite the different branches in a single course—functional mathematics. Arithmetic, algebra, geometry, and trigonometry are taken out of their watertight compartments and the fundamental and working ideas of each become an integral part of the functional mathematics courses.

Realizing that mathematics cannot be meaningful and function in the life of the individual if he does not have a clear understanding of the concepts upon which the processes are dependent, the teachers who were building the functional program used the basic mathematical concepts as the foundation of the structure. After much discussion and work, 61 concepts were agreed upon as being basic. These concepts may be classified under the following broad headings:

1. Concepts of Number
2. Concepts Basic to Operations
3. Concepts of Per cent and Percentage
4. Concepts Basic to Measurement
5. Concepts of Measurement
6. Concepts of Functional Relationship
7. Concepts of Comparison
8. Concept of Locus.

The next step in constructing the program was the decision as to the grades in which the development of these concepts should take place. It was agreed that the whole story of any one concept should not be attempted in any one grade, but that after the concept had been introduced there should be a continued unfolding of the concept through each of the succeeding grades. For example, consider some of the concepts of number and the grades in which the development of these is placed. The concepts of integer, common fraction, decimal fraction, approximate numbers, exact numbers should be developed through Grades VII–XII; literal numbers and directed numbers should be taught through Grades VIII–XII; rational and irrational numbers through Grades IX–XII; imaginary numbers through Grades X–XII.

If the concepts are to function, the student must also have an understanding of the basic mathematical principles. These principles are what give him a *reason* for performing a task in a certain way. In the functional courses constant emphasis is placed on the following and other basic principles in order that the processes may be meaningful rather than mechanical. As a result the student has a satisfying experience in solving problems.

1. Only like quantities may be combined by addition or subtraction.

2. The numerator and denominator of a fraction may be multiplied by the same number (except zero) without changing the value of the fraction.

3. The position of the digits in a number determines the value of the number.

4. Whatever operation you perform on one side of an equation you must perform on the other side in order to maintain the equality.

In the functional mathematics curriculum the student has little opportunity to forget the concepts and principles learned in a previous grade. These mathematics courses provide for spiral learning, repetition of the concepts and principles within each grade and from one grade to another. Concepts whose development is begun in Grade VII continue to unfold in materials suitable for Grade VIII, with growth in understanding of these concepts in each grade through Grade XII. This treatment is not through drill but through their use in materials which are different, more advanced in nature, and selected to meet the interest, learning readiness, and age level of the group. For example, consider the concept of per cent and the way the concept is applied in different situations from one grade to another:

Grade VII: The concept of per cent is used in finding simple interest, simple discounts, and commission.

Grade VIII: The concept of per cent is broadened by use in finding the rate of simple interest, rate of increase and decrease, rate of discount, and in figuring city and county taxes.

Grade IX: The same concept is applied in problems relating to city, county and state budgets, to state taxes, and to fire insurance.

Grade X: The use of per cent is extended to finding the rate of interest on installment purchases, to investments bearing compound interest, to federal taxes, and to life insurance.

Grade XI: Per cent is used in problems of taxes of a small business, of insurance of employees, of depreciation of automobiles, buildings, and equipment.

Grade XII: Per cent is used in problems of mortgages on real estate, of borrowing money from a bank, from small loan companies, and from credit unions, of compound interest in connection with annuities.

The content of the functional mathematics courses is so planned that each idea is taught when there is a need for the understanding and use of that topic or method. For example, when it is found that a particular quadratic equation cannot be factored, there is a reason to find a method by which any quadratic equation can be solved; thus attention is given to the quadratic formula. When it is found that the discriminant of the quadratic formula is not always rational, there is a reason to learn to find the approximate square root. The different topics are not taught as separate ideas but they are closely related and connected with ideas previously studied or developed.

The materials suggested for the functional mathematics courses involve applications in various fields of endeavor. The relation of mathematics to economics, to science, to industry, to engineering, to music, to art is emphasized. Considering the learning process to be the interaction of the personality of the student with his total environment, applications within the interest and understanding of the student are used. The student is led to realize the many uses of mathematics in specific ways so that he may make the transfer of his mathematical training to situations outside the classroom.

The functional mathematics courses are developed with the philosophy that the student learns best by doing and remembers longest those things which he discovers for himself. Experiments, investigations, reports, and projects are essential parts of these mathematics courses which are meaningful and functional. The student is challenged to think and to discover mathematical truths and relationships for himself. For example, by experiments and planned activities the student is guided step by step to reach such generalizations as the following:

Two triangles are congruent if three sides of one are equal respectively to three sides of the other.

The ratio of the areas of two similar polygons equals the ratio of the squares of the corresponding sides.

To add two negative numbers, find the sum of their absolute values and prefix a minus sign.

The courses of the functional mathematics program may be summarized in statement of their objectives as follows:

1. To give the students a workable understanding of mathematics through interrelation of the basic ideas of arithmetic, algebra, geometry, and trigonometry.

2. To make the mathematical processes meaningful rather than mechanical by constant emphasis on the basic mathematical principles.

3. To strengthen and enlarge the understanding of the basic mathematical concepts through repetition and application in new situations.

4. To aid the student in the transfer of training in mathematics to the solution of problems which he meets now or will face later in life.

5. To encourage students to think and to discover mathematical relationships for themselves.

6. To create a sense of appreciation of the great importance of mathematics in the world of today and of its contribution in the development of civilization.

7. To develop ability to reason logically and to think critically in nonmathematical as well as in mathematical situations.

8. To help each student to attain the level of mathematical competence which he needs to deal successfully with the problems of everyday affairs.

9. To provide a rich background for further mathematical and scientific training.

As mathematics courses filled with interest, activity, and understanding are offered in the secondary-school curriculums, more students are choosing to continue mathematics beyond Grade IX. Because of the nature of these courses surely the students will attain that mathematical competence expected of today's high-school graduates.

The teachers of Florida are happy to share with others their solution to the problem of providing a mathematics curriculum which is closely related to the needs and interests of the boys and girls in the secondary schools.

A Curriculum Development to Capitalize on the Interrelationships of the Many Areas of Mathematics

William Holt Glenn

For the past four years teachers in the Pasadena City Schools have been considering together a major revision of the secondary-mathematics curriculum. This report is mainly concerned with two large aspects of the problem: (a) the technical details of how the project was organized and carried forward and (b) some illustrative examples of material developed for classroom use.

In the summer of 1949 one of the members from the teaching staff in Pasadena attended the summer conference of the National Council of Teachers of Mathematics at Denver, Colorado. The reporting of this conference to the secondary-mathematics teachers in Pasadena resulted in the desire of the group to study the content of our mathematics curriculum with the objective in mind to break down the rather rigid compartmentalizing of mathematics as it has been traditionally taught. There had been a long-felt need for a more complete integration of the areas of arithmetic, algebra, geometry, trigonometry, solid geometry, analytic geometry, and calculus.

A number of years prior to this time a group of teachers of the analytic geometry and calculus classes had developed an integrated program of analytic geometry with differential and integral calculus. This was so successful that they felt something similar to this was definitely in order for the subjects below this level.

In the fall of 1949, therefore, it was decided to establish a number of Curriculum Content Committees, as well as a number of Problem Committees, to revise the mathematics curriculum from Grade VII through Grade XIV. The Steering Committee consisted of persons representing all levels of instruction, as well as co-ordinators from the central administration.

There were four Curriculum Content Committees, as follows:

1. Content for Grades VII and VIII
2. Content for Grades IX and X
3. Content for Grades XI and XII
4. Content for Grades XIII and XIV.

There were five Problem Committees organized under the subject headings of:

1. Physics, Chemistry, General Science, and Geology
2. Shops and Trades
3. Astronomy, Optics, Navigation, and Surveying
4. Meteorology
5. Sports.

The members of the Problem Committees were asked to make lists of practical problems in their respective fields and to submit them to the Curriculum Content Committees. As the individual committees submitted their materials to the Steering Committee the information was mimeographed and distributed to all other committees, so that there was an interchange of ideas. During this first year there were six general meetings to which all secondary-mathematics teachers were invited to hear committee reports and to offer further suggestions.

At the beginning of the school year 1950–51 it was decided to take the findings of these committees and to develop textbook material, since teachers felt that there was no single textbook which was adequately meeting the type of organization desired. The group decided that the greatest need for revision was at Grade IX and Grade X, and it was proposed to start the writing of these materials first. Four persons volunteered their services as authors. One was a central office co-ordinator in the fields of science, mathematics, and homemaking; the other three were teachers in the schools, two from one of the junior colleges and one from a junior high school. The central office co-ordinator agreed to write the general descriptive material and to do the editing, while the other three submitted problem material. This procedure was followed in the main for the first volume, with the exception of some specific sections. However, for the second volume one of the instructors wrote the main portions with suggestions from the other three.

Approval of this writing project was obtained shortly after the appointment of the new acting superintendent. Released time was granted the three teachers from their teaching assignments, in the amount of an average of five hours per week for both school years 1950–51 and 1951–52.

Two professors of the University of California at Los Angeles agreed to serve as consultants. One is a professor of mathematics and the other a professor of education responsible for the training of mathematics teachers. On two occasions they met with all the secondary-mathematics teachers in Pasadena and offered many valuable suggestions. Other assistance was given by means of correspondence or meetings with the four authors.

Early in 1951 the authors had completed about one-half of the first semester of Grade IX and had submitted the material to all secondary-mathematics teachers for their suggestions. During this time the material was used in mimeographed form in three classes at Pasadena City College, which includes Grade XI through Grade XIV. On the basis of suggestions of teachers, both those using the material in their classes, as well as others, this material was revised and used in five classes at Pasadena City College in the fall of 1951. As the year proceeded additional revisions were made in the ninth grade material and the writing of the tenth grade text commenced. Another revision of the ninth grade material was made for use in all algebra classes at the Pasadena City College in the fall of 1952. Also, the tenth grade text was completed during the summer of 1952 and made available for use in all classes where the students had had previous instruction in the integrated ninth grade course. A revision of the first half of the geometry was made in time to use with new classes starting in the spring of 1953.

A few additional statistics may be of some interest. A total of 13 teachers were involved in the actual classroom use of the materials, and from 1951 through 1953 there were 436 students in algebra and 444 students in geometry who used this material exclusively.

It should be noted that students using the material were those who, for one reason or another, postponed taking algebra and geometry until the eleventh or twelfth grade. It would have been desirable to use it also with the students of Grade IX and Grade X, but because of the numbers involved, it was agreed to carry the experiment forward with the smaller group only.

In the fall of 1952 meetings were held at regular intervals in all seven junior high schools (Grade VII through Grade X) with algebra and geometry teachers, in order to obtain further reactions and suggestions for revision. Through this process teachers became better acquainted with the material and also gave the authors valuable assistance in improving the content.

The following are some examples of problem material used in Grade IX and Grade X courses to aid in unifying the program:

1. The topic of *exponents* is first introduced with a discussion of areas and volumes. The area formula for a rectangle is compared to that of a square. Instead of writing the area of a square as $A = SS$, which is similar in appearance to $A = LW$, the student is introduced to the new notation, $A = S^2$. In a similar manner the formula for the volume of a cube is written $V = S^3$, instead of $V = SSS$.

Multiplying or dividing by powers of 10 offers an opportunity to review the principles of the number system with particular emphasis on place value.

Closely allied to this is the use of the standard notation of writing numbers such as

$$.000268 = 2.68 \times 10^{-4} \quad \text{or} \quad 154000 = 1.54 \times 10^{5}.$$

Astronomical distances or dimensions of atomic particles dramatically illustrate the usefulness of this notation. It also lends itself readily to estimating answers to problems involving several products and quotients such as

$$\frac{(.00042)(8720)(765000)}{3,740,000}$$

This can be written as

$$\frac{(4.2 \times 10^{-4})(8.72 \times 10^{3})(7.65 \times 10^{5})}{3.74 \times 10^{6}}$$

and, as an approximation, this is

$$\frac{(4)(9)(8)}{4}\ (10^{-4})(10^{3})(10^{5})(10^{-6})$$

which reduces to 72×10^{-2} or .72. Slide rule computation gives a result of .75.

Exponents are also used effectively by introducing the metric system to show how powers of 10 simplify the relationships of the metric units compared to the more complex English system. Applications to areas and volumes make the simplicity of the metric system even more striking.

Thus exponents are not exclusively used in literal algebraic expressions but there is a definite connection between arithmetic and algebra and a direct utilization of geometric figures for applications.

2. Another topic is *percentage*, which is reintroduced through the many formulas involving percentage. Estimating answers suggests the study of percentage error. Mixture problems require typical algebraic equations which require an understanding of percentage.

Geometry has much to offer in picturing percentage as a ratio. It is suggested to teachers that they use a meter stick to represent the 100 per cent scale. A one-to-one correspondence, set up between any other scale and the meter stick when the two scales are parallel to one another, results in a visual aid based on similar figures. Equating the ratios of corresponding parts of the similar figures leads to the proportion that will solve any type of percentage problem.

3. Geometric representations of *algebraic expressions* can often be found which will point up the necessity for each term that appears in the expression. For example the expansion of $(a + b)^3$ can be visualized by the use of solid blocks. This can be accomplished by having one block of volume a^3; three blocks of volume a^2b; three blocks of volume ab^2; and one block of volume b^3. When these blocks are assembled properly they form a block of volume $(a + b)^3$. Thus the identity $(a + b)^3 = a^3 + 3a^2b + 3ab^2 + b^3$ is verified by a geometric model.

4. *Ratios* of corresponding lines, areas, and volumes of similar figures lead to important generalizations. It is suggested that students first construct similar figures and measure the lengths of corresponding sides. They might also compute areas of faces, and volumes of solid portions. By taking ratios of corresponding parts they might discover for themselves that the ratios of corresponding line segments are equal, or that corresponding areas are in the same ratio as the squares of the corresponding lengths, or that corresponding volumes are in the same ratio as the

cubes of the corresponding lengths. These proportions offer a wealth of problem material in which any three members of the proportion may be given and the fourth member solved.

5. The subject of *graphs* is important and can be treated in an integrated manner by considering four major aspects of dealing with data: (a) organizing data in tabular form, (b) graphing the data, (c) considering how the data might be discussed or summarized in a verbal statement, and (d) representing the data by a formula, where this is possible.

6. The work with similar figures leads naturally to a special study of right triangles and the use that can be made of *trigonometric functions* to solve triangles. A project recommended to students is to draw a series of right triangles with acute angles of 10°, 20°, 30°, $\cdots$, and 80°. Then by measuring the sides of each right triangle and computing all possible ratios, they can organize the data to see if conclusions can be drawn. Here is an excellent example of the interrelationship of arithmetic, algebra, geometry, and trigonometry.

7. The *Pythagorean Theorem* can be proved in many ways but one that has much appeal utilizes a combination of algebra and geometry.

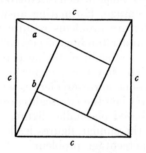

Suppose that the right triangle has legs of lengths a and b and an hypotenuse c. Cut out four of these right triangles and place them in a way that forms a large square of side c. The total area is c^2 and this is made up of 4 triangles, each with an area of $(\frac{1}{2}ab)$ and an inner square of area $(b - a)^2$. Thus equating the areas gives

$$c^2 = 4(\tfrac{1}{2}ab) + (b - a)^2$$

which reduces to the desired result

$$c^2 = a^2 + b^2.$$

8. The organization of a formal *geometric proof* is not introduced until Grade X although algebraic proofs such as the one above are given in the ninth grade work. In Grade X an appeal is made to analyze the kind of logical thinking that should be done in dealing with problems in everyday affairs. The student is urged to discover what assumptions and definitions are used and agreed upon; what facts are known; and what

conclusions are reached. In case more than one conclusion is reached, the students are urged to see if the reasons for differing opinions can be discovered. Differences may be due to different assumptions, definitions, or sets of facts. The students try their skill in dealing with everyday problems while they learn to apply this technique to the more well-defined geometric proofs.

9. In Grade IX the Pythagorean Theorem introduces the topic of square root and the student solves equations of the form $x^2 = n$. It is not until Grade X, however, that the general case of the *quadratic equation* arises through such applications as mean proportion relations in right triangles where an altitude is drawn from the right angle to the hypotenuse, and circle-chord-tangent-secant relations.

10. After properties of *parallelograms* are established by geometric proofs, there is an excellent opportunity to use scale drawings and solve practical problems of parallelogram of forces including some of those in basic air navigation.

11. Introducing the principles of *logarithms* in Grade X enables the student to review the concepts of exponents and to solve trigonometric problems by the use of logarithms. A knowledge of this tool leads naturally into the use of the slide rule to solve simple proportions.

In summary it can be stated that this project has served several useful functions:

1. It has brought secondary mathematics teachers together citywide to consider a major revision in the courses.

2. It has caused teachers to examine problems critically to determine whether or not they feel that the problems are meaningful to the students.

3. It has stimulated thinking to see how the various areas of mathematics can be brought together in a functional manner.

4. It has promoted an interest in the cultural value of mathematics through the collecting of historical notes pertinent to the topic at hand.

5. It may offer suggestions to others who are considering curriculum revision.

The Development of a Differentiated Mathematics Curriculum

DALE CARPENTER

THE student body of the present-day high school is a cross section of the youth of this country. Our high schools are no longer college preparatory institutions but have become a basic part of the educational training for all boys and girls who wish to use this training.

There is no average boy or girl in the high school. High-school students vary greatly in intelligence, economic background, and vocational interests. One student may need a business emphasis to his mathematics, another an engineering emphasis, and still another a technical, or trade emphasis. In addition to special vocational needs, all students need to be familiar with the mathematics of home measurement and personal and home finance.

We need to analyze and understand the major factors that have a bearing upon the problem of planning, organizing, and operating a program that meets the mathematical needs of all secondary students. Those factors are: (a) purposes and outcomes of instruction, (b) teacher and administration attitudes, (c) administrative problems, (d) agreement upon a differentiated mathematics program, and (e) a plan of administering a differentiated program.

The major purposes and objectives of mathematics instruction must be kept in mind when planning curriculum content, curriculum materials, and when planning daily instruction. *The Guidance Pamphlet in Mathematics*, prepared by the Commission on Post-War Plans, gives us a practical breakdown of the mathematics needed in four major areas. These areas are listed as follows (9):

1. Mathematics for Personal Use
2. Mathematics for Skilled and Semiskilled Workers in Industry and Business
3. Mathematics for College Preparation
4. Mathematics for Professional Workers.

In order to plan an effective mathematics curriculum we must keep in mind the nature of the secondary-school population as well as the specific mathematical objectives which must be met by such a curriculum. The following information assisted us in understanding the nature and the mathematical needs of secondary students.

The personal problems of living are faced by 100 per cent of the high-school graduates. Approximately 15 per cent of the high-school graduates enter college. Of this group less than half receive four or more years of college work. Less than 7 per cent of the labor force in the United States are classified as professional, whereas approximately 60 per cent are industrial workers, skilled and unskilled, and approximately 30 per cent are in commercial occupations. Also we must remember that approximately 40 per cent of the students who enter the ninth grade do not graduate from high school. When considering any secondary curriculum problem we cannot dismiss these drop-outs as unimportant. Many of them leave high school because of lack of interest and failure to see that the high school has anything valuable to offer to them.

Many mathematics teachers believe that arithmetic is an elementary subject, that the main purpose for learning arithmetic is to prepare for algebra, and that the cultural values of mathematics transcend its utilitarian and vocational values. These same teachers are quite apt to lack any background of teacher preparation in the field of arithmetic and therefore do not understand how children learn arithmetic nor how to teach arithmetic.

Many high-school administrators think of mathematics only as a specialty for engineering and science students and of high-school arithmetic as a review or refresher course for poor students. Such administrators are therefore slow in accepting the idea of a complete and well-rounded mathematics program.

Administrative problems such as assignment of teachers to classes, size of classes, and student transfers tend to restrict mathematics curriculums to the so-called standard academic courses. Since many mathematics teachers have little interest in teaching courses other than the traditional ones, administrators often find that it is difficult to assign an interested teacher to any of the so-called nonacademic mathematics classes. Maintaining a minimum class size and teacher load is also an administrative and budgetary problem, particularly in small schools. Therefore administrators tend to frown upon the formation of the nonacademic mathematics classes since multiple-track plans are apt to lower both class size and teacher load. Student transfers further aggravate the problem of running a varied type of mathematics program because of the difficulty of obtaining agreement upon such programs between schools and of placing the student who has transferred in a mathematics class that is comparable to the class in which he was previously enrolled.

Mathematics teachers, administrators, and teacher-training representatives should plan together and reach agreement upon a mathematics program that can meet the varied needs of high-school students and yet is sufficiently flexible to be administered in different geographical locations and in different types of high schools. There have been many plans for a differentiated program developed during the past few years. In fact, a recent nation-wide survey of general mathematics in high school reveals that mathematics curriculums are in a state of unrest and that many schools are planning changes in their mathematics program that they hope will make it more flexible and of greater help to all students.

The new plans for improving mathematics curriculums vary greatly as to organization and content emphases. However, most of these plans have some important characteristics that should be noted here.

First, teachers have participated in formulating the plans and in putting them into effect. This participation helps to insure the success of the plans and helps the teachers to develop a broader attitude toward mathematics education.

Second, the new plans are, in large measure, the result of a new look at the objectives of mathematics education. Although no two groups of teachers will agree wholeheartedly upon the objectives, the curriculum planning that is being done has a remarkable amount of agreement concerning the objectives and place of secondary mathematics in secondary education. The universal activity in planning mathematics programs and the basic agreements upon objectives, may be the direct results of the work of the Commission on Post-War Plans, since it was this group that so clearly stated the major areas of mathematics education and the mathematical needs of each of these areas.

Third, the organization of most of the new plans calls for a greater degree of integration of the basic ideas of secondary mathematics at each level of instruction. Integrated, or unified, secondary mathematics has been successfully taught in many countries other than the United States. Integration of mathematics has been taking place at the college level in the United States. Perhaps one of the most important of the results of the present activity in mathematics planning will be a greater degree of integration of our traditional mathematics courses.

Fourth, another common characteristic of the new plans for mathematics curriculums is the increased emphasis upon the practical uses of mathematics. One of the chief criticisms of formal mathematics has been that it lacked interest because of its formality, dryness, and remoteness from ordinary life experiences. The increased emphasis upon the practical phase of mathematics indicates that many teachers have come to realize that even a mathematics program should be useful and interesting for all high-school students.

The following plan for a differentiated mathematics program shows the basic courses that are, in our opinion, needed for a completely functional curriculum.

A PLAN FOR THE ORGANIZATION OF A DIFFERENTIATED MATHEMATICS PROGRAM

Course	Time	Grade Level
Basic Arithmetic	1 semester	9 to 12
Business Mathematics	1 semester	10 to 12
Mathematics of Personal and Home Finance	1 semester	10 to 12
Industrial Mathematics	4 semesters	9 to 12
College Preparatory; basic integrated mathematics or algebra and geometry	4 semesters	9 to 12
Mathematics-Science Major; basic integrated mathematics or algebra and geometry	4 semesters	9, 10
plus 4 semesters of advanced integrated mathematics	4 semesters	11, 12.

Counselors and mathematics teachers work together so that each pupil will obtain the mathematics education that is best suited to his interests and abilities. The major factors that are considered by the counselor and teacher in determining the mathematical placement of a pupil are mental ability, mathematical achievement, reading achievement, mathematics grades previously received, and teacher judgment.

Mathematics tests have been found helpful when employed as a basic part of the guidance and placement program. However, test results should not be used as the sole means of placing students in appropriate mathematics. Great care is used in the selection of the tests to make sure of their validity for our purposes.

A well-constructed power test in arithmetic is proving to be the most satisfactory type of test for use in placing students in appropriate mathematics classes. Such a test may be constructed by teachers and appropriate standards established for admission to the business mathematics, mathematics of personal and home finance, industrial mathematics, and beginning algebra. Not only is a valid test secured by co-operative teacher efforts, but also in making the tests the participating teachers improve in their understanding of the use of the test in helping pupils to obtain the most suitable mathematics instruction.

Reasonable standards of achievement in arithmetic are maintained not only for admission into the college preparatory course but also for admission into the various types of nonacademic mathematics courses. The basic nonacademic courses will not succeed if they are considered to be dumping grounds for poor pupils. Each of these courses should function by helping students progress toward the specific objectives for which the course was established.

In spite of good counseling, pupils frequently are enrolled in classes for which they are not suited. A flexible system of transfers helps pupils obtain the best instruction for themselves without loss of face or credit. For example, a pupil who is doing failing work in industrial mathematics or beginning algebra is transferred to the basic arithmetic class. Also, if a pupil is doing excellent work in the basic arithmetic class he is often transferred to another mathematics class that is more suited to his needs and ability.

One of the most difficult of the administrative problems relative to any multiple-track plan concerns normal class size and the time continuity of course offerings. We meet this problem by offering some classes in alternate semesters and by combining two small classes under the same teacher for one semester. It should be remembered that it takes more than algebra, geometry, and trigonometry to build a mathematics program and that a complete offering of mathematics courses tends to create interest and to expand the total program. Teachers are willing to do a little extra in order to maintain such a program.

Present-day vocational and home needs in the field of mathematics are so varied and the areas of application so broad that teachers find that it is a necessity to have more than one textbook available if good instruction is to be given to all pupils. Administrator and teacher see to it that several texts varying in difficulty and types of applications are purchased and used in the mathematics classes. The use of supplementary texts is just as desirable in the more orthodox, academic type of mathematics classes as in the other mathematics classes.

Both preservice teacher training and inservice teacher training are of grave concern to administrators and mathematics teachers. Those students who have had primary academic background in mathematics do not necessarily become good secondary-mathematics teachers. In fact, there is good reason to believe that, in many cases, such students are not interested in teaching any courses other than the traditional ones, and tend to belittle all efforts to broaden the teaching of mathematics so as to make it useful to all secondary pupils.

A broad background of college mathematics, methods courses in the teaching of arithmetic and mathematics, courses in related areas of science and engineering, work experience, and inservice training experience will go far in helping a differentiated mathematics program to be successful. With such a background teachers are more apt to realize that their job includes the teaching of all types of mathematics to all types of students.

Any school program, new or old, is subject to evaluation at all times by the public. A school program is evaluated by the administrators and teachers who are responsible for that program.

We believe a mathematics program is subject to continuous evaluation in terms of major objectives of the program. If the purpose of a course is to help students improve in basic arithmetic, then the evaluation of that course is directed toward determining whether or not the pupils have improved in their ability to use arithmetic when faced with problems that involve ideas such as measurement, graphs, money, rate, and percentage. The course is also evaluated in terms of its success in helping pupils to succeed in the other more advanced mathematics courses and in terms of the pupils' success after leaving school.

Courses in industrial mathematics, business mathematics, and academic mathematics are evaluated in a manner similar to that described in the preceding paragraph. Each course contributes toward its avowed objectives and hence is evaluated in terms of those objectives.

In addition to the evaluation of each mathematics course, the entire program of mathematics is evaluated from time to time and any needed changes put into effect. This evaluation is of the same nature as the evaluation for each course that is outlined above. Answers to questions such as the following ones are sought:

1. Do most of the pupils enrolled in each course achieve well in that course?

2. Do all pupils in the high school succeed reasonably well in one or more semesters of mathematics?

3. Are most students interested in their mathematics classes?

4. Is the percentage of failures small?

5. Do the mathematics teachers co-operate in planning the program and in putting it into operation?

6. Does the content of the courses function in the lives of the students after they graduate?

SUMMARY

A successful differentiated mathematics program requires the continuous, co-operative effort of teachers, counselors, and administrators. Reasonable agreements are reached concerning objectives of the program, the place of mathematics in the total school program, policies of teacher assignment and class size, types of courses and content of the courses to be offered, scheduling of classes, testing policies and tests, student transfers, and the manner by which the program is to be evaluated. The teachers co-operatively develop specific courses of study, select materials, and develop suitable tests. The entire program is evaluated from time to time by teachers, administrators, and business, industrial, and PTA representatives. By such continuous and long-range co-operative planning, mathematics teachers and administrators are developing programs that meet mathematical needs of all high-school pupils.

Mathematics for the Consumer

FLORENCE S. MITCHELL
VERYL SCHULT

CAN I AFFORD TO GET MARRIED ON
FORTY DOLLARS A WEEK?

A CLASS in Applied Mathematics at McKinley High School, Washington, D. C., recently included several pupils who were planning to marry as soon as they graduated. A discussion of the units which the class might study during the year brought out the fact that many pupils were interested in the cost of setting up and running a home. "Can I Afford To Get Married on Forty Dollars a Week?" was the title of a unit that was chosen, and interest ran high as plans got under way.

In the planning sessions, the class listed the following expenses to consider: shelter, food, clothing, personal care, transportation, medical care, recreation, donations, and savings. Since the problem was a real one, current, authentic data were needed. A folder was supplied to each pupil who used it to keep the material he collected. At the end of the course, pupils could take their folders home, and many pupils continue to use the materials, especially the budget books.

The first problem that the class considered was job prospects on graduation. Each pupil prepared a personal sheet analyzing the prospects of the jobs for which he could qualify upon graduation, the advantages and disadvantages of such jobs and the probable salary. The sheets closed with these statements:

My estimated monthly basic salary = ?
Social Security, or 2 per cent of my basic salary = ?
Income tax, or 18 per cent of all over $52 per month = ?
Estimated monthly take-home pay. = ?

One pupil wrote: "When I get out of high school, I plan to marry within a few months. My husband will work for the

State Department and will make $3800 a year. I will also work for a while to help out, and I should make at least $35 a week. With these plans in mind, we will have an income of about $110 a week."

Shelter was the first budget item studied. A guide supplied by the teacher to the pupils for the study of advertisements for shelter included such important points to consider as costs, location, ventilation, plumbing and kitchen facilities, kind of building, condition of building, privileges (laundry and phone), and pets. Upon studying the newspaper advertisements of homes and apartments, and the material in the textbook, and discussing them in class, each pupil formulated his summary on the subject of shelter. One girl's summary follows:

In looking for an apartment, you should not pay a rent price that is higher than your weekly pay check.

If utilities are included in the price of an apartment a couple can afford to pay a higher rent as they do not have to pay for bills such as electricity, heating, and such items.

An apartment for a couple should at least be three rooms and a bath. It should have good ventilation and plenty of light. The rooms should be in good condition. A couple should make sure there are no insects or mice. The windows and doors should be placed so that furniture can be arranged easily in many different styles. It is best for a newly married couple to move into a furnished apartment as they will want new furniture when they buy their own home. If they bought new furniture for an apartment, when they bought their home it might not be suitable for the different types of rooms.

The neighborhood should be pleasant and cheerful and with nice surroundings. If there are children, you should not move into an apartment that is near a highway or busy street, as the children are liable to get hurt.

The location of stores such as large chain stores and little grocery stores should be nearby.

Transportation should also be within walking distance. If there is not a family car, transportation that is nearby comes in handy when you are almost late for work or for an appointment.

A church of your religion is always nice if within walking distance and also helps in making friends with your new neighbors who are of your religion.

Entertainment such as theaters and restaurants should be close, as everyone enjoys some kind of relaxation at some time or another.

All these things and many more are essential when renting an apartment.

In connection with the study of shelter, maintenance bills for one month were brought in by pupils and averages were found to be as follows:

Item	Per Month
Electricity	$ 3.38
Gas	3.80
Water	1.18
Telephone	3.16
Coal	4.83
Total utilities	$16.35

Food was the next important item. Pupils made a study of the actual cost of food in their own homes. Each day the actual accounts from the homes were posted on the bulletin board. The average cost per meal was computed after the costs of hundreds of meals were summarized. Part of one such account follows:

	Number of Meals	Money Spent on Food
Saturday, March 1	14	$8.79
Sunday, March 2	10	—
Monday, March 3	10	4.53
Tuesday, March 4	10	—
Wednesday, March 5	10	1.63
Thursday, March 6	17	8.26
Friday, March 7	10	2.42
Weekly totals	81	$25.63
Average cost per meal		$.3164

The class found that the average cost per meal based on the number in the family varied from $.56 in a family of two to $.25 in a family of eight. Menus were made out based on current costs in newspapers. This work correlated with the study of nutrition in physical education which made it doubly interesting. Two boys became so interested in the study of food costs and nutrition that they prepared an excellent exhibit on the subject for the city Science Fair.

Clothing. First of all, each pupil took an inventory of his own clothing. Everyone was amazed at the large amount of money his parents had had to expend for clothing for just one person. Then committees made up clothes budgets with costs given in newspapers. Following is a proposed annual clothes budget which one of the committees of boys considered "essential for a well-dressed young man."

ANNUAL CLOTHES INVENTORY

Quantity	Cost	Years Used	Yearly Cost
2 hats @ $7.50	$15.00	2	$7.50
1 overcoat @ $50	50.00	2	25.00
2 suits @ $50.00	100.00	2	50.00
1 sport jacket @ $25	25.00	2	12.50
3 slacks @ $11	33.00	3	11.00
3 sweaters @ $6.67	20.00	2	10.00
6 dress shirts @ $4	24.00	2	12.00
3 sport shirts @ $3.50	10.50	2	5.25
1 flannel shirt @ $10	10.00	2	5.00
6 T shirts @ $1.00	6.00	1	6.00
6 shorts @ $1.00	6.00	1	6.00
10 socks @ $.85	8.50	1	8.50
2 pr. dress shoes @ $10	20.00	1	20.00
1 pr. dungarees @ $4.50	4.50	1	4.50
1 pr. tennis shoes @ $5	5.00	1	5.00
5 ties @ $1.00	5.00	1	5.00
Total Cost:	$342.50	Total Yearly Cost:	$193.25

Operating an automobile seems essential for transportation purposes in many families. Pupils who were also enrolled in Auto Shop prepared a budget for running a family car that cost $2000, for 45,000 miles in four years:

FAMILY CAR

Cost $2000

45,000 miles in four years

Depreciation, $200 per year	$ 800.00
Gasoline at 25¢ per gallon, 15 miles per gallon	750.00
Oil at 30¢ per quart, 6 qt. capacity, change 1500 mi	54.00
Tires, recapping and replacement	65.00
Lubrication, $1.00 every 1000 miles	45.00
Repairs and adjustments	75.00
Insurance, $40 per year	160.00
License, $40 per year	160.00
Drivers license, $3.00 for three years	4.00
Miscellaneous, as antifreeze, washing, and such incidentals	25.00
Total cost for four years	2138.00
Cost for one year	534.50
Cost per month	44.54
Average cost per mile	.0475

A Savings and Loan Association became interested in the class project and kindly supplied budget books for the use of the class. These books encouraged pupils (and the teacher as well) to keep neat and careful records. Also, the many categories helped remind pupils of the many and varied expenses of running a home.

The culminating activity of the unit was the preparation of a budget for a $40 a week income, and one for a salary of about $80 a week in which the couple was buying a home. The latter budget included picture advertisements of the house they were proposing to buy, with all the expenses of owning and operating.

Can two live on $40 a week? The class found they could— but with difficulty. The study of running a home opened the eyes of the students to the many financial problems of home-makers; it made them appreciate their own parents more; it gave them a sense of responsibility in the family budget; and it gave them an appreciation of the great extent to which running a harmonious home depends on mathematics.

2

Providing Differentiated Curriculums In Schools Where Homogeneous Grouping is Feasible

A Differentiated Curriculum for Homogeneous Groups

REUBEN A. BAUMGARTNER

THE Commission on Post-War Plans of the National Council of Teachers of Mathematics has pointed out the desirability of a double-track ninth grade mathematics program. Thesis 12 of the Post-War Commission states (8) "The large high school, with more than 200 pupils, should provide in Grade IX a double track in mathematics, algebra for some and general mathematics for the rest.''

A two-track program gives an opportunity to take the pupil with interest and ability in mathematics along much further than otherwise possible. This is the place to develop mathematical power. In such a plan, those pupils in general mathematics now have an opportunity to work at the type of mathematics which is to their interest and which will help make them more functionally competent.

The double-track program will not in itself give the complete answer to an effective mathematics program. The organization must be flexible enough to give each pupil a chance to change from one track to another.

One method of setting up a double-track mathematics program is by homogeneous grouping. Homogeneous grouping has been in use at Freeport, Illinois, Senior High School for over 25 years. It was started by L. E. Mensenkamp (30), now principal of the high school. The plan now in operation, which modifies somewhat the original plan, went into effect in September 1950.

In Los Angeles three different year courses were set up for ninth-grade pupils, namely: Basic Mathematics, General Mathematics 1 and 2, and Algebra. Basic Mathematics is remedial in nature. It is designed for pupils with low arithmetical ability or for those who need remedial work in arithmetic. General Mathematics 1 and 2 are designed for those with a fairly good arithmetical background. Algebra is organized for pupils who have an interest and ability in this field.

It cannot be emphasized too strongly that no hard and fast rule can be given for subject placement. Any method of homogeneous grouping adopted must try to place the pupil in the course where he is capable of doing his best work. An effective guidance department is essential to see that pupils are placed, as far as possible, in the proper course.

Opportunity should be given pupils to transfer from one course to another after the school term begins if it is felt a pupil has been misplaced. Some of the factors that need to be taken into consideration are: (a) a test of algebraic ability, (b) pupil's previous arithmetic grade, (c) previous teachers' recommendations, and (d) pupil's reading ability.

All the above information should be secured in the spring in order that it may be analyzed before school begins in the fall. If a test of algebraic ability is given it should be given in the spring. If adequate information concerning the mathematical background of pupils entering in the fall is available, there will be a minimum of shifting from course to course after school begins.

The number of pupils in each course will vary from school to school and from year to year. At Freeport Senior High School about 50 per cent of the pupils take algebra. An ideal situation would exist if each pupil could be placed according to his or her interest and ability. The plan outlined is an attempt to approach that ideal. One must keep in mind that the pupil should be placed in a course that gives him a challenge but not in a course where the content is so difficult that he cannot understand the work of the class and will thereby become discouraged.

Many schools complain that a plan of homogeneous grouping attaches a stigma to pupils taking general mathematics. Much can be done to eliminate this attitude by a thorough explanation of the content, purpose, and organization of each subject. General mathematics can be thought of as helping pupils become more functionally competent, and as additional preparation for tenth year mathematics, which may be algebra if the pupil desires to take this course.

The main emphasis in basic mathematics is upon the ability to understand and do arithmetical operations involving whole numbers, fractions, and decimals. Since some of these pupils have previously failed arithmetic courses, the teaching approach and the content should draw from new illustrations and examples. Time must be taken to find out where these pupils are so that learning goes forward from this point. The use of visual materials helps in teaching such a course. There should be a flexible organization so that content can vary from class to class. It is probably better to do a few things well than to cover a great many topics.

With this organization, the content of General Mathematics 1 and 2 can be organized around topics which are not remedial in nature. The objectives for this course as set up at Freeport Senior High School follow closely the objectives as set forth in the Wisconsin Bulletin on general mathematics (12):

1. To develop the ability to work accurately and with speed in arithmetical computations with whole numbers and decimals.

2. To understand and appreciate the need for accurate measurement.

3. To appreciate the concise language of algebra and acquire the ability to use formulas in the solution of simple problems of everyday living.

4. To develop an understanding of elementary geometric construction.

5. To interpret and to make graphs as a way of expressing relationship.

6. To develop the ability to use and apply the Pythagorean law.

7. To develop skill in scale drawing and an understanding of its application.

A course organized around these objectives is both respectable and desirable.

Algebra now will include pupils who have an ability in this field. This gives teachers an excellent opportunity to present a challenging course. A great deal has been written about the objectives and content of algebra, so no attempt will be made to include this topic.

MATHEMATICS IN THE TENTH YEAR

Mathematics is required in Grade IX and Grade X at Freeport. This requirement may be met in a number of different ways as listed in the table below. The column on the left indicates the course taken in Grade IX and the column on the right indicates the course taken in Grade X:

Grade IX	*Grade X*
1. Basic Mathematics	General Mathematics 1 and 2
2. General Mathematics 1 and 2	General Mathematics 3 and 4
3. General Mathematics 1 and 2	Algebra
4. Algebra	Plane Geometry
5. Algebra	General Mathematics 3 and 4

General Mathematics 3 and 4 continues the process of trying to make the pupil more functionally competent. The objectives of this course follow closely the Wisconsin Bulletin on General Mathematics (12). They are as follows:

1. To understand and appreciate the simple trigonometric relationships used in indirect measurement.
2. To extend pupil's knowledge of simple algebraic processes and to develop skill in using them.
3. To become familiar with the basic ideas of simple algebraic graphs.
4. To develop an appreciation of the value of statistics and the dangers in their use.
5. To develop understanding and proficiency in the common business application of mathematics with emphasis on percentage.
6. To investigate geometrical facts and to develop a mathematical way of thinking.
7. To develop skill in the use of the slide rule.
8. To learn about modern means of travel and the mathematics involved.
9. To appreciate the contribution of mathematics in the wise use of money.
10. To develop an appreciation of the wide variety of items covered by insurance and the importance of insurance in modern living.
11. To develop an appreciation of taxation as a co-operative effort to pay for protection and services rendered by various governing bodies.
12. To develop an appreciation for a knowledge of mathematics problems involved in owning and operating a home and automobile.

Under this plan pupils in Basic Mathematics in the ninth grade take General Mathematics 1 and 2 in the tenth grade. After taking Basic Mathematics, pupils are now, it is hoped, on the same level as those ninth grade pupils entering General Mathematics 1 and 2. If this is true, these pupils can be placed in the same class.

Pupils taking General Mathematics 1 and 2 in Grade IX have two choices in Grade X. They can take General Mathematics 3 and 4 or Algebra. Most of these pupils take General Mathematics 3 and 4. However, if a pupil desires or if his ability indicates an aptitude for Algebra after a year of work in General Mathematics 1 and 2, he is encouraged to take Algebra. Most pupils in algebra in the ninth grade take Geometry in the tenth grade; however, they may take General Mathematics 3 and 4.

This system leads to a flexible mathematics program. Here is an opportunity for pupils to go from one track to another. At the same time Algebra and Geometry are now courses that can develop mathematical power. Such a program does have the advantage of taking a pupil as far as he wants to go in mathematics, taking into consideration his interest and ability.

MATHEMATICS IN GRADE XI AND GRADE XII

Since pupils in algebra and geometry have had an excellent background many more topics can be covered in junior and senior years. Junior year mathematics consists of a semester of algebra followed by either solid geometry or a fourth semester of algebra. This last semester of algebra has as its emphasis such topics as statistics, slide rule, and trigonometry of the right triangle. Seniors follow these courses with trigonometry and college algebra. Many pupils begin their college work with analytic geometry or calculus with excellent results. In fact, the University of Illinois gives college credit for trigonometry and college algebra if a pupil enters the University of Illinois without using these courses for entrance credit.

For those juniors and seniors who feel they need additional mathematics for everyday living, a one-semester course in consumer mathematics has been organized. Its objectives follow the Wisconsin Bulletin on General Mathematics (12):

1. To become aware of the use of money as it affects the standards of living.
2. To develop an appreciation of the services offered by banks and to master the mathematical skills involved.
3. To understand better that taxation is a co-operative effort to pay for protection and services rendered by the government.
4. To appreciate the important role insurance plays in personality, security, and community welfare.
5. To acquaint wage earners with their rights and responsibilities, in regard to social security benefits (30).
6. To study further the problems of ownership as related to business, home, and automobile.

The development of an effective high-school mathematics program depends on many things. To institute any program one must consider the size of school, type of community, interest of pupils, and other such things. A good program in one school may not work as effectively in another school.

However, experience does seem to indicate the two-track program does secure effective mathematical instruction. Homogeneous grouping is an aid to implementing such a program. Any plan devised must be flexible to take into account the needs and interests of all pupils.

Using Homogeneous Grouping To Lead Pupils to Their Own Highest Level of Achievement

Mary A. Potter

To THE gifted child, to the slow pupil, to the teacher, homogeneous grouping affords an excellent opportunity for adjusting the curriculum to the needs, abilities, and interests of the students. If there is more than one youngster in a class this segregation does not produce a group of uniform homogenity, but it does reduce the range of differences to be found in any one section.

What criteria should be used for dividing students into ability groups is a question frequently posed. At one time the intelligence quotient was considered a sufficient basis for sectioning, but experience has shown that the process is not that simple. Intelligence is still a determining factor, but other facts that should be carefully considered include:

1. The drive for work possessed by the boy or girl
2. Teacher judgment of his skill and information as shown by marks and cumulative records
3. Scores on standardized tests in both reading and arithmetic
4. The health of the pupil
5. The type of course desired by the student often prompted by his current vocational interest
6. The wishes of the parents
7. The educational background of the family
8. The economic status of the parents which often determines whether or not the student will need to be prepared for college.

There will always be borderline cases where a more complete knowledge of the circumstances noted above will be of great assistance in classifying the pupils. Moreover, in some of these borderline cases it will be seen that a pupil may profit by shifting him to a faster or a slower group since he may be misplaced due to a change of conditions or due to a mistake in judging his ability. The door into each group should be kept open at all times for such adjustments.

In the early experiments with ability grouping many teachers and administrators assumed that both the able and the slow children should be taught the same subject matter by the same methods from the same textbooks. They thought that if children were grouped with others of their kind all pupils would arrive at the same goals. This ambition has proved to be wishful thinking. Continued experiments have shown that the subject matter, the methods, and at times the choice of teacher, have needed considerable adjustment to fit the homogeneous groups. When these accommodations have been made, ability grouping has proved to be very successful, perhaps of greater value to the abler children than to their less capable classmates. With the slow-learners eliminated the teacher can quicken the pace of the class, can present challenging material, can give the superior boys and girls a chance to expand to their greatest powers. Confronted with a heterogeneous group the teacher needs to spend the majority of her time with the slow pupils who have difficulty even with simple work, but with homogeneous grouping the teacher of a gifted class can be released to give her full attention to the development of the gifted.

In classes by themselves, the less able pupils find new leaders. They are no longer frustrated by being constantly confronted by superior achievement which they themselves can never attain; they lose their feelings of inferiority; they are happy in being able to complete tasks and master materials within their ability and within their range of interests; they become mathematically educated even if to a limited degree.

The traditional secondary course in mathematics of yesterday contained those topics chosen largely by the college professors which they considered necessary as a foundation for the successful pursuit of college courses in mathematics. This work was geared to the mentality of pupils of superior ability who were to enter one of the professions, or to become scientists, engineers, or teachers of mathematics. Confidence in these excellent high-school courses has been disturbed by two factors—the influx into high school of all teen-agers who may not be interested or profit from the traditional academic subjects, and the necessity of training an army of technicians, many of whom will not go to college, but who must be proficient in a more practical form of mathematics so they may service the countless inventions of the past 50 years.

Present-day courses for the bright children are based upon the high-school courses of the past with minor modifications. They include many of the traditional topics of algebra, geometry, and trigonometry with a healthy emphasis upon the mastery of the skills of arithmetic. However, the various subjects are seldom separated into watertight compartments. The difficulties of algebra, geometry, and trigonometry are introduced gradually in a spiral development through successive years as was advised in the earlier part of the century. The title of a textbook may not be an accurate description of its contents but a concession to tradition.

With the pressure caused by more extensive training of engineers and scientists, certain universities have been urging that more mathematics be taught to the better students in the high school including some topics in analytical geometry, the calculus, and statistics. Other educators disturbed by consumer problems of modern living and the poor adjustment made to financial difficulties by some competent adults have urged that consumer topics in mathematics such as taxes, insurance, and installment buying be inserted in the regular work for gifted children, or taught as a separate course.

If an able boy is p'anning to enter the trades or industry instead of attending college, he will profit greatly by electing this course usually des'gnated as college preparatory. Such work as that of the pattern maker and machinist—widely expanding fields—are surprisingly mathematical. Recent technical advancements are based upon a foundation of mathematics that makes promotion difficult, even if the worker is equipped with the ever-helpful handbook, unless he is grounded in arithmetic, algebra, geometry, and some trigonometry.

Does the average man or woman need any training in mathematics in the secondary school in order to do his job well and conduct his personal affairs? Before World War II many educators answered this question with a "No" and considered mathematical training in high school a needless luxury. But the low degree of mathematical competence and subsequent inefficiency of the average man enlisted by the armed services received wide publicity during World War II and led to the appointment of the Commission on Post-War Plans of the National Council of Teachers of Mathematics. Their exhaustive study of the mathematical skills and information needed by the common soldier and accepted as equally necessary for the common man, produced a check list which has been generally accepted as the basis of courses for the less able section of our population. This list (8: 3–5) is of sufficient importance that we print it again as the best inventory yet devised of mathematical knowledge and skills essential for efficient daily living and everyday occupations of the average citizen.

THE CHECK LIST

1. *Computation.* Can you add, subtract, multiply, and divide effectively with whole numbers, common fractions, and decimals?

2. *Per cents.* Can you use per cents understandingly and accurately?

3. *Ratio.* Do you have a clear understanding of ratio?

4. *Estimating.* Before you perform a computation, do you estimate the result for the purpose of checking your answer?

5. *Rounding numbers.* Do you know the meaning of significant figures? Can you round numbers properly?

6. *Tables.* Can you find correct values in tables; e.g., interest and income tax?

7. *Graphs.* Can you read ordinary graphs: bar, line and circle graphs? the graph of a formula?

8. *Statistics.* Do you know the main guides that one should follow in collecting and interpreting data; can you use averages (mean, median, mode); can you draw and interpret a graph?

9. *The nature of a measurement.* Do you know the meaning of a measurement, of a standard unit, or the largest permissible error, of tolerance, and of the statement that "a measurement is an approximation"?

10. *Use of measuring devices*. Can you use certain measuring devices, such as an ordinary ruler, other rulers (graduated to thirty-seconds, to tenths of an inch, and to millimeters), protractor, graph paper, tape, caliper micrometer, and thermometer?

11. *Square root*. Can you find the square root of a number by table, or by division?

12. *Angles*. Can you estimate, read, and construct an angle?

13. *Geometric concepts*. Do you have an understanding of point, line, angle, parallel lines, perpendicular lines, triangle (right, scalene, isosceles, and equilateral), parallelogram (including square and rectangle), trapezoid, circle, regular polygon, prism, cylinder, cone, and sphere?

14. *The 3-4-5-relation*. Can you use the Pythagorean relationship in a right triangle?

15. *Constructions*. Can you with ruler and compasses construct a circle, a square, and a rectangle, transfer a line segment and an angle, bisect a line segment and an angle, copy a triangle, divide a line segment into more than two equal parts, draw a tangent to a circle, and draw a geometric figure to scale?

16. *Drawings*. Can you read and interpret reasonably well, maps, floor plans, mechanical drawings, and blueprints? Can you find the distance between two points on a map?

17. *Vectors*. Do you understand the meaning of vector, and can you find the resultant of two forces?

18. *Metric system*. Do you know how to use the most important metric units (meter, centimeter, millimeter, kilometer, gram, kilogram)?

19. *Conversion*. In measuring length, area, volume, weight, time, temperature, angle, and speed, can you shift from one commonly used standard unit to another widely used standard unit; e.g., do you know the relation between yard and foot, inch and centimeter, and similar relationships?

20. *Algebraic symbolism*. Can you use letters to represent numbers; i.e., do you understand the symbolism of algebra—do you know the meaning of exponent and coefficient?

21. *Formulas*. Do you know the meaning of a formula—can you, for example, write an arithmetic rule as a formula, and can you substitute given values in order to find the value for a required unknown?

22. *Signed numbers*. Do you understand signed numbers and can you use them?

23. *Using the axioms*. Do you understand what you are doing when you use the axioms to change the form of a formula or when you find the value of an unknown in a simple equation?

24. *Practical formulas*. Do you know from memory certain widely used formulas relating to areas, volumes, and interest, and to distance, rate, and time?

25. *Similar triangles and proportion*. Do you understand the meaning

of similar triangles, and do you know how to use the fact that in similar triangles the ratios of corresponding sides are equal? Can you manage a proportion?

26. *Trigonometry.* Do you know the meaning of tangent, sine, cosine? Can you develop their meanings by means of scale drawings?

27. *First steps in business arithmetic.* Are you mathematically conditioned for satisfactory adjustment to a first job in business; e.g., have you a start in understanding the keeping of a simple account, making change, and the arithmetic that illustrates the most common problems of communications and every day affairs?

28. *Stretching the dollar.* Do you have a basis for dealing intelligently with the main problems of the consumer; e.g., the cost of borrowing money, insurance to secure adequate protection against the numerous hazards of life, the wise management of money, and buying with a given income so as to get good values as regards both quantity and quality?

29. *Proceeding from hypothesis to conclusion.* Can you analyze a statement in a newspaper and determine what is assumed, and whether the suggested conclusions really follow from the given facts or assumptions?

No school is any better than its teachers and the most important job of the administrator is to choose the teacher best adapted to the type of pupils in the class. For a superior group he will select an alert teacher of excellent mental caliber and of sound mathematical training who will also have the qualities of leadership, which will demand the respect of young people and appeal to them. She will be familiar with the current content of the college courses, will be interested in the more difficult applications of mathematics, will be able to point her instruction toward the value and uses of the subject, and will be able to inspire her students to continue their studies.

Great care should be taken in choosing a suitable teacher for the slow-learning classes since the boys and girls in them are often not interested in school or in academic subjects, and may be difficult to handle. Their teacher must be a good disciplinarian, a person devoted to duty, resourceful, not too academically minded but with a broad field of interests. Being personally attractive is no hindrance to success, but she needs the working knowledge of psychology that makes a ward politician successful, must combine enthusiasm with tolerance, patience, perseverance, and sympathy. She must be emotionally stable and must find it easy to adjust to a new situation. It is axiomatic that she must be skillful in presenting subject matter and in devising drill. A knowledge of teaching arithmetic and experience as an elementary school teacher are helpful.

Since most of the volumes on methods have been discussions of problems of instructing the superior and average children, perhaps space should be given to a few suggestions about teaching mathematics to the dull-normal.

Methods of teaching are based upon an understanding of the individuals to be taught, and certain mental characteristics seem to be found in most slow-learning children. Fortunately they differ from the normal not in kind of intelligence but in degree. Like most of humanity, they have uneven mental abilities and these traits vary around a low level of capacity. Every teacher knows that slow children are poor readers which defect hinders their progress in mathematics. They are not logical; they are weak in forming associations; they find abstractions difficult, but enjoy the concrete; they have little power to transfer training; they lack imagination. Their rote memories are not so inferior, but they do have poor associative memories. They lack the discrimination to detect their own errors. Perhaps the most important difference between the dull and the bright is the ability to create, which is almost lacking in the dull and a great motivating factor with bright children. In common with the rest of the world they love to succeed.

By the time slow learners have reached the secondary school many of them have developed a block against mathematics. Little teaching can be effective until that block is removed, and how to remove it depends upon the mind-set of the youngster and the personality of the teacher. Starting a topic with work so easy that even the slow can readily master it, praise for work well done, teaching the value of the thing to be learned, adorning the topic with interesting applications all help to break down this protective shell of indifference or hatred of the subject. Many teachers forget the role that emotions have played in the theory of education in the past; but if a child knows that a teacher cares for him, he will release his energies to learn; pleasant emotions yield the largest harvest of learning, but arousing even unpleasant emotions is more efficient than an attitude of indifference shown by the teacher.

To achieve satisfactory results the pace of presenting material should be kept slow. Each topic should be analyzed to find the minute steps of learning and all these steps taught in their proper order so that the student will have a clear understanding of the meaning of the concepts he is trying to master. If the youngster cannot learn from one method of approach, new methods should be used until the meaning is made clear. Since dull children think more easily in terms of the concrete, it is advisable whenever possible to approach the necessary abstractions through concrete channels. Here visual aids are of great assistance. Not only projected materials may be used, but of even greater help are things which require physical activity of the students, preferably using things they themselves have made.

Since their span of attention is short, variety in a class period is essential. It has been found that in general most efficient teaching is done when an interval of not more than 20 minutes is devoted to one type of effort, that mental work should be occasionally interrupted by physical activity. After intense application, there should be a rest period before beginning a new task.

Although drill is a necessary part of teaching both the bright and the dull, it is fortunate that slow children enjoy drill because they need so much of it.

The teacher needs to give careful assistance to the less able children in making a transfer from one situation to a nearly related situation, and from one principle to a closely related principle, since these children find difficulty unless the path is clearly pointed out to them. The teacher does well to multiply associations and suggest clues and reminders.

SUMMARY

With homogeneous grouping, pupils at the same grade level may study different topics which are necessary for their later life, suited to their intellects and within their ability to master. They may proceed at a pace suited to their natural mental rate of progress with methods suitable for their full development, and taught by a teacher who is chosen for her understanding of the psychology of the students in the group. When properly administered, homogeneous grouping affords an unusual opportunity for the teacher to lead young people with varying abilities to their own highest level of achievement.

A Mathematics Program for Grade XII

JACKSON B. ADKINS

THE Phillips Exeter Academy takes boys from Grade IX through Grade XII. Mathematics is required in Grades IX, X, and XI. It is elective in Grade XII. In a typical year, out of a senior class of 230, 165 take mathematics. The IQ's of this group range from 98 to 156 with a median of 120. Thirty-six per cent of them have spent three previous years at the Academy, 27 per cent of them two years, 26 per cent of them one year, and 11 per cent of them are in their first year at the Academy. The latter small group presents special problems with which these notes will not deal.

Twenty years ago the Academy began to teach second-year algebra and plane geometry concurrently in Grades X and XI. The senior course that followed consisted of more or less conventional advanced algebra, solid geometry, and trigonometry. As the years went on, an introduction to demonstrative geometry was added in Grade IX and the algebra and geometry of Grades X and XI became quite interdependent. This interdependence produced a great strengthening of both subjects. The program described below is a complete revision of the 20-year program. This revision was begun in 1953–54 in Grade X and will continue in Grade XI in 1954–55; the new senior course will be taught for the first time in 1955–56. To understand this new senior course it is necessary to look first at the new courses of Grades IX, X, and XI.

The program in Grade IX is essentially a thorough course in elementary algebra. This course includes radicals, the general quadratic equation, numerical trigonometry, and a brief introduction to demonstrative geometry. There is thorough drill in algebraic mechanics and arithmetic with considerable emphasis on the postulational bases of the fundamental operations.

The course in Grade X carries plane geometry through the usual work in congruence, rectilinear figures, similarity, the Pythagorean Theorem with three-dimensional applications, areas of rectilinear figures, and volumes and areas of prisms and pyramids. It does not include circles or areas of regular polygons. The algebra of Grade IX is continued and expanded by adding exponents and logarithms, the solution of right triangles, and a rather extensive study of the linear function and the analytic geometry of the straight line. The latter brings in the locus concept.

Grade XI begins with a study of the quadratic function, $f(x) = ax^2 + bx + c$. The locus concept is emphasized in the graphing of $f(x)$. The range of values of $f(x)$ is studied, also the roots of $f(x) = k$, complex numbers, sum and product of the roots, formation of functions, and equations under given conditions. Area formulas, the distance, rate and time relations are used to build quadratic functions. The turning point of the parabola is determined.

The circle is introduced with the locus definition. Locus is discussed generally and there are three-dimensional applications like the sphere and the cylinder. The usual work with circles in plane geometry is completed.

Analytic geometry proceeds with the derivation of the equation $x^2 + y^2 = r^2$. The graphical intersection of lines and curves is studied with the algebraic solution of linear and quadratic pairs. The discriminant of the quadratic function is used to find tangent lines to curves. Detailed analytic study of the parabola, ellipse, and hyperbola is optional.

Trigonometry goes through the laws of sines and cosines, the general angle, $K = \frac{1}{2}ab \sin C$, and simple equations and identities. The usual study of the measurement of the circle and of the regular polygon is expanded to include work with the areas and volumes of cylinders and cones. Brief surveys of arithmetic and geometric progressions and the binomial theorem are included.

It may be noticed that no mention is made of verbal problems. A fair number of conventional verbal problems appears in Grade IX. They are almost entirely eliminated in Grades X and XI. Their place is filled by the studies of quantitative relationships in geometry and in trigonometry.

A systematic study of the polynomial function, with emphasis on the cubic, involves synthetic division, the factor theorem, and leads to a method for approximating irrational roots of higher degree equations.

Varying speeds of absorbing this course make two programs in Grade XII desirable. The slower groups will be expected to spend 10 or 12 weeks on analytic trigonometry, six weeks on a review of the linear, quadratic, and polynomial functions. They will spend four weeks on permutations, combinations, and probability, one week on the binomial theorem, two weeks on the analytics of the circle, and six to eight weeks on an introduction to the calculus. The time factors may change as experience with the course is gained.

This introduction to the calculus is primarily designed to teach the pupil how to read a calculus book. The meaning of differentiation and of integration is emphasized. Real skill in either operation is not sought. Work in the theory of limits is confined to an effort to present as clearly and simply as possible the underlying ideas, and to prepare for the more rigid treatment it will receive in college. Familiarity with the vocabulary and the basic concepts is the goal. For the student who takes no further mathematics in college this course should provide a glimpse of the place and power of mathematics in modern civilization. The student who continues his mathematics in college will take a course in beginning calculus.

The better group in Grade XII—about half those taking the course—is expected to spend about eight weeks on analytic trigonometry and the rest of the year on analytic geometry and calculus. This calculus course not only emphasizes meaning and understanding; it also achieves considerable skill in differentiating and integrating algebraic, logarithmic, exponential, trigonometric, and inverse trigonometric functions. The analytic geometry is introduced as needed, in accordance with common practice these days. A fair amount of it is already at the student's disposal from the previous courses. Integration of algebraic functions appears early and the definite integral follows immediately after. The fundamental theorem is not rigorously proved. Many applications of the fundamental theorem are included. Some discussion of indeterminate forms and of the theorem of mean value are included as time permits.

The amount of rigor conforms with the usual practice in the better college freshman courses. Precise language is used in discussing the theory of limits though some of the proofs are omitted. Points in the course where rigor is lacking are carefully pointed out. At the conclusion of this course the student is ready for the second course in calculus given in most colleges.

The textbook for the senior course is a standard text in Analytic Geometry and Calculus. Books for Grades IX, X and XI have been written by members of the department.

During the last 20 years special sections have been formed in Grade X and slowly increased by the addition of new boys in Grades XI and XII. In the senior year these groups, totaling from 20 to 30 boys, have been given a stiff calculus course that included, in addition to the material of the course described above, considerable work in the analytic geometry of the conic sections, very thorough drilling in differentiation and integration, and some work with polar co-ordinates and parametric equations. The better pupils of this group have frequently started college with the second half of the college sophomore course. It seems likely that there will still be, under the new program, about a dozen pupils who will carry the calculus this far. Also, about every other year, from one to three boys appear who absorb the subject so fast that a special course is provided for them in their senior year. This course commonly consists of mechanics, advanced calculus, and differential equations in varying amounts depending on the wishes of the boys. Thus, while there are essentially two programs planned for Grade XII, in practice there will be boys progressing at four different rates.

3

Providing Differentiated Curriculums in Schools Where Homogeneous Grouping is not Feasible

Adjusting Work Within the Class to the Varying Abilities of its Members

ONA KRAFT

THE title of this section suggests two interpretations. Curriculums can be differentiated by offering alternate subjects, such as algebra or general mathematics, geometry or shop mathematics. This important problem is receiving widespread attention in today's professional writing. Differentiated curriculums can also be obtained by adjusting the work in a class to the varying abilities of its members. It is this second interpretation that I shall discuss.

Again two ways emerge to accomplish this end. The class can be divided into two or three sections with different classwork and assignments for each. This plan has some professional backing, but my own experiences with it have been unsatisfactory. An ideal class is a laboratory where boys and girls make discoveries through their own efforts as much as possible. Each section needs the teacher's constant attention and direction and cannot succeed with only a fraction of them. Divided classes often deteriorate into an explanation by the teacher of a certain type of problem, with the class working 10 more exactly like it. While a divided class may learn, the arrangement seems unsatisfactory to me.

You may name the sections A, B, and C; or right, middle, and left; or, in elementary-school fashion, the lilies, the roses, and the lilacs; but to the pupils they will be the geniuses, the regulars, and the dumbbells. The dumbbells have two strikes on them at the start, as they see the others concerned with projects they have been labeled too dull to undertake. They may not complain, but they are resentful. Only the lazy ones among them are pleased that they can now relax and just sit.

Instead of dividing a class into sections, each limited by the teacher's estimate of its average ability, it is better to differentiate the curriculum by planning the lessons so that each pupil can perform to the limit of his ability. This is my method, but my pupils would probably tell you that everyone in the class had the same work to do, with no distinctions made among them. Everyone should seem to be on the same basis with no genius or dumbbell ratings. A system which works without clamor is more effective. The most helpful professional articles I have read have been by other teachers who have met my problems. Theory has an honored place in education, but to hear what someone has actually made work is sometimes of more immediate aid. With this in mind I shall speak of some of the ways I have found most successful in adjusting the curriculum to individual ability. They are not original discoveries; I am only calling them to your attention.

To develop a differentiated curriculum, first obtain an outline of the term's work. As you read it through, mark in some certain way those topics so essential that they must be mastered by everyone who receives a passing mark. Mark in a different way those which ought to be learned but are not so basic, and devise a still different mark for those strictly optional or enriching. This is the basis of differentiation. The poorer pupils will receive a passing mark, through not a high one, if they do acceptable work on only the essential topics. They will be permitted to try anything under discussion but you will remember that they cannot be required to master everything. The average pupils must do considerable work in the second group of topics you have marked. No one, no matter how well he does the minimum required work can receive an honor mark unless he has done something with optional topics or shown some originality or solved some of the difficult problems assigned for extra credit. Over and over again I say to my classes, "Remember that it is not what you have done that counts in mathematics, but what you can do." What has been gained by solving several pages of fractional equations correctly, if you cannot deal with one later on? What good did it do you to learn all the types of congruent triangles, if you cannot apply the proper one to the situation you are considering?

For a long time I have required as a basis for passing that every pupil must pass all the class tests, each one covering four or five weeks work. If he fails a test, he is given time for further study and extra help, and then he takes another on the same work. Sometimes pupils take the first test as many as four times before they pass it, but they usually soon realize that it would be better to study, and there is little further trouble. I know of no other one thing which reduces the number of failures so sharply. Even the lazy or uninterested ones make an effort, if only for the sake of peace. You must make sure that enough test questions depend upon the essentials to enable the poor but industrious ones to make a passing mark, but that more searching questions make an honor mark impossible without actual effort. Add something really difficult for extra credit. You will find that the first test has divided your class into definite groups, and you know what you can expect from each.

Instead of separate assignments for the different levels of ability that you recognize, make elastic ones: solve at least six of the equations; prove at least two of the exercises. This establishes a minimum but leaves the maximum to the pupil's choice. The real students will do as many as they can, knowing that no one will receive a high mark on the minimum assignment. Keep an extra credit assignment going, the originals in geometry too difficult for most of the class, tricky concrete algebra problems, unusual trigonometry problems difficult to diagram. The pupils will bring in problems, which are good to assign if they can be solved mathematically.

Careful planning enables the teacher to differentiate the classwork as well. Choose part of it simple enough for everyone, but add challenging material, too. Give the poorer ones a chance to help in the difficult work, even though they prove to be wrong. Keep your eye on the lazy ones. I still remember several boys who were practicing a German poem before school. One of the group was silent and when I asked him if he knew it, he answered that Miss Brown wouldn't be foolish enough to expect him to know it.

Someone should devise a punishment horrible enough for the teachers who murder geometry by making it a memory course. Memorizing proofs is futile nonsense. After a theorem has been proved, it can be used without recalling the steps of the proof. We study the proofs given wholly or partly in the text to learn methods. Reeling them off like a parrot does not guarantee that anything has been learned, but if the pupil can prove other theorems in the same way, then there is real accomplishment. Make a test of six new originals, with the understanding that the highest marks go to those who prove the most. If some poor but determined pupil succeeds in proving only one, he has still accomplished infinitely more than if he had written accurately from memory the proofs of five book theorems. If you are not already doing so, try to prove most of the theorems in the text in class. After making sure that the meaning and the *given* and *to prove* are clear and after a general plan has been agreed upon, pause for a few minutes while everyone turns the pages hunting necessary information. The important theorems are quoted so often in proofs that they are soon known without conscious memorizing. Make these proofs a class affair with anyone free to contribute. The duller pupils get a thrill out of helping with something, though giving all the steps may be beyond them. Vary the procedure by letting only the girls make suggestions for one proof, only the boys for another. Sometimes have everyone write the statements and find out whose work is best. Occasionally write the statements on the blackboard as they are suggested, and let the pupils find the reasons. However you vary such a procedure, you are dividing the proof into parts of varying difficulty to suit the abilities of different pupils, and only original work is going on, no canned memorizing.

Similar methods are applied to the other mathematics classes. In algebra we solve equations by writing on the blackboard the steps given by different pupils. If it is understood that you will put down everything, right or wrong, the class becomes keener in detecting errors. If concrete problems are bothering too many, work many of them at the blackboard, using the steps suggested by different pupils. Even the lowest group will get the idea by watching the methods constantly applied, and by taking some part themselves. Another apt place for differentiation is in the study of formulas. Derivations are sometimes simple enough for everyone to work out and understand, but occasionally they are difficult. I prefer to derive them all, even if only half the class can follow. The others have learned at least that they were derived and not invented. A pupil who had been handed formulas ready-made once complained to me that anyone could have made up an easier formula for solving quadratic equations.

As a final suggestion for the highest group, refer whenever you can to more advanced mathematics. Make your study of graphs more interesting by bringing in a little analytic geometry now and then, or when something comes up that reminds you of calculus, take a few minutes for a glimpse into it. A fascinating number to them is ϵ, not made up by anyone, but like familiar π just appearing. When projections are in the lessons, a few words about projective geometry will catch their attention. You seldom know what interest has been aroused. A boy in my intermediate algebra class brought me a so-called self-teaching calculus he had found at the public library. He had worked one-third of the way through the book, doing the problems and getting the correct answers. The one that stumped him was a tricky one beyond what he had learned. In only his third term of algebra, he had found out for himself something basic about calculus.

In this short discussion I have tried to show by a number of illustrations that a class of varying abilities can apparently follow the same curriculum, but with careful differentiation by the teacher; that the class can be truly divided into sections, if only in the teacher's mind; and that both homework assignments and classwork can be so planned that each section will be adequately served. We teachers are always proud when our best pupils rate high on citywide tests or win college scholarships by competitive examination, but in our striving to reach all our pupils there is more to warm our hearts in the below average child's tribute, "I like geometry because it makes so much sense."

Methods Used To Provide Differentiated Curriculums Within the Classroom

H. George Murphy

It is now common knowledge that the individual pupils in any school group vary widely in academic ability, in mathematics and emotional backgrounds, in interests, and in educational or vocational aspirations. They differ in their rates of learning and their degrees of retention and understanding. Our schools are now trying to adjust their curricular offerings to these variations and differences. There is a general trend toward establishing differentiated mathematics courses in the high school. Many schools are establishing what is often called a second-track course in the ninth grade with the possibility of offering another one at Grade XI or Grade XII level. Some are establishing third-track courses for strictly vocational interests.

On the other hand, the establishment of separate courses and the use of so-called "homogeneous" or "ability" grouping of pupils *by classes* is generally unacceptable in grades below Grade VII, and "homogeneous" classes in Grade VII and Grade VIII appears to be diminishing. There are many of our high schools which are too small to offer a variety of course selections. It is clear then that if a vast number of schools are to adjust their curricular offerings to the variations and differences between pupils such adjustments must be made within the classroom. The weight of responsibility for doing this falls heavily upon the classroom teacher.

It is the purpose of this section to discuss how such adaptations within heterogeneous classes are being made. As a matter of fact, even when many separate courses are provided in the high school only a degree of homogeneity of pupils is accomplished. Variations in abilities and differences in achievement and in interests between pupils still exist. Thus many of the methods for differentiating instruction *within the classroom* discussed here will be useful, even necessary, for use by teachers of separate courses for which the pupils have been carefully selected. Adaptations of this kind will probably be made to a greater degree in general mathematics than in the academic courses.

In recent years teachers of mathematics have been accumulating a storehouse of experience in dealing with heterogeneous classes. They have developed methods of differentiating mathematics curriculums and instruction. Mathematics teachers are using different topics with a single class. They are varying the amount of concrete background within a topic to be given to various pupils and they are adjusting the extent of the topics to be studied to the pupils in the class.

Subgrouping Within the Classroom. If there is only one class in a given course, or if homogeneous grouping by classes is not desired, then within each class we are learning how to use subgrouping. Sometimes subgrouping is used to teach two parallel courses in a single period. Sometimes the subgroups are ability groups. Sometimes subgroups are organized within a class to carry out special projects or to execute the various aspects of a unit. Subgroups are often used to organize a class for remedial work. In grades below Grade VII, pupils are most often grouped within classes in terms of their present stage of development in mathematics. In few instances is instruction completely individualized.

There seems to be a growing tendency to keep subgrouping flexible and varied from purpose to purpose. Flexibility in the use of subgrouping is not so common when the groups within the class are organized according to mathematics ability or achievement, or when two parallel courses are taught in the same class; but even here we find groups being set up to do certain jobs or to carry on committee work. Thus pupils have opportunities to work with each of their classmates at one time or another. Usually pupils belong to more than one subgroup at a time.

The first and most important job of the teacher who uses subgroups is to discover the amount and kind of mathematics learning possessed by each pupil. There are several ways of doing this; a combination of the following is usually employed:

1. Study the records and reports of the previous teachers.
2. Give achievement, diagnostic, or prognostic tests.
3. Watch each pupil's performance informally and note his needs.
4. Make and give tests on suspected areas of weakness.
5. Ask the pupils to record the things they understand and do well and those things in which they are uncertain or want more practice.

Once a teacher understands the stage of development for each pupil in mathematics, the strengths and weaknesses of each pupil and their special interests and needs, there will be little difficulty in organizing subgroups within the class. Several topics will be selected from the list of class needs. The children will fall naturally into one or more of these groups. If there is a question as to which group is correct for a pupil he might in some cases make the selection himself unless it is a case involving sequential learning and then he should be placed in the more basic of the groups. Placement in subgroups should, of course, be flexible and should change according to the pupils' needs from topic to topic.

Subgrouping is carried on in such a way that no stigma is attached to any group. Rigid grade requirements are replaced by a concept of pupil progress based on an understanding that each pupil progresses according to his individual rate, according to his growth and maturity and according to the meaning he is able to attach to an operation. Teachers of mathematics seek to develop their ability to judge when a pupil is ready to go on, and when a pupil can move from concrete experiences to abstract thinking.

Parallel Courses. In schools which are so small that only one course in mathematics can be offered at the ninth grade level, two subgroups are sometimes formed within the algebra class— one to deal with college preparatory algebra and the other to deal with general mathematics. To do this requires much skill on the part of the teacher.

Actually what is done is to have two different courses taught by the same teacher during the same period. Here at least two programs are provided: one for pupils who display ability to do specialized mathematical work and another for the noncollege preparatory pupils which is geared to immediate or near immediate needs. These two programs are usually administered by using two subgroups and without altering either course of study. The two programs often are entirely different and neither is less important than the other. They merely meet different needs.

As teachers gain experience, however, with teaching such parallel courses and as they gain experience in using subgrouping within the classroom, it is likely that minor adjustments will be made in each of the courses. It is often found feasible to combine the two subgroups for certain particular phases of the work and organize additional subgroups for special purposes as suggested elsewhere in this section.

Ability Grouping Within the Classroom. Subgrouping within a mathematics class strictly according to ability is not often resorted to. Nevertheless when a teacher has a heterogeneous class —as do most teachers of grades below the ninth, and as do many teachers of the ninth—consideration is given to the varying abilities of the pupils in the class. In order to maintain the meaning and continuity of mathematics for the individual, the teacher attempts to reach each pupil at his own level, so that each pupil may work up to his own capacity to learn. The teacher does not deal with the slow pupils in the same manner he uses with the superior pupils even if he is developing a topic with the whole class at almost the same time.

The slow pupils require a longer time to develop a concrete background of understanding for the topic or process and some may never leave the concrete level. The superior pupils will be able to move very rapidly to the abstract thinking level and are not be held back. The formation of subgroups within the class is being used to meet this problem.

In addition to the fact that pupils of a class differ in their lack of understanding of a topic or process, teachers of heterogeneous classes have found that superior pupils usually need less practice for mastery of a topic or process. Such superior students are being directed to independent work in the library, in supplementary books, and on special projects. They need less routine work.

A system of individual pupil folders is often used to advantage. Each pupil has his own folder which he works from in the class period or study period. Mimeographed material suitable to the needs of individual pupils can be quickly inserted in the folders, and the superior pupils proceed with little direction or difficulty. The teacher is thus free to work with the slower pupils who need closer supervision, more practice, and assignments of a more specific nature. Periods of work for the slower pupils are shorter and more frequent than those for the superior pupils and there is more discussion and explanation. Here again teachers of heterogeneous classes are using flexible subgrouping as a classroom management technique.

Subgroups often use mathematics crossword puzzles suited to their level of development. An example of such puzzles used in New York State is presented here:

ANS.

1. $21\frac{3}{8} + 1\frac{5}{8} - .3$ ——

2. $25.6 \div 3.2$ ——

3. $7\frac{3}{4} + 2\frac{1}{4} - 9$ ——

4. Find 8% of 250. ——
5. Find the area of a rectangle whose dimensions are 5 and 4. ——

6. What is $\frac{2}{3}$ of 12? ——

7. $\frac{7}{16} \times \frac{48}{49} \times \frac{35}{3}$ ——

8. What is 3.23 ÷ .17? ——
9. What is 74.7 − 69.7? ——
10. What is 131.2 ÷ 32.8? ——

11. $\frac{1}{64} \times 320$ ——

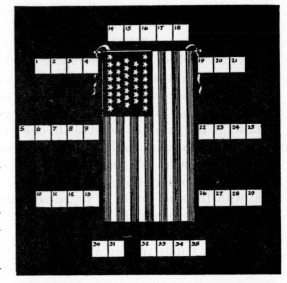

In 1863 there were 35 states in the Union

12. $\frac{1}{2} \div \frac{1}{2}$ ——

13. Find .5% of 800 ——
14. Round off 19.4 to the nearest whole number. ——
15. Add: 6.2, .4, 1.4 ——
16. Find 5% of 20. ——

17. Find the perimeter of a rectangle if the sides are 4 and 2. ——

18. $\frac{144}{26} \times \frac{13}{6}$ ——

19. What is 126 ÷ 9? ——
20. What is 52.6 − 37.6? ——
21. 10 ÷ 5 ——
22. $2\frac{2}{3} \times 3$ ——

23. $\frac{4}{27} \times \frac{3}{8} \times 18$ ——

24. What is 4% of 550? ——
25. 145 ÷ 29 ——
26. If the perimeter of a square is 16, what is one side? ——
27. Find 150% of 6. ——

28. $6\frac{1}{4} \div 1\frac{1}{4}$ ——

29. 2.64 ÷ .66 ——

30. $\frac{24}{5} \div \frac{8}{15}$ ——

31. 471 − 457 ——

32. What per cent is .22? ——

33. $8 \times 12\frac{1}{2}$¢ ——

34. Find the total number of lbs. in 6 lbs. 9 ozs. and 2 lbs. 7 ozs. ——
35. How many feet are there in 168 in.? ——

CODE for Puzzles 1 and 2

(To be furnished after the pupils have finished the necessary computations)

A	B	C	D	E	F	G	H	I	J	K	L	M
1	2	3	4	5	6	7	8	9	10	11	12	13

N	O	P	Q	R	S	T	U	V	W	X	Y	Z
14	15	16	17	18	19	20	21	22	23	24	25	26

Note: Of course, it is advisable to change the code from time to time.

Adaptations of this idea will occur to the alert teacher. Superior pupils could construct such puzzles for themselves and for use by other subgroups within the class.

Special Purpose Subgroups. Differentiation in depth and scope is also provided by teachers of heterogeneous classes by the use of subgroups within the class. Subgroups are formed to carry out special projects. Sometimes these special projects or assignments are aspects of the central topic or unit on which the entire class is working and sometimes these special assignments are independent of and unrelated to the central unit.

This kind of subgrouping or committee work is a good way to begin subgrouping for a teacher who has not had previous experience, or for a class which has not learned to work in subgroups. Usually only one subgroup is organized as a beginning. Its assignment could be as uncomplicated as taking care of the bulletin board and it could work on its assignment during the supervised study period. As one group learns to work successfully, others can be added. Subgroups of this kind construct multisensory aids and demonstrate and explain them to the rest of the class. Special groups report on current topics involving mathematics. Some keep materials illustrating mathematics principles in notebooks. Some make scrapbooks depicting the uses of mathematics found in daily living.

The bulletin board is used to great advantage in this kind of teaching. It can be of service to all kinds of subgroups. Responsibility for its care, when delegated wisely, leads to awakened interest in mathematical problems. For instance, in junior high school, a set of Napier's bones, constructed by one or more subgroups and hung upon the bulletin board for actual use by the pupils, provides some motivation in multiplication.

Sometimes group projects involve the school, the home, and the community. Such group projects tend to develop genuine motivation for the learners when the tasks to be accomplished are set in terms of the pupil's individual capacities for success.

Subgroups for Remedial Work. Diagnostic procedures will reveal weaknesses and gaps in the mathematics learning of pupils in any class, but particularly in heterogeneous classes. As such gaps and weaknesses are found, the pupils with similar difficiencies are organized into subgroups within the class for special instruction or practice. Subgroups for remedial work are only temporary and are disbanded as soon as the specific weaknesses have been corrected. With those pupils who are generally weak, as is more usually the case with heterogeneous classes, use of the other forms of differentiation mentioned here are considered.

In Small High Schools, Many Purposes— Many Curriculums

ALBERT I. OLIVER, JR.

Two INTERRELATED slogans—"Meet the needs of the learner" and "Provide for individual differences"—are ever present in modern educational discussions. Since the secondary schools of America are enrolling and retaining an increasingly complete cross section of our adolescent population, the average classroom teacher is now working with a pupil group which has tremendous range in abilities, interests, backgrounds, and purposes. Some schools have attempted to meet the situation by grouping their pupils homogeneously. At best this but reduces the range and still does not guarantee that the pupils thus grouped are homogeneous in all respects. Furthermore, there are many educators who do not subscribe to this particular philosophy of grouping.

There is also the fact that at least two-thirds of the high schools in this country have fewer than 200 pupils enrolled, and many of this group have less than 100 pupils in the four-year program. Such small high schools have but few teachers and can consequently offer relatively fewer courses than in the large city schools. Furthermore, this small pupil population makes it impractical to set up more than one section in any subject. How, then, can such schools, as well as those who do not favor grouping, provide mathematical offerings suitable for the varying needs and abilities?

When thinking of differentiation, the curriculum maker considers at least two aspects. First, there is the matter of purposes to be served. This typically has resulted in certain courses such as business arithmetic or college preparatory algebra. A second consideration in differentiation relates more to varying abilities. This affects the level of instruction. In the paragraphs which follow some guide lines will be presented to suggest how small schools are providing for both factors of differentiation.

Basic Philosophy. When a school is limited in its offerings, it is important to examine the proposed program in mathematics and make sure that first things are put first. Some searching questions, such as those following, are being considered:

1. Are we overdoing the concept of mathematics as a preparation for mathematics itself?
2. Have we tended to build a program aimed at college preparatory mathematics whereas very few of our pupils are going to college?
3. What does the community demand for its young people in terms of high-school preparation?
4. What have been the occupational choices and experiences of graduates and dropouts of the school?
5. Do we believe in a background of everyday mathematics for all pupils regardless of future special goals?
6. What local resources may be utilized in implementing any program of mathematics education?

In 1948 the writer made a survey of the educational programs of the small high schools throughout the United States. The study included opinions and experiences by curriculum workers and supervisors who had close contact with these small schools. Whereas the experts would emphasize such goals as citizenship training, maintenance of health, how to study, development of self-reliance, reading critically; the schools themselves were stressing English grammar and mathematical processes. An analysis of the details would indicate that we are challenged to spend more time on the development of long-range traits rather than devoting so much time to the mechanics of manipulating words and symbols.

Another guide may be found in studying carefully the aims of secondary education as related to mathematics. The recent *Bulletin 360* published by the Department of Instruction in Harrisburg, Pennsylvania, suggests the following objectives:

Learning experiences and materials in mathematics should be selected with due consideration to their contribution toward the attainment of desirable pupil growth. The following are goals for pupil development and therefore are guideposts for teachers in helping secondary-school pupils to:

1. Develop those mathematical behaviors which will better fit pupils for useful service to their community and for ethical living

2. Gain an appreciation of the importance and power of mathematics in the development of societies—past, present, and future

3. Discover vocational possibilities which open if pupils attain certain competencies in mathematics

4. Develop the ability to analyze and to solve problems of living

5. Recognize the various relationships within the field of mathematics

6. Recognize the relationships of mathematics to other fields of learning

7. Develop an understanding of concepts of time, space, and quantity

8. Build foundations which will permit the study of higher levels of mathematics

9. Analyze themselves as to their abilities to deal with quantitative relationships

10. Develop proficiency in mathematics as a method of communication

11. Establish desirable work habits and study skills.

The findings, the questions, the statements outlined above suggest that the mathematics program of the small high school rests primarily upon a program which may well be entitled Basic Mathematics. The Pennsylvania *Bulletin 360* suggests four areas as the nucleus for a separate course in each of the four years of high school. On the other hand some small schools may not find it possible to offer mathematics for each year and will thus select certain topics from each of these areas and present them in whatever plan they offer for the common learnings in mathematics. The four centers of emphasis suggested are:

Mathematics 9—Mathematics for the Individual
Mathematics 10—Mathematics for the Earner
Mathematics 11—Mathematics for the Citizen
Mathematics 12—Mathematics for the Consumer.

Teachers' Viewpoints. The effectiveness of any plan, however desirable on paper, depends upon the understanding and the philosophy of the individual teachers. For this reason it is important that the teacher-training institutions give even more attention to developing in mathematics teachers a belief in the value of basic mathematics. Furthermore, it should give them practical aids in teaching techniques which will allow a class, regardless of the subject designation, to be carried on in such a way that the instruction can be effectively differentiated. How can a teacher handle a multiple program in one classroom? Those who believe that this is important, are finding ways to do it. The first hurdle will be overcome when the teacher looks upon teaching as the guidance of learning rather than as the presentation and the checking of a lot of facts.

Important also are administration attitudes in these schools. For example, a young teacher undertook to teach mathematics in a community located in a coal mining region. Having some of the viewpoint outlined above, he made a survey of his classes and found that in a beginning algebra class of 29, only one pupil had any intention at all of going to college. The course itself was geared to college preparation; so this teacher began to incorporate more everyday mathematics into the course. Very soon, however, he was visited by the principal of the school who said, "What is this I hear about your tampering with the algebra class? At the beginning of the year I gave you the course outline. That is the way I want it taught!"

In general it is felt that the common mathematical needs of all pupils can be met through the basic courses previously mentioned. The special needs of certain small groups will call for material often found in shop math, business arithmetic, college algebra. A teacher skilled in the multiple class technique will work with the class on basic mathematics during general sessions and then set up the specialized work to be done by individuals or small groups during the supervised study period. Basic mathematics is thus a point of departure for individual purposes and interests.

The extent of a teacher's training, ability, and interest, the demands of a community, and individual student purposes may make it advisable to establish courses under the more conventional names of algebra and geometry. However, even with this group the pupils are entitled to have opportunities to become acquainted with the mathematics of everyday living.

A few practices are presented below to show how expanded programs are being operated.

Both solid and plane geometry are being incorporated into one course, henceforth known as geometry. From an educational point of view this is sound anyway since we are living in a three-dimensional world and not in "flat-land." Teachers will readily see how they can extend relationships of two dimensions into the third dimension without the necessity of undertaking formal proofs.

Some pupils undoubtedly will profit by a study of courses of advanced algebra and trigonometry. Whether or not these can be offered as separate courses in the regular schedule is dependent upon the school size and the teacher load in each situation. For the small school, however, two administrative devices are mentioned at this point to indicate what can be done to offset some of the usual limitations. First of these is alternation of subjects. By this plan, geometry might be offered to tenth-and eleventh-graders in the school year 1954–55. For the next school year the offerings for the tenth and eleventh graders would be advanced algebra or perhaps a half year of algebra and a half year of trigonometry. The reversing of the order of these two subject areas should bring no serious consequence if the teacher does careful planning and keeps in mind the background of the group before him each year.

Correspondence courses are particularly valuable in Grade XI or Grade XII of small high schools where only one or two pupils may want some more advanced courses such as trigonometry, solid geometry, or possibly even an introduction to elementary calculus. These supervised correspondence study courses work out especially well in the cases of individuals who really have the ability to do mathematics on an independent basis. In such courses the usual practice is to have the student assigned to the classroom or study hall where a mathematics teacher is present so that he may occasionally check upon the progress of the work or answer questions. The prepared lessons themselves, however, are sent back to the correspondence center. Excellent correspondence courses are available through extension centers of the University of Nebraska and the University of Wisconsin, among others.

While it is a fairly common experience to find people thinking of "curriculum" as synonymous with "course of study," it should be apparent from this article that curriculum is a highly individualized concept. An honest recognition of individual differences requires teaching techniques which will allow each pupil to learn in the way that is best for him. "Differentiated curriculums" means ultimately, then, more than several courses of study; it means improved methodology.

At the beginning of the year each pupil tells why he is taking the course. A summary should be made with the teacher asking, "How can we serve all these purposes?" One answer will be to group within the class in terms of similar *purposes*. Secondly, it should be emphasized that this is a class in mathematics with its many possibilities and is not just an arbitrarily limited branch such as Algebra I or Plane Geometry. The success of this approach is founded upon establishing some procedures, such as those mentioned below, and upon developing independent work habits in each pupil. Above all, it is important for the teacher to recognize and utilize the many opportunities for *guidance* in its many manifestations.

Unit Approach. Teaching by units offers several possibilities for meeting individual differences. Many units have limitations such that their potential has not been realized. For example, it is common to find units subject-centered, such as "A Unit on Circles", rather than pupil-centered, such as "How Does Geometry Help Me in My Daily Living?" While the first topic may have value for some pupils, it is too abstract and meaningless to satisfy the purposes and be within the comprehension level of all pupils. For the teacher trying to present differentiated curriculums, it is better to start the class in broad areas of mathematics and then to specialize within the unit activities.

Another limitation of many units is the lack of sufficient learning activities. Most units do not have *enough* activities or fail to have *variety* within the amount. Some of the more intelligent pupils do well with creative work or with research; others make their contribution through construction work, by manipulation, through cartooning, or by art ability. The key is to discover and utilize the abilities and the special interests of each one in the class. It is also desirable to include situations which call for group work as well as individual study. Group investigations and reports are important in noting social applications, in discovering underlying principles, in identifying problems and suggesting their solutions, and in summary activities.

Supervised Study. Teachers are more and more discovering the flexibility of supervised study. After a general session for introducing a new topic, the members of the class proceed on activities designed to develop the desired concepts and skills. The teacher spends her time going from desk to desk to provide the necessary guidance. If she finds a common difficulty, she calls this to the attention of the class as a whole and provides a brief explanation. If the difficulty is found with a small group, she gets those few together—perhaps at a corner of the blackboard—and goes over the matter with them. Sometimes there will be an individual presentation for the slowest. This personal visitation by the teacher allows on-the-spot corrections and thus reduces the chance of a pupil's doing the whole exercise incorrectly. As a teacher becomes skilled in supervised study, she uses but 10 minutes or so to present the topic and the rest of the hour is a work period.

In the matter of assignments not all will be doing the same thing at the same time. For the teacher preferring to keep the class together it is a common practice to present, on the board or by mimeographed outline, a weekly list of extra credit problems to be done after the minimum work is finished. Above all, one should avoid any plan whereby all work on a skill until the majority have mastered it; some will get bored, others will be proceeding to the next step too soon.

Another assignment plan is to have available a number of supplementary projects which each one works on as he finds time. These can be related to a special topic such as "Geometry in Advertising Signs," "Geometry in Tire Treads," "Geometry in Nature," and other such topics, or they can be long-range projects which do not depend too much upon any sequential mathematics, such as "Cost of Running My Father's Car" or "Cash Accounts." Some of the more capable pupils find a challenging experience in making review questions and problems to be given to the rest of the class. Others develop "Crossnumber Puzzles" which utilize numbers instead of letters in the familiar crossword pattern.

Correlation. How is mathematics related to other subjects? Here is a chance to differentiate according to special interests. The class is studying the measurement of time. For the girl interested in literature, there is an opportunity to investigate how Shakespeare, or some other author, mentions time and its measurement. A boy, fond of history, reports on how time was measured in George Washington's time. A girl discovers the importance of time in cooking. Through co-operation with the shop teacher some boys (and why not girls?) make sundials, sand-clocks, and many such articles.

Mathematics Laboratory. The whole procedure of individual and small group work is facilitated by the establishment of a mathematics laboratory (39). In a few schools an actual laboratory might be set aside as we do for chemistry and physics, but the majority will not be able to do this. At any rate, the greater value comes when every mathematics classroom takes on the appearance of a workshop. There should be a circulating library of books and pamphlets to be read during the supervised study period or at home. It is important to provide resource material for different reading levels since a pupil with a ninth-grade label may have a sixth-grade reading ability, and another in the same class might have twelfth-grade ability.

It must be realized that the laboratory concept as used here refers to more than physical items in a classroom. It is as an *atmosphere* in which problems may be worked out realistically through the medium of mathematics.

Class Supplements. To enrich the limited time available in the regular class periods, many schools have mathematics clubs available. Often these take on the nature of an "Einstein Club"— that is, they cater to those with a superior mathematical competence. This may help meet some needs of the gifted, but it overlooks the fact that many of the less gifted can gain much from the informal approach of a club. The same can be said of the seminar technique. Some interested teachers have given up one of their free periods per week or have taken an afternoon or evening to meet with a select group to investigate all kinds of mathematical situations. Nevertheless this is one way to provide expanded curriculums for a few.

SUMMARY

It is the individual pupil and not the group that learns, or fails to learn. In view of this some schools have tried grouping pupils homogeneously in terms of one or a very few limited factors. Some schools are too small to consider grouping. Others do not believe in homogeneous grouping as a principle. In the last analysis no group is ever really homogeneous in all factors. Many purposes call for many curriculums. Administrative devices such as alternation, correspondence courses, and selected acceleration are adjudged helpful in certain cases. Some teachers may be called upon to handle several classes within one class period. All such provisions challenge the teacher to conduct each class in such a way that each pupil has an opportunity to learn at the level and in the way that best suits him. Units, supervised study, mathematics laboratories, differentiated assignments are some of the most common classroom methods. We need, however, to experiment much more. The zeal, vigor, and enthusiasm of the experimenter will soon pay dividends in a more mathematically literate student body. The clue to success will come when more and more pupils say, "Oh, Miss Jones, don't tell us any more; we're getting on to these!"

4

Differentiated Curriculums Resulting From Pupil, Parent, Teacher, and Community Planning

Geometry Developed Through Pupil-Teacher Planning

ROBERT CASTATOR

IN THE field of mathematics, geometry is important in giving instructive experiences in the procedures of gathering and organizing data, presenting data, and drawing conclusions. Geometry has too often been treated solely as geometry and not as a subject which in addition to being a splendid example of deductive reasoning, important and interesting in itself, can also serve the purpose of creating a critical attitude of mind toward deduction and thinking in general.

It is perhaps these possibilities of geometry, even over its practical usefulness, which has caused most colleges and universities for so long to require the course of its entrants.

Geometry achieves its highest possibilities if, in addition to its direct and practical usefulness, it can establish a pattern of reasoning; if it can develop the power to think clearly in geometric situations and to use the same discrimination in nongeometric situations; if it can develop an appreciation of the place and function of definitions and postulates in the proof of any conclusion, geometric or nongeometric; if it can develop an attitude of mind which tends always to analyze situations, to understand their interrelationships, to question hasty conclusions, to express clearly precisely, and accurately, nongeometric as well as geometric ideas.

During the school year 1951–52 I taught a course at University High School, Iowa City, Iowa, which in my experiences has most closely approached fulfillment of these ideas. The following is a brief discussion of that course of study.

In the past years there has been a growing tendency in geometry to shift the emphasis from proving theorems and corollaries to solving or proving original exercises. Fewer and fewer theorems are proved in their entirety in the textbooks, many of the details being left to the pupil as an exercise. This trend has undoubtedly placed the emphasis where it belongs and has consequently helped eliminate the senseless memorization of proofs.

Four other developments are worthy of mention but none has been accepted to such an extent that it could properly be called a trend (28).

1. Introduction of nonmathematical situations into the course. The principal reason for this procedure is the belief that transfer of training is most likely to take place when that transfer of training is the direct aim of the teaching.

2. Inclusion of some solid geometry in the plane geometry course. There has been spasmodic experimentation with this procedure for a number of years and a few textbooks, particularly recent ones, have reflected a possible trend. For the most part, the three-dimensional work

is of an informal nature, serving largely as a means of applying two-dimensional relations. Reasons for such a policy are numerous; probably the most prominent one is the fact that some solid relations are of more practical value than much of the material included in plane geometry.

3. Emphasis on the nature of proof: its dependence upon definitions and assumptions only.

This procedure, as exemplified by Fawcetts' research (14), gives the pupil a more meaningful insight into the manner in which geometry is constructed. Taught by an experienced teacher, probably without a textbook, the pupil learns through his own efforts how a science develops in a logical fashion.

4. Reduction of the number of theorems and original exercises to be proved.

Recently many leaders in the field have become convinced that it is a waste of time to prove everything in the geometry course. After a certain number of relations have been formally demonstrated it is doubtful if the pupil gains much from further proof. The common recommendation calls for some proofs throughout the course, but many exercises (far more than is now common) are to be treated informally.

All four of these developments have been considered in the planning of this course of study along with the desire and attempt to get our students "into the game." As Dr. Kilpatrick points out, "as teachers we are concerned not merely with the objective goals reached by the pupils, but quite as truly with the actual searchings themselves. The good teacher of mathematics nowadays knows, perhaps as do few others, that to have searched and found leaves a pupil a different person from what he would be if he merely understands and accepts the results of others' search and formulation" (25).

In this school, mathematics is required through Grade IX and elective thereafter. Since functional competence embraces roughly one semester of algebra and a large part of the domain of informal geometry, Grade X is devoted to a study of second and third semester algebra, and Grade XI to plane and solid geometry. The first half of the twelfth year provides a review and extension of geometry while the second half is a study of trigonometry.

The eleventh year course consists of a study of the most important properties of the common geometric figures in two and three dimensions: triangles, rectangles, pyramids, cones, circles, spheres, and such. A few of these facts are discovered by measurements and ruler-and-compass construction, but the principal purpose of the course is to develop relationships by a process of reasoning. It is not absolutely essential that algebra be studied before geometry but it is strongly recommended. Since the student is to have the opportunity to reason about the subject matter of geometry in his own way, no definite sequence of theorems can be arranged in advance. The sequence for an individual pupil will vary with the environment, and it should not be overlooked that the teacher is a factor in this environment. He is acquainted with the domain which the pupil is about to enter, and it is his responsibility as guide and counselor to assist the pupil in developing whatever sequence will give him the greatest sense of accomplishment. What particular theorems are covered is not a matter of great concern, since the emphasis is to be placed on the nature of the process by which these theorems are proved and not on the theorems themselves. H. Vernon Price has taught this course since 1946, and through fairly intensive testing of available sorts has found several indications, two of which may be of considerable importance (36). The first of these is that a complete fusion of plane and solid geometry may produce better results than is now obtained through separate courses. This should be expected since geometry would then assume the "review and extend" quality which characterizes our algebra courses. Such overlearning is an important factor in promoting retention. The second, and by far the most interesting and far-reaching, is that, given proper content, organization, and methodology, one year of instruction may provide sufficient training for all but the most exacting curriculums. This is particularly promising for the thousands of schools in the country in which only one year of instruction in geometry can be provided.

No textbook is used for this course, due in part to the fact that no suitable textbook is available as a basic reference for our purposes. With the background established in the junior high school, a substantial number of relations are already somewhat familiar to the pupils and, although the laboratory approach is utilized extensively, many of the facts are simply recalled rather than discovered. In such cases, the major purpose becomes one of stating relationships accurately and organizing them into a logical sequence.

The content is ordered very much as it is in standard texts, with parallel and perpendicular lines and planes appearing early in the course and circles and spheres toward the end. Considerable care is exercised at the outset in familiarizing pupils with elementary concepts and with the essentials of perspective drawing. After the course gets underway, the work carries from two to three dimensions and vice versa quite naturally. Relations discovered in one space frequently have their counterparts in the other, with or without restrictions. Pupils quickly learn that such propositions as, "two lines which are perpendicular to the same line are parallel to each other" hold only in a plane and the knowledge forces upon them a super-carefulness of statement. Moreover, it tends to discourage those who would lift a few theorems from dad's old textbook in order to impress their fellow pupils.

A typical classroom activity is to have pupils work together in small groups in the development of a unit, using whatever materials—sketches, models, or perhaps tinkertoys—are available. Each group then presents its research to the class and few PhD candidates are subjected to a more rigorous grilling then these rivalries occasion. Once a proof has been accepted and is deemed important by teacher and pupils, it is incorporated into the class textbook. Each class member keeps an up-to-date copy of this class textbook to refer to in his work. The classbook contains three sections: definitions, assumptions, and theorems. Many theorems have been adopted for some time only to be revised later or perhaps deleted entirely after more knowledge and information have been gained by the students.

The problem of measuring achievement and of comparing the results with established norms is somewhat perplexing. Standardized tests are available for pupils completing plane geometry or solid geometry, but not for those who have studied parts of each. Very likely the average plane geometry class is less capable in mathematics than ours and the average solid geometry class more capable. In spite of these discrepancies, the only possible solution is to administer those examinations which exist. By far the best means of evaluation will consist of the teacher-made test with select questions supplemented by applicable questions suggested by the various available standardized tests.

From a pedagogical point of view, the major objectives of the course are:

1. To review the geometric concepts, relations, and skills which the pupils have already learned.

2. To develop many other important relationships of geometry.

3. To organize this body of material into a logical sequence.

4. To develop in the pupils a realization of the need for, and an understanding of, the nature of proof.

5. To promote an attitude of open-mindedness and critical evaluation of the results of experimentation and observation.

6. To provide adequate opportunity and guidance in the application of geometric principles and relations to practical problems.

From the standpoint of organization, the major objectives of the course are:

1. To unify the content of plane and solid geometry.

2. To organize this content in such a manner as to fit the needs of present-day pupils with their wide range of abilities.

3. To include the core material necessary to meet the entrance requirements of technical schools and colleges.

4. To place the course in the program of studies so the pupil will have the work concurrently with, or just prior to, the advanced courses in science.

The nature of this course is such that no proper sequence of content matter or material can be listed to be taught verbatim as a complete course. Rather it is considered as a guide for the teacher who must act as an interlocutor to direct the pupils' searches along paths of reasoning which lead to these goals. This calls for excellent teaching technique and the ability to see ahead of the pupils' reasoning in order to select those thoughts which eventually develop the course aims. The teacher must call upon the right pupil at the right time. The subject matter outline is as follows:

I. Introduction to plane and solid geometry
   A. Geometry highlights, past and present
      1. Early historical development
      2. Modern applications
      3. Brief biographical sketches of outstanding geometers.
   B. Foundations for plane and solid geometry
      1. Basic concepts and definitions
      2. Basic assumptions
      3. Angles and angle measurement.
   C. Fundamental constructions and drawings
      1. The protractor

　　2. Constructions with straightedge and compasses
　　3. Practice in drawing and lettering figures which involve combinations of lines, planes, and curved surfaces.
II. Figures formed by straight lines and planes
　A. Triangular figures
　　1. Development of the nature of formal proof
　　2. Assumptions and theorems
　　3. Constructions
　　4. Practical applications of triangles and pyramids
　　5. Original exercises
　　6. Fundamental concepts and definitions.
　B. Parallel and perpendicular lines and planes
　　1. Theorems and assumptions
　　2. Indirect reasoning
　　3. Forming converses and testing their validity
　　4. Constructions
　　5. Original exercises
　　6. Practical applications
　　7. Fundamental concepts and definitions.
　C. Angles of polygons and polyhedrons
　　1. Assumptions and theorems
　　2. Constructions
　　3. Practical applications in nature, architecture, and industry
　　4. Exercises applying the assumptions and theorems
　　5. Fundamental concepts and definitions.
　D. Quadrilaterals and prisms
　　1. Assumptions and theorems
　　2. Constructions
　　3. Exercises and practical applications
　　4. Fundamental concepts and definitions.
　E. Ratio, proportion, and similar figures
　　1. Assumptions and theorems
　　2. Constructions
　　3. Original exercises
　　4. Practical applications
　　5. Fundamental concepts and definitions.
III. Loci in two and three dimensions
　A. Fundamental locus theorems in a plane and in space
　B. Construction of loci in two-dimensions, drawing loci in three dimensions
　C. Intersecting loci
　D. Concurrent lines in a triangle
　E. Applications of loci.
IV. The circle and solids having a curved surface.
　A. Circles
　　1. Basic assumptions and theorems

      2. Constructions
      3. Uses of circles
      4. Practical problems and original exercises
      5. Fundamental concepts and definitions.
  B. Cylinders
      1. Basic assumptions and theorems
      2. Uses of cylinders
      3. Theory of limits as applied to cylinders
      4. Practical problems
      5. Fundamental concepts and definitions.
  C. Cones
      1. Basic assumptions and theorems
      2. Practical problems
      3. Fundamental concepts and definitions.
  D. Spheres
      1. Basic assumptions and theorems
      2. Practical problems
      3. Fundamental concepts and definitions.
V. Additional solid figures
  A. Figures on a sphere
  B. Applications
  C. Frustrums.

The above list is only a check list which the teacher will use as guideposts. Many of the theorems deemed important by the teacher may not be discovered by the class. In such a case the teacher must plan an attack in order to aid their discovery, but she must not become impatient or discouraged when such an instance arises and key theorems are passed by. On the other hand, many situations arise whereby a unit will produce an enormous amount of pertinent information. Many of these the teacher knows are unimportant in the development of the course, but in the eyes of the class they represent a magnificent accomplishment and probably are.

My experience suggests that many of the relations in three dimensions should be treated informally, perhaps postulated after experimentation and observation. The amount of emphasis to be placed on proof will depend upon the individual class. In general, however, the teacher will probably want to require formal demonstration for most of the relationships in unit two and then taper off to only an occasional proof in succeeding units. At no time would I completely abandon rigorous treatment.

No time allotments are necessary in this course of study due in part to the nature of the course but mostly because of the sequential study. As previously discussed, the first half of the twelfth year is a third semester of this course. It is very flexible and is altered from year to year depending upon the results of the geometry classbook of the preceding year. Suffice it here to say this represents the filling of gaps and bringing together of loose ends into a well-rounded complete study of the plane and solid geometry.

Working Together in Developing the Mathematics Curriculums

Lottchen Lipp Hunter

When the school and community put their heads together to plan some co-operative undertaking, results are often so successful that the thoughtful are left with the feeling that vast community resources for the furtherance of the welfare of boys and girls remain untapped. The earnestness and sincerity with which each participant in an educational council lends his best thinking to the identification of what boys, girls, and adults need is impressive and stimulating. The discovery of means of actually providing some solution for the fulfillment of these needs, though sometimes all too apparent, and making sure that the solution results in action, not just a surface display of good intentions, is important.

There is now discernible a trend towards improved school and community relations and towards better curriculum and community integration. The multiplicity of outcomes which reward joint effort has encouraged leaders of each group to discover avenues for communication with each other and to search for and remove blocks to planning and achievement. Although the true community school exists in a few situations, most localities attempt only small projects somewhat experimental in nature, or larger ventures with the core curriculum, multiple-track classes, and grouping within the classroom. The trend toward more adequate school and community integration is gradual, but it is real.

Educational groups are discovering that there are many interested people in a community who can help find home-grown solutions to prickly problems. These can be specific problems as well as those general objectives and policies with which lay people have usually been concerned. One of the most prickly and most persistent of problems is that of differentiating the curriculum, or arranging learning experiences which allow every student to get his "money's worth." It is an enormous responsibility to provide for such differentiation, knowing that each boy and girl has a growth pattern and rate, individually his or hers; that every pupil is growing in attitudes, emotions, intellect, and physique simultaneously; that every pupil must remain in school until a given age whether he is academically gifted or not. Wise educational leaders have started sharing this information and are looking to students and citizens for help in planning the discriminating program demanded by these variables.

When a girl helps her mother double a recipe, or a boy observes a carpenter figuring the dimensions of lumber needed for new porch steps, each is learning about fractions at some distance from the classroom and teacher. Countless other learning experiences are obtained outside the school, and the community should know that teachers, limited as they are by time and equipment, appreciate and value the educational possibilities offered by informal experiences with mathematics. Many school leaders are accepting the responsibility for co-ordinating the more formal efforts of various agencies interested in boys and girls and are acting as advisers in envisioning a differentiated program for the maximum, continuous development of young people. Community mores, economic and educational status, and institutions exert such powerful conditioning factors that there undoubtedly should be a pooling of these forces with those of the school lest there be much straining at cross-purposes. The curriculum for modern living should be amalgamated with every community activity of a desirable educational nature.

That the benefits from joint discussion and planning for curriculum development are mutual is widely recognized. Children, above all, profit when parents, employers, school personnel, and they themselves to a certain extent, are well-informed about the findings of research and experience in regard to the importance of maturity, interest, goals, individual differences, and other factors that influence learning. Business and industry profit when they receive into their ranks young men and women who, in their school years, have developed the work attitudes and skills which people in business and industry have felt were needed for economic competence and have recommended for inclusion in the curriculum. Parental hopes and dreams for their children are either more exactly fulfilled, or else modified toward realistic and attainable goals, when parents make use of the guidance information collected by the school.

Some school administrators view with doubt the entry of citizens and pupils into any phase of educational activity other than policy making. That they are neglecting potential support and creative suggestions for other phases—selection of content, materials, evaluation—is apparent from the enthusiasm and approval with which experiments involving everyone concerned with education are summarized. Wise leaders, by allowing parents and pupils to be in on plans from the very beginning, take them along on the same plane of understanding needs as themselves. By this process wrangling dissatisfaction with newer educational techniques, arising from lack of comprehension of the purposes and principles back of the newer practices, may in large part be avoided. For example, the community learns that far from neglecting fundamentals, there is more and more recognition of the importance of the development, extension, and maintenance of arithmetic skills. This is particularly true of the four fundamental operations, use of common and decimal fractions, problem-solving, ratio, and proportions, even for Grade XII students. Teachers have derived their knowledge that such emphasis upon fundamentals is important by giving heed to recommendations made by people in the community.

Knowledge about the way boys and girls learn anything, let alone mathematics, is sufficient reason why pupils should sit in on plans for utilizing classroom materials and community resources. Pupils can see their goals more clearly when they have had a part in setting them. A clear recognition of goals is primary to effective learning. Pupils are more interested—and interest is another factor which induces learning—in their school work when they have helped decide what is valuable for them to study and which methods will best obtain results. Such a large part of life activity takes place in committees or other groups these days that social learnings are a part of the mathematics curriculum. Even scientific research, to a great extent, is carried on by teams working purposefully toward well-planned goals.

From the larger community of nationally known industrial leaders, authors of mathematics textbooks, national commissions, and educational experts there is gradually accumulating a substantial amount of material resulting from their combined thinking about educational needs and problems. Nearly all large corporations maintain a division of their public relations department especially devoted to the production of educational materials and a request for a list of such materials is promptly supplied. A rapid survey of some of the publications (17, 18, 19, 27, 41) shows immediately that they are helpful in providing curricular material for different types of pupils. Some contain suggestions for the guidance of future scientists and engineers; others explain the opportunities open to craftsmen; some of the booklets, prepared in comic book style, are unusually attractive to younger pupils as well as informative.

Mathematics textbooks indicate that authors have consulted people in industry and business, since books are now obtainable (4, 26, 42) which suggest things to do or make that will lead students in the community to become acquainted with different job requirements and common business practices.

An entire issue of the widely known magazine, *The Mathematics Teacher*, was devoted to reports of talks given by industrial leaders before a meeting of the National Council of Teachers of Mathematics. Many hints for differentiating the curriculum may be obtained from suggestions offered in these talks (13, 29, 44). Further evidence that lay-school co-operation proves worthwhile is presented in articles and books such as, "School and Community Look at the Content of Consumer Mathematics," "A Job Survey as Class Motivation in General Mathematics," and *The Community School* (6, 20, 23, 24, 31, 33, 34).

A weekly radio program is supported by some communities, not only to interpret the work of the schools to the public, but also to bring special programs to classrooms and to present panels of students, teachers, parents, and other interested citizens in the discussion of timely issues. Of greatest importance, although it involves but a relatively few people, are the preplanning and meeting of minds which occur ahead of time, since the broadcast may or may not reach the audience for whom it is intended. In all planning, the requisities of effective communications are given thoughtful attention. Educational labels are used with caution or when used are carefully explained; time is allowed for an interchange of ideas.

It may be of interest to see the questions pondered by one of the panels of a regularly prepared educational series, "Pop Goes the Question." The topics are those which a member of the staff of the broadcasting station, two personnel directors from a large department store, a representative of a trucking service, two pupils, three teachers from different educational levels, and two parents, believed would be of interest to the audience listening to "Mathematics in the Wichita Public Schools." Modern ways of individualizing the curriculum were reported upon as the following questions were proposed and discussed:

1. Do students today know as much mathematics as they used to know when I went to school?
2. What mathematical skills do business and industry expect high-school students to have?
3. Parents often say, "They don't teach mathematics like they did when I went to school." Have methods of teaching mathematics changed much in recent years?
4. What is a sixth-grader and a twelfth-grader in our schools supposed to know about mathematics?
5. Is one year of mathematics (the present Kansas requirement) enough for the average student? What per cent of students take more than the one year in high school?
6. What specific changes have been made in the content of mathematics courses?

A skit for another program in the series "Citizens of Tomorrow" was entitled, "Why Take Mathematics?" It was planned and enacted by representatives from the staff of the radio station, students and teachers from mathematics classes in two different high schools, and the director of the state employment bureau.

How to tap the rich supply of human and physical resources in a community is a major problem. Teachers in one school received an enthusiastic response when they decided to uncover possibilities by conducting a Survey of Parents (22), a compilation of items from the 387 families represented in their classes. Information was filed on 4" x 6" cards and contained help for almost every phase of the curriculum. As pupils, teachers, and parents laid plans for the appropriate use of people having had unusual experiences or having held interesting positions, the curriculum was greatly expanded and enriched. The participating teachers believe that they are thus opening new avenues to better school-community relations and that the teaching-learning process is becoming more interesting and meaningful. Gifted, average, and nonacademic students are enabled to find enrichment adapted to their particular levels of maturity, their interests, and their capacities.

A group of teachers of mathematics in another community (43) believed that a collection of true "story problems" which could be discovered by pupils as they questioned parents, other relatives, business acquaintances, and their own experience, would help boys and girls appreciate the reality of mathematics and the worth of earnestly trying to understand mathematical processes. They also believed students would be impressed by the widespread use of mathematics and the importance of accuracy in even the simplest of computations performed by meter readers, mail clerks, truck drivers, and others in the less glamorous occupations. The schools seemed to be doing fairly well by their college-bound students, but students needing general mathematics were still offered experiences to a large extent lacking in interest and appropriateness.

All participation was voluntary and included Grade VII through Grade XII. Methods of collecting stories and their accompanying solutions and diagrams were optional. Here follows one of the guides developed to make sure parents understood their share in the project and to simplify the work of the committee of students and teachers who would later organize the stories into a usuable form.

REAL LIFE PROBLEMS FOR MATHEMATICS CLASSES

Pupils learn faster when they are interested in their problems and when they think that what they learn will be of actual use to them. To make problems seem realistic, students have used newspaper and magazine clippings, recipes, and other data for information in making up their own problems.

Some of the pupils have suggested that a collection of ways their fathers, mothers, and friends use mathematics would help them feel that problem-solving is important; other pupils and their teachers have agreed. For this reason, we are inviting your co-operation and are hoping you can send us worthwhile problems for our collection.

The contributions may involve any form of mathematics and any degree of difficulty. A committee will see that problems are distributed to the proper grade level. We are hoping to get one or more ordinary, typical problems from parents who are druggists, truckers, homemakers, cashiers, grocers, workers for the city, lawyers, salespersons, farmers and those holding many other kinds of jobs. The following items are suggestions only and any other types of mathematical processes, pictures, graphs, or bulletins of mathematical data will be usable and very much appreciated.

Addition, subtraction, multiplication, and division of whole numbers, common fractions, and decimal fractions

Percentage problems of all kinds

Squares, square roots, cubes, areas, volumes, board feet

Ratios and proportions, scale drawings

Tables of statistics, graphs

Constructions—any use of compass, straightedge, or other drafting tools

Formulas and some realistic values to use in them, equations.

TYPE OF JOB _____

YOUR NAME AND THAT OF EMPLOYER (if desired) _____

NAME OF STUDENT CONTRIBUTOR _____

STORIES AND SOLUTIONS OF PROBLEMS:

Stories were collected by an organization committee and placed in the usual categories of arithmetic, algebra, geometry, and trigonometry. They were also sorted into three approximate levels of difficulty—a, b, and c. It was the hope of the committee that by using letters, the nonacademic students as well as the average and the superior learner of mathematics could, without embarrassment, find that certain occupations use mathematics within the range of everyone's interest and capacity. Differentiated reading materials for students on the same grade level but at varying stages of maturity are available to teachers of the language arts and it was with the idea of providing themselves with similar arithmetic materials that certain teachers of the committee advised ranking problems a, b, c, rather than marking them for Grade VII and so on.

A 55-page booklet was prepared from the selected problems which were gleaned from the hundreds of contributions. The paper shortage limited the number included. Forty copies of the booklet were allowed each school in order that an entire class might use the booklets at one time. Teachers were informed that the problems were not intended for practice of skills as would be the scientifically selected problems of a textbook, but instead were to be used for motivating purposes. The stories make interesting reading:

Baby-sitter: multiplication of decimals, (a) arithmetic

37. Delores Morton says that this is one of her own business problems: I took care of Mrs. Miller's little boy, Jeff, for four hours one day, three hours the next day, and two hours the next day. At 25¢ an hour, how much money did I earn in those three days? (Ans. $2.25)

Sheet music librarian: addition of fractions, (a) arithmetic.

41. "I certainly found a funny use for fractions", reports Jimmy Burns. Sheet music is estimated at so many dollars per foot. Three piles have $12\frac{1}{2}$ inches, 20 inches, and $10\frac{1}{2}$ inches of music. Find out for Bob Strong's band, the total amount of sheet music in the three piles, in feet. (Ans. $3\frac{7}{12}$ ft.)

Upholsterer: division of fractions, (b) arithmetic

22. An upholsterer in the West Side Mattress Company told Carol Lassiter that he needed to know the exact center of the pieces of furniture to be covered. He asked her, "What is the exact center of a frame for a daveno $71\frac{3}{4}$ inches long?" (Ans. $35\frac{7}{8}$ in. from either end)

Photographer: evaluation of formulas, (a) algebra

2. Ronald Hill, an amateur photographer, tells us that an interesting use of the formula is in finding the diaphragm opening (the F number) on a camera. The F number = guide number/distance.

If the guide number, according to the table is 170 and the camera is placed at a distance of 20 feet away from the subject for the picture, find the F setting. (Ans. 8.5)

MULTIPLE VALUES MAY BE DERIVED FROM PUPIL-TEACHER-PARENT-
COMMUNITY PLANS FOR A DIFFERENTIATED CURRICULUM

A summary of the outcomes of the above project to adjust curricular materials by the inclusion of interested adults in school planning lists the following possible values:

1. From the Pupil's Standpoint:

    a. The committee agrees with Noland Wallace who said, "The greatest good from these problems has already been realized. It is the good the students got when they hunted out the problems."
    b. Pupils obtained an idea of what business people think important: accuracy, a favorable attitude toward work, mathematics, and co-operation.
    c. Pupils have a tendency to overlook the fact that the use of mathematics in one form or another can be found in almost any job. (Homemaking was considered a job.) This project of collecting problems emphasizes the multitude of uses for mathematics.
    d. Helping with the collection was better for students than simply looking at problems which might have been collected solely by the teachers. Active pupil participation facilitates learning.
    e. Verbal problems are usually approached by students with an attitude of fear, and hence dislike. Clothing problems with the details and background of actual jobs may help remove these unfortunate attitudes.
    f. Pupils have become more disposed, we hope, to want to use their mathematical skills in their everyday quantitative experiences outside of school.
    g. Pupils were given the experience of participating in a project where they learned to plan co-operatively with students and teachers in other schools as well as in their own.
    h. Pupils learned to take advantage of the opportunities offered by community resource people.

2. From the Teacher's Standpoint:

    a. The committee knows that few teachers limit themselves to a single textbook, and that they already have a large collection of illustrative problems which they use to create student interest and understanding. The committee hopes that some of these problems assembled here can be used to add further interest and variety to this stock of each teacher's own materials.
    b. New teachers may appreciate some of these supplementary problems to provide a nucleus of illustrative problems.
    c. Teachers may obtain suggestions from this project which will help them in carrying out some similar project in the future.
    d. Activities such as this offer teachers improved opportunities to know students and their parents. Teachers will then be able to offer guidance appropriate to individual students as an integral part of classroom teaching.
    e. This project provided opportunity to try teacher-pupil planned experiences and democratic work procedures.

3. From the Community's Standpoint:

a. Public relations were bettered when parents saw that an effort was made to obtain useful problems instead of those which are tricky and improbable.

b. Industry is pleased to see that the schools are trying to improve workers' attitudes, accuracy, and skill.

c. Parents were enabled to show their concern for their children's welfare, and children were benefited by knowing that their parents took an interest in them.

d. Many adults remember mathematics with dislike and are apt to pass this attitude on to their children. Projects showing that mathematics has improved since their day and is no longer something obtained entirely from a textbook help eliminate this distaste.

e. Mr. Crellin, of the Santa Fe Trailways, Inc., Trucking Division, volunteered to come to the schools at any time to talk to students and participated in the North High School Career Day. Mrs. Mike came to a classroom to help with a discussion of measurement in the home, giving explanations of, "A pint's a pound the world around," and what one does about half an egg for a recipe. These two persons are representative of many parents or nonparents who could spare a little time to the schools and whose interest it would be to our extreme advantage to utilize.

5

Guidance for the Optimum Use of Differentiated Curriculums

The Importance of Early Guidance at the Junior High School Level

ALICE M. HACH

THERE is, perhaps, no better place to start a guidance program in mathematics than when a child enters the seventh grade. Here is a point in a child's education where the broad general offering of the elementary school is beginning to narrow down to the place where children will have to make decisions and choices.

After one more year most children will be confronted with the important question, "Should I take algebra or general mathematics?" It is then that he may suddenly become aware of these facts: that his arithmetic foundation is not strong enough to give him unlimited choices in higher mathematics; that he should have developed better work habits in order to be recommended by a teacher for a particular course; that he should have built up his arithmetic skills in Grade VII and Grade VIII because success in the new course he desires depends on a good foundation. He may also realize that certain types of careers require certain programs of study, and that although he liked the introduction to algebra, general mathematics might be more useful to him in his future plans.

The child may show his bewilderment by such remarks as: "What is algebra, anyway?" "What is geometry?" "I know I can get it if I work, but I just didn't work in the seventh and eighth grades." "Do I need these courses to get into college?" "Do I need algebra and geometry to graduate?" "Can't I take algebra, even if I don't want to take the remedial arithmetic?" "Will general mathematics give me the same credit as algebra?"

Added to the bewilderment of the child is the concern of the parents. They, too, may suddenly become aware that the child is not qualified to make a choice of the courses offered. It is now that they realize the importance to the child of good mathematics grades.

What can we do to ease the tension, the disappointment, the bewilderment for a child at the age when there is already considerable nervous tension? What can we do to help the parents?

First let us look at a few facts regarding the mathematics program in junior high school:

1. Most children will have only two more years of a single-track program in mathematics.

2. In these two years there is an opportunity and often the last opportunity to build understandings and skills in arithmetic.

3. The course in arithmetic taken in the elementary school changes to a mathematics course in junior high school. Therefore, arithmetic is no longer the only objective, but intuitive geometry and an introduction to algebra are also a part of the course.

Whether a child recognizes these facts depends to a great extent on whether his teacher guides him in developing this perspective.

It seems too bad to delegate this responsibility to a homeroom teacher, guidance teacher, or a social studies teacher when the mathematics class can utilize this guidance information to strengthen the course and motivate the work. Likewise, it seems unfortunate to confront the child with these important ideas in a limited period of time. Regardless of where the guidance is done or who does the guiding, it is difficult for a child to get a proper perspective when the guidance is crowded into a few weeks.

Let us analyze the program in mathematics to determine *where* there are opportunities to guide a child so he will be able to make a wise choice at the time when it will be needed. If we were to compile a list of the ways guidance can be carried on as a part of the regular mathematics program it might consist of the following:

1. To use the first few days of the seventh grade to acquaint children with the true nature and purposes of the junior high school mathematics program.

2. To use the grades at the end of the first grading period to point out how grades are a measure of progress and to stress the relationship of this progress to the child's future choices in mathematics. Each subsequent grading period then offers an opportunity for a child to evaluate his growth.

3. To use a check list of work habits on report cards, *only* when the habits listed can be objectively measured by the teacher and pupil. Only if this is true can an evaluation of work habits be of any value in determining the growth and development of those characteristics needed for specific types of study.

4. To use standardized tests to provide specific information for the teacher, the child, and the parents. Ways can then be provided for a child to overcome specific deficiencies. It is important that the child and parents understand the place of standardized tests in the child's total mathematics program.

5. To have parent conferences early enough in junior high school to give parents an opportunity to understand the needs of a child while he is still on the single-track program in mathematics. The more nearly a parent understands the progress of the child throughout the junior high school the better able he is to help the child in making wise decisions regarding the selection of future courses.

6. To use professional articles, guidance bulletins, and all such helps as special project material. This might be offered throughout a child's mathematics program.

7. To show the relationship of the material that is being studied to future courses in mathematics. For example the section on banking,

budgets, and business accounts might be related to general mathematics. Plane figures might be related to plane geometry, solids to solid geometry, while formulas might be shown as developing fundamental principles of algebra. In each case the respective future textbook might be examined. This gives the child an opportunity to see not only the relationship of the new material to that which is familiar, but also to recognize its place in future courses.

8. To use talks by pupils regarding mathematics courses. A student from an algebra class and one from a general mathematics class might be invited to talk to the eighth grade students, and a student from a geometry class might talk to the algebra students.

9. To use a display of advanced texts with notations explaining the prerequisites needed for each of the courses and the grade level at which the course can be studied.

10. To use aptitude tests to give the pupil another measure of his chances for success in a particular course. Pupils and parents need to understand the limitations of such a test as well as its value to the pupil. It is helpful for the parents and the child to know that when aptitude tests are used with *other* measures, they can be useful devices for guidance.

In these various ways guidance becomes a regular part of the mathematics program. This gives a child two years rather than a few weeks to study his needs, his weaknesses, and his strength. He may then be prepared to make a wise decision when needed.

Guidance in the Mathematics Program

LEE IRVIN

DURING the schoolyear of 1951–52, the Southern section of the California Mathematics Council sponsored a research project concerned with the offerings in arithmetic and other nontraditional mathematics courses at the high-school level. (For purposes of this report, the term "nontraditional" mathematics courses will refer to all high-school mathematics courses other than the "traditional college preparatory sequence" of Algebra 1, Plane Geometry, Algebra 2, Trigonometry, and Solid Geometry.) The nature of the study was that of "action research" such as was recently proposed by the Commission on Life Adjustment Education. Representatives of 92 schools, situated in 35 states and the

District of Columbia, took part in the project by supplying information concerning their present offerings and by outlining certain plans in progress for the improvement of their mathematics programs. The reports from participating schools included information regarding three main aspects of the problems involved in the reorganization of the mathematics program: (a) the administrative aspects, including guidance and the programing of students, (b) the problems of selecting and organizing materials and subject matter content for the different courses, and (c) matters regarding teaching procedures and methods of evaluation.

Information obtained from the five-page questionnaire was supplemented by classroom visits to 10 of the schools in question, by a library survey of related literature, and by a detailed study of the work being offered by 15 of the selected schools, each of which gave one or more of 19 courses that appeared to be representative of current nontraditional mathematics offerings.

It is with portions of the first division of the research project that the present report is concerned.

PROGRAMS OFFERED

It was found that 74 of the 92 co-operating schools offered a multiple-track mathematics program; 16 offered a double-track program at the ninth or twelfth grade level or at the ninth and twelfth grade levels; and 38 offered "related mathematics" in connection with industrial arts, agricultural, homemaking, or prenursing curriculums. These courses were offered by 43 of the schools in a two-to-four-year sequence, and 33 of the 74 were offering two or three differentiated nontraditional courses.

It might be noted here that the Committee for Economic Development has formed several local research projects for the purpose of improving the teaching of economics in secondary schools. There were 25 workshops held in 1952 and 30 more were scheduled to be set up during 1953. There have been 14 research centers established, and 10 more will be formed this year. One of the CED's recent workshops in economic education was attended by 70 school administrators from 22 states. CED believes that both business men and educators can contribute importantly in national economic affairs. This group feels that business men are practical but that they tend to overlook basic principles and theories, while educators and other "masters of theory" have a tendency to overlook the practical side. Teachers, especially mathematics teachers, could find much of value in a review of the economic workshop discussions because many of the ideas are based upon mathematical principles. Teachers of upper level high-school pupils could point out the growing fields in business and economics, as well as in industry, where there is a need of young people who have good mathematical backgrounds.

It may be seen, then, that the offering of a sequence of well-planned mathematics courses in the various areas of mathematics education becomes a matter of deep concern to the interested administrator. Not only must he and his mathematics department head lead in the work of curriculum reorganization but he must help in the selection of teachers who are in sympathy with the ideas behind the changes, and it is he, too, who must worry about the matter from the financial standpoint. It is the administrator, too, who must plan for counselors who will help the students to take advantage of the various types of courses according to their individual needs, plans, capacities, and abilities.

COUNSELORS PROVIDED

While it is to be understood that plans for a multiple-track mathematics program are not made without careful consideration of the school population, it must also be understood that the best-planned program will fail to meet its objectives unless pupil programing is accompanied with proper counseling. The mathematics teachers and the counselors must have a meeting of minds concerning the value of the courses offered and regarding the type of pupils to be counseled into those courses. Certain mathematics teachers "beating the drums" for the value of the traditional "college preparatory" program and one or two "academic minded" counselors can completely sabotage a well-planned multiple-track program. It may be seen, therefore, that adequate and informed counseling, both from the mathematics teachers and from the counseling staff, is a necessary factor in handling the problems of a multiple-track program.

The 88 of the 92 selected schools co-operating in the study (96 per cent) reported definite guidance programs and well-defined procedures for selecting and enrolling students in the various mathematics classes. The reported plans varied from simple commonly used methods to some rather complex procedures. The majority of the plans, however, included a consideration of the following items: (a) the pupil's past achievements, (b) the teachers' recommendations, (c) reading comprehension test results, (d) the pupil's special interests or vocational preferences, (e) his IQ scores, and (f) his parents' wishes.

It was interesting to note that 81 of the co-operating schools (88 per cent) reported increasing mathematics enrollments, and that 86 schools (94 per cent) reported decreasing failures in mathematics classes. Thus it would seem that something of value is gained from encouraging pupils to enter classes from which they can profit most and that adequate, informed counseling during programing will undoubtedly aid in the adjustments of students, thus lowering the percentage of failures in the classes.

Many of the schools presented detailed information regarding their programing procedures and continuing work in guidance through the various mathematics classes. Worthy of special note were the plans from the following schools: the Shorewood High School in Milwaukee, Wisconsin; one of the large schools in Delaware; the San Diego City Schools in San Diego, California; the Waukegan Township High School, Waukegan, Illinois; the Rosemead High School, Rosemead, California; the schools of Washington, D. C.; the schools of Portland, Oregon; and the Smith High School, and other community high schools of Atlanta, Georgia.

For illustrative purposes, two of these plans will be reviewed briefly at this time; namely, the plans of the Waukegan Township High School and those of the Rosemead High School.

Members of the mathematics department of the Waukegan Township High School, Waukegan, Illinois, including Grade IX through Grade XII, have done an enormous amount of work during the last few years in reorganizing the mathematics program and in planning means of giving guidance to the students. This school has already set up a two-year sequence of a double-track mathematics program, and extensions of the plan are now in process.

All eighth grade pupils in Waukegan are given the Advanced Arithmetic Test of the Stanford Achievement Test Battery. The Snader General Mathematics Test is also used at times in this program. The resulting scores, together with such items as intelligence scores, reading achievement level, teachers' recommendations, parents' wishes, and the student's choice are used to program the pupil into the beginning mathematics course of one of five curriculums offered in Waukegan.

The different curriculums offered at Waukegan are as follows: (a) general studies, (b) commercial field, (c) technical preparation, (d) general college preparatory, and (e) scientific and professional. Enrolling pupils are advised concerning the various mathematics courses offered within the limits of these curriculums. The pupil will be guided, according to his abilities and previous record, into the program which would be most likely to meet his needs. The mathematics courses offered, corresponding to the curriculums listed above, are as follows: (a) basic mathematics or general mathematics, (b) business arithmetic, (c) shop mathematics, (d) algebra for general college preparation, and (e) algebra for science, mathematics, and engineering majors.

This school made a special report concerning its ninth grade basic mathematics classes of which there were, at that time, six sections with others in the process of formation. These classes were being taught by special teachers who like to teach such sections and who have had training in guidance techniques, in elementary methods, and in methods of teaching remedial arithmetic and remedial reading. Thus, the guidance process is continued as a part of the teaching program, and the way is prepared for fewer programing problems as the students begin to realize their needs and capacities.

In the Rosemead High School, Rosemead, California, the counselors and the registrar spend several days each spring in each of the "feeder" schools, talking with the prospective freshmen and preparing preregistration cards. Some time before the visit of the counselors and the registrar, the school's *Registration Manual for Freshmen* is given to each homeroom teacher of the classes to be visited. For approximately a week before the scheduled visit, the pupils and their homeroom teacher discuss the information given in the manual which describes the high school courses open to entering freshmen. Each pupil also takes a manual home with him for a day or two in order to discuss the program with his parents.

At the time of the preliminary registration, the counselors and the registrar consider all test data and other records of achievement and activities for each pupil as his card is prepared. The pupils are programed into classes which seem most suitable for them and which, in most cases, have the parents' advance approval.

In regard to the mathematics registration, the counselors and registrar are guided by each pupil's grades, his expressed like or dislike for mathematics, his vocational and recreational interests, his reading ability, and scores made on tests of the fundamentals of arithmetic and of problem-solving ability.

There are five classes into which the entering students may be scheduled: (a) basic mathematics, Type 1, for students scoring below 7.0 grade placement level either in fundamentals of arithmetic or in problem-solving ability; (b) intermediate mathematics for the student scoring 7.0 to 8.5 on the tests used; (c) secondary mathematics for those students of average or above average ability who do not care to take algebra; (d) algebra for those students who wish it and whose scores in both arithmetic and reading ability justify such scheduling; and (e) a class in everyday business training, which is a core subject for the secretarial training program.

After these students reach the various mathematics classes, guidance continues in connection with class work. The students have access to the high-school *Guidance Pamphlet* published by the National Council of Teachers of Mathematics. They also have reading privileges during one class period each week from a classroom reading shelf containing several books describing various occupations, and numerous magazines dealing with topics in the fields of engineering, science, industrial arts, business, and economics.

The pupils are given a department prepared booklet which

they may keep in their notebooks and which will be found useful during the preregistration period in the following spring. This little booklet, *Your High School Mathematics Program*, describes the mathematics courses offered by the school and lists 150 occupations which demand a knowledge of mathematics. The first page of the booklet is reproduced below:

YOUR HIGH SCHOOL MATHEMATICS PROGRAM

1. What kinds of mathematics are offered at *your* high school?

    a. See the "eighteen programs" sheet in this folder.

    b. Talk with the shop teachers, the business education teachers, the science teachers, the mathematics teachers, and your counselors.

2. What are some of the occupations that require the use of mathematics?

    a. Study the National Council's *Pamphlet.*

    b. See the "Occupations" sheet of this folder.

    c. Talk with the counselors, your parents, and friends in several different occupations.

3. What kinds of mathematics are required by different jobs?

    a. Notice the divisions of the "eighteen programs" sheet in this folder.

    b. Talk with people in different occupations.

4. Should a high-school pupil take four years of mathematics?

    a. Consider the answers you have found to the three questions asked above.

5. What kind of mathematics program should *you* plan for *your* four years of high school?

    a. Do you want mathematics for personal or business use?

    b. Do you want mathematics for semiprofessional and industrial use?

    c. Do you want mathematics as background for professional trainng in science or engineering?

As was mentioned in the reproduced page from the booklet, students in this particular school have a choice of 18 different programs of four years of mathematics. Thus, for each of his four years of high school, a pupil may take some course that will contribute both to the development of functional competence in mathematics and to the growth of his special interests.

The "Eighteen Suggested Programs," with mathematics courses named (but not described as they are in the booklet) are listed below:

FOR BUSINESS USE

Basic Mathematics
Intermediate Mathematics
Secondary Mathematics
Business Arithmetic

Intermediate Mathematics
Secondary Mathematics
Business Arithmetic
Bookkeeping

Everyday Business
Intermediate Mathematics
Machine Calculation
Bookkeeping

Secondary Mathematics
Bookkeeping
Machine Calculation
Office Training

Intermediate or Secondary Math-
  ematics
Business Arithmetic
Bookkeeping
Machine Calculation

Basic or Intermediate Math-
  ematics
Business Arithmetic
Machine Calculation
Office Training

FOR SEMIPROFESSIONAL ENGINEERING OR FOR
INDUSTRIAL USE[1]

Basic or Intermediate Math-
  ematics
Secondary Mathematics
Practical Geometry
Industrial Mathematics

Basic or Intermediate Math-
  ematics
Business Arithmetic
Secondary Mathematics
Algebra 1

Secondary Mathematics
Algebra 1
Practical Geometry
Algebra 2 or Trigonometry and
  Solid Geometry

Secondary Mathematics
Practical Geometry
Industrial Mathematics
Advanced Shop

Intermediate Mathematics
Secondary Mathematics
Algebra 1
Plane Geometry

Secondary Mathematics
Practical Geometry
Algebra 1
Trigonometry and Solid Ge-
  ometry

---

[1] All advanced shops—electrical, wood-working, machine, radio, and such—are double periods which include related mathematics. Also, as has been mentioned in other reports of the presently described investigation, the print shop work includes certain instruction both in related mathematics and in related English.

Intermediate or Secondary Mathematics   Secondary Mathematics
  ematics   Algebra 1
Business Arithmetic   Machine Calculation
Bookkeeping   Industrial Mathematics
Algebra 1

FOR PREPROFESSIONAL TRAINING IN SCIENCE OR ENGINEERING[2]

Secondary Mathematics   Algebra 1
Algebra 1   Plane Geometry
Plane Geometry   Algebra 2
Algebra 2   Trigonometry and Solid Geometry

Secondary Mathematics   Algebra 1
Algebra 1   Industrial Mathematics
Plane Geometry   Plane Geometry
Trigonometry and Solid Geometry   Algebra 2

Science majors are counseled to take some form of preprofessional mathematics credit during each year of their high-school careers, and shop majors are counseled to take some form of semiprofessional mathematics courses during at least three years of their high-school work. Such courses would be of special importance to students majoring in electrical, machine, or radio shop.

Home-making majors are counseled to take either business arithmetic or bookkeeping for a thorough understanding of household and business methods in buying and budgeting. They are also advised that secondary mathematics and machine calculation might be useful should the pupil ever wish or need to obtain part-time work in addition to her homemaking career.

Business majors, as they progress through school, will realize that their mathematical abilities should be kept at working level at all times. They will probably want to become familiar with algebra, too, as it is used in many banking and insurance problems.[3] By reading the vocational information regarding jobs in the world of business, the pupils will find that a knowledge of

---

[2] Grades of "A" or "B" are required in this group in order to count as preprofessional training. In general, the courses are from the "traditional" mathematics sequence.

[3] The secondary-mathematics course includes a nine-weeks unit in algebra.

mathematics is the key to many doors in the areas of business, finance, and the social sciences.

In this particular school, the advertising and salesmanship pupils find a need for mathematics, and the art and music pupils are also advised to take "brush-up" courses if they feel that they are weak in the fundamentals of arithmetic. Thus, finally, all the students are not only required to take at least one year of mathematics (a graduation requirement) but they are led to a realization of the importance of mathematics in the world today.

CLASSROOM ASPECTS OF THE GUIDANCE PROBLEM

Almost all personnel in the teaching profession are aware of the fact that guidance is a continuous process, that it does not end with the programing of the student, and that it cannot be confined to the counselors' offices. Guidance is a definite part of the classroom work; it becomes background for the motivation offered the pupil, for the teaching techniques used, for the subject matter included in the courses, and for the evaluation which follows and which accompanies all good teaching.

MOTIVATION OFFERED

The teachers and department chairmen replying to the council's questionnaire listed many methods of motivating the student. The methods mentioned most frequently may be grouped as follows: (a) Using discussions and reports regarding the relation of mathematics to the world of work, (b) Using problems taken from other school subjects and from school activities of the extra-class type, (c) Building a classroom library of books, newspaper clippings, and magazine articles that deal with mathematical topics, (d) Using the bulletin board for displays of posters, pictures, graphs, charts, and maps, (e) Using a variety of plastic containers for measurement experiments; using blocks, cubes, spheres, and other solids; using counting or computing devices of various kinds; using certain films, filmstrips, and slides, (f) Using selected recreational mathematical problems or puzzles, and (g) Changing methods and types of work from time to time.

It is significant to note that the majority of the co-operating reporters included the above-listed items under "Motivation" rather than under the heading of "Teaching Techniques." It is conceivable that mathematics subject matter can be taught, and has been taught, without the use of some or any of the procedures listed above, but much of the motivating force and many of the guidance possibilities, both of the educational and vocational types, would thus be lost or ignored.

TABLE 1

MOST FREQUENTLY REPORTED PRACTICES IN PROVIDING FOR INDIVIDUAL DIFFERENCES WITHIN THE CLASSROOM

PRACTICE	NO.	%	NO.	%
Differentiated assignments			67	86
Special lessons for weaker pupils	54	69		
Special lessons for stronger pupils	33	42		
Special reports on current topics	14	18		
Small groups within the class			29	37
Work on different aspects of same topic	17	22		
Work on different assignments	12	15		
Projects			34	44
Construction of visual aids	28	36		
Demonstration of mathematical principles	7	9		
Scrapbooks	12	15		
Notebooks	22	28		
Taking charge of bulletin boards	9	12		
Work almost entirely individualized			8	10
Supervised study within the classroom			42	54
Use of Strathmore Sheets (word problems; *not* computation exercises)			11	14
Use of Arith-O cards and similar games			7	9
Use of much supplementary work			62	80
Duplicated materials	42	54		
Several different textbooks for supplementary work and a "reading or reference corner"	15	19		
Use of many diagnostic tests (locally prepared; not standardized)			49	63
Use of resource units tailored to fit the mathematics sequence being taught			14	18
Special sections of the class work with Adapted Materials			3	4

This table includes replies from 78 high schools in which the mathematics program has been revised to include a two-to-four-year sequence of second- or third-track mathematics. The first line of the table may be read thus: There were 67 of the schools, or eighty-six per cent of them, using differentiated assignments as a means of providing for individual differences within the classroom.[4]

[4] Data taken from a report of a Special Research Project (1951-52) sponsored by the Southern Section of the California Mathematics Council.

INDIVIDUAL DIFFERENCES CONSIDERED

A mathematics program which would provide adequately for individual differences must be so planned as to make provisions in each of the following ways: (a) through the offering of differentiated courses, (b) through the offering of at least one series, or sequence, of nontraditional courses as well as the offering of elective courses for special-interest groups, (c) through the use of carefully developed mathematical learning sequences and the use of a spiral treatment of mathematical topics, and (d) through the motivation offered and through the teaching procedures used.

Table 1 indicates to some extent the ways in which the fourth method of providing for individual differences may be used. In much the same way that making provisions for pupil motivation is a part of teaching procedure, making adequate plans to provide for individual differences within the classroom is also a part of teaching procedure.

The Mathematics Teacher's Part in Effective Guidance for Optimum Use of Differentiated Curriculums

DOUGLASS BROWN

THE writer has taught junior and senior high school mathematics in two different schools for 13 years and he has served as a counselor and guidance administrator in four different high schools for 16 years. Naturally, during these years (five of which overlapped) the writer has almost daily faced the vital question, "Who should take what mathematics?" Gradually he has arrived at the tentative judgment that there are four categories of secondary school mathematics pupils and that there should be consequently four categories of curricular offerings. These offerings would be for: (a) The pupil who feels no interest in mathematics and would be studying it unwillingly and primarily or solely as a present and future consumer; (b) The pupil who has some interest and is studying it primarily as a part of a liberal education; (c) The pupil who may or may not have interest in mathematics, but who is studying it because he does have interest in applied mechanics and knows his need for it as a machinist, toolmaker, draftsman, or other such trades; (d) The pupil who has high interest in mathematics, and average or superior ability, and who expects to use mathematics as a professional worker in the field of teaching, chemistry, insurance, engineering, or other such professional fields.

There seems to be a consensus of professional opinion that differentiation in curricular offerings, including those in mathematics, should begin at the ninth-grade level. It is logical then to conclude that guidance work, in an effort to effect proper placement in the high-school mathematics curriculums, must begin at least as early as the seventh grade. Indeed some guidance efforts might well be expended as soon as the pupil makes his first more or less fanciful vocational choice, which may occur as early as the third grade. The counselor or homeroom teacher or principal (or whatever a particular school's special guidance functionary is called) and the mathematics teacher should share co-operatively the responsibility of aiding the pupil in the making of his curricular choice in mathematics. The parents, too, should share in this work. Unfortunately the parents' "help" sometimes begins and ends with such an admonition to his child as, "Jane, whatever you do, don't take geometry. I almost failed it!"

The writer believes that the counselor's principal functions in providing guidance for optimum use of differentiated curriculums are: (a) encouraging the teacher to contribute, and showing him how he can contribute to the pupil's cumulative record; (b) administering standardized tests of interest, ability, and achievement (which will, of course, become a part of the cumulative record); (c) interpreting, through individual interview, the pupil's cumulative record and showing pupil the relationship of his individual characteristics to the curricular offerings and to occupational opportunities; (d) helping provide material for the teacher's classroom use concerning the relationship of specialized curriculums to vocational opportunities; (e) revealing to the teacher special interests and abilities of the pupil.

Neither the seventh and eighth grade mathematics teachers— nor those or any other level—should abdicate their guidance responsibility. The writer has known some mathematics teachers who took the attitude, "They've hired a counselor; that's his job. Let him do something to earn his pay." Where that attitude exists in all probability it is partly the counselor's fault. However, the pupil's best interests cannot possibly be served unless the teacher of mathematics assumes some guidance responsibility. And if the teacher is emotionally mature enough to do his part, in the face of the counselor's seeming inefficiency or lassitude, then the counselor very probably will be motivated to fulfill his responsibility to the pupil more thoroughly. If the counselor and the classroom teacher both focus their attention on *serving the pupil* there need never be any real conflict.

Here are 10 specific ways in which the writer, especially at the junior high-school level, tried to provide effective guidance for optimum use of differentiated curriculums in mathematics:

1. Teach for understanding, not for mere facility in manipulation. The writer had taught mathematics for several years before anyone helped him to grasp the importance of this concept. Afterward then, by contrast, he realized that an appreciable percentage of mathematics pupils who have not been taught to understand it fail to realize their highest potential as mathematics students. Many such pupils who do not truly belong there would then place themselves eventually in the first category mentioned above, namely, among those who feel no interest and who study mathematics unwillingly. Surely whenever this occurs it is tragic for several reasons.

2. Provide orientation for each of his own mathematics classes regardless of how much or how little orientation the school's organized guidance program provides. This orientation during the first three weeks, perhaps, of the class should attempt to accomplish these four goals: (a) establishment of rapport between the pupils and the teacher; (b) establishment of a friendly feeling among the pupils of the class, which would include the ability of each to call every classmate by name; (c) some understanding by the pupils of the purpose of the particular course and its potential contribution to their total education; (d) a rather complete comprehension of how to study this particular subject which will have elements of difference from the study of literature, of social studies, and other such courses.

3. Ascertain individual differences and recognize them by providing differential assignments and projects which will tend to give some satisfaction to each pupil by enabling him to do something which he likes and can do. The writer is very conscious of how extremely difficult it is for the teacher to do this with 100 per cent success, but the teacher

cannot have even 20 per cent success in providing for individual differences unless he strives for 100 per cent success.

4. Provide a definite challenge to the ability of the above-average pupil. This is, of course, similar to point three above, but it is mentioned separately because of the importance to society of having people of high intelligence function at or near their highest potential. Some years ago the writer had as one of his counselees a 14 year old boy whose Stanford Binet IQ was 160. He was performing below average in first year algebra until counselor and algebra teacher, by working together, provided sufficient challenge to the boy. Six months later he was performing at the superior level, owing principally to the efforts of the algebra teacher. The counselor's chief contribution was informing and convincing the teacher that the boy really was superior in potential. He is now a successful civil engineer.

5. Insofar as is reasonably possible, show practical applications of the mathematics he is teaching. And every time he does so he should take pains to mention the occupation or occupations in which the application occurs.

6. Spend two or three minutes a day three or four days a week in giving the class information about the various different occupations in which mathematics other than arithmetic is used. The counselor could be a helpful resource person here. Various pupils might be assigned a two minute report on the various different occupations, the teacher then perhaps supplementing the report for one half to one minute. Of course, both professional level and mechanical level jobs should be covered— by appropriately chosen pupils. Lester Schloerb's 48-page booklet, *School Subjects and Jobs* (38), can be helpful in suggesting many of the occupations which should be included.

7. Make each course, to a degree, an exploratory course in the field of mathematics. Every pupil at the end of a given course should have some conception of what lies ahead in mathematics in each possible curriculum which is available to him. Ideally this goal would be reached by incidental allusions throughout the course, with a concentrated recapitulation in one day near the end of the course.

8. Sponsor some club or nonclass activity; from the point of view of the present discussion he should sponsor a mathematics club or a life career club. In any case the club activities ought to help both teacher and pupils to know one another better as real persons.

9. Supply pertinent information, concerning some or all of the individuals in his classes, for the office cumulative record. Just exactly what information is supplied or how it is reported will depend upon the organization in a particular school. The anecdotal record may be used. The types of information would include family background, individual interests, individual strengths, and individual weaknesses.

10. Strive to become the "new" teacher described by Arbuckle in his

book, *Teacher Counseling.* "The new teachers are no longer thinking of themselves as being judges, moralists, disciplinarians. . . . Instead, they are concentrating on creating an atmosphere of understanding and permissiveness in which the child may feel free to express his true feelings; they are concerning themselves with the individual child rather than the problem itself; they are concerned with causes at least as much as with effects; they are beginning to see that the child lives by his emotions as well as by his intellect" (1). This type of teacher will love his pupils at least as much as he does his mathematics; he will occasionally initiate an informal type of counseling interview and he will be available, sometimes, when a pupil wants to drop in during the lunch period or after school.

If, as was indicated above, curriculum differentiation begins at the ninth-grade level, then the eighth-grade mathematics teacher becomes the key person in mathematics curricular guidance. The 10-point program discussed above will apply especially, but certainly not solely, to the eighth-grade teacher. Some important groundwork can be laid earlier. Help must also be given by the mathematics teachers at ninth- and higher-grade levels because *changes of interest and vocational goal do occur after the ninth grade.* How many mathematics teachers today could honestly state that they determined definitely before the end of their freshman year in high school that their life career would be the teaching of mathematics?

Every pupil should have help in his curricular choice from his counselor and his mathematics teacher and, perhaps, from other sources. But, finally, *he must be free to make his own choice.* If he chooses wrongly and fails one semester, so be it. What one of us has not failed, at least once, in life outside of academic walls? No counselor and no mathematics teacher is omniscient enough to make important life decisions for some other. Few pupils, if they have the help outlined above, will make grave errors in their own decisions.

PART TWO
Laboratory Teaching in Mathematics
Introduction

LABORATORY techniques have long been used in the public schools in such areas as science, dramatics, home economics, and shop. Teachers have long been urged to use laboratory techniques in the teaching of mathematics. Enough teachers are doing that, so that we may well consider laboratory teaching as one of the emerging practices in teaching mathematics.

Perhaps there is not perfect agreement among teachers as to the specific techniques of laboratory teaching. Let us here consider some goals and techniques which do seem to characterize the method. Let us concede that laboratory teaching is a method of teaching which provides for individual experimentation, for discovery of mathematical facts and generalizations through the manipulation of objects as well as through reading and discussion, and that pupils need to see and feel mathematics at work as well as to think it.

LABORATORY TEACHING REQUIRES SPACE

Laboratory teaching places emphasis upon the scientific method of thought. The student is encouraged to isolate his problem, to decide on the facts known, to investigate possibilities for solving it, to draw logical conclusions, to solve the problem, and to test the validity of the solution. Any one of these steps may require research in books or magazines, the making of drawings, the cutting or hammering or soldering of materials. Any one of these activities requires space. Space for books and magazines, workbench, filing cabinets and storage cabinets may be available at the back of the discussion room or in an adjoining or nearby room. Teachers are beginning to request such space for mathematics rooms and architects are planning for such space in new buildings.

LABORATORY TEACHING REQUIRES EQUIPMENT

No two mathematics laboratories will be furnished with the same equipment. Students and teachers will want to work together in planning and making laboratory materials. Available space and money and imagination will determine the amount and kind of equipment. Minimum equipment would probably include:

1. Sturdy work tables
2. A sink
3. Storage space
4. Books and magazines
5. Bookcases
6. Drawing instruments
7. Various kinds of paper
8. Field instruments
9. Bulletin boards and display cases
10. Materials such as: cardboard, plastic, tin, cord, rubber bands, plywood, fasteners of various kinds, scissors and other cutting instruments.

LABORATORY TEACHING REQUIRES DIRECTION

Adequate space and equipment will not in themselves assure that laboratory techniques are being used. In fact without proper direction much time can be wasted and poor habits of work encouraged in aimless manipulation of materials. For most students individual laboratory work needs preliminary discussion for determining goals, guide sheets for selecting profitable areas of investigation, and careful evaluation. When goals are determined and the investigation of possible solutions well guided laboratory work will proceed from the manipulation of things to the grasp of ideas.

J. E. M.

Laboratory Techniques with Specific Practices

SHELDON S. MYERS

LABORATORY teaching which is worthy of the name necessarily involves goal-seeking activity on the part of pupils. These goals may be essentially mathematical in character, such as the discovery of geometry propositions from measurements made on geometric figures. On the other hand they may be both non-mathematical and mathematical in character, such as taking an opinion poll in the school. In this case the pattern of opinions of the student body would represent a nonmathematical goal, while the experience and skill achieved in statistical techniques would represent a mathematical goal. Both types of goals contribute to the motivation of pupils. Furthermore it might be said that laboratory activities with both types of goals provide for significance and transfer of mathematical processes. A reminder might also be made that mathematical concepts and processes themselves might be products of laboratory activities in one case and instrumental in other cases. For example, the concept of congruence might be the product of activities involving the measurement of triangles, while statistical techniques would be instrumental in a community survey.

It seems that laboratory teaching can be analyzed into two levels—one dealing with the specific activities of pupils, the other dealing with larger, goal-seeking projects in which the specific activities are involved. Too often in traditional classes pupils are engaged in aimless, specific activities without the unity, significance, and motivation provided by larger, goal-seeking projects. This section will attempt to enumerate the specific activities which characterize laboratory teaching and to suggest some of the larger, goal-seeking projects in which these activities have been a part.

ENUMERATION OF SPECIFIC ACTIVITIES

Measurement. There are two large mathematical ideas associated with measurement—the arbitrary nature of the unit of length, time, weight, and other quantities; the inverse relation between the size of the unit and the amount of the measure. The latter idea is the basis for the conversion of measures from one set of units to another, such as feet to yards, or ounces to grams. These concepts can be formulated by pupils from experiences with the following operations, or types of measurement:

1. Length—use of hand spans, shoe lengths, paces, metric and English rulers, tape measures, calipers, micrometers
2. Weight—use of beam balance, spring balance, analytical balance, bathroom scales
3. Volume—use of dry and liquid quarts, bushel and peck baskets, kitchen measuring cups and spoons, tin cans, graduates, burettes, pipettes, gallon jugs, milk bottles, cubic inch, cubic foot, cubic yard, cubic centimeter, cubic meter, liter, milliliter

4. Angle—use of protractor, transit, sextant, hypsometer

5. Time—use of stop watch, study of time zones, study of calendar, world calendar

6. Temperature—use of Fahrenheit and centigrade thermometers, use of thermocouple, optical pyrometer, pyrometric cones

7. Revolutions per unit of time—measuring speed of rotating wheels such as an automotible tire or airplane propeller

8. Heat—calories in food, calories or British thermal units in fuel, relation of heat to mechanical energy such as running upstairs and the calories expended, calories and diet

9. Electrical units—measuring volts with a voltmeter or potentiometer, ohms with an ohmmeter, amperes with an ammeter

10. Power—horsepower in relation to automobiles, airplanes, boats and tractors, electrical power in watts.

Construction. Because of the time-consuming nature of construction activities, some teachers prefer to encourage these activities as out-of-class assignments. In any case construction activities include the making of plane and solid geometry models, the making of devices such as linkages and planimeters, curve stitching, paper folding, the construction of apparatus to exhibit forms of variation, such as a train of gears. Alert teachers will often correlate mathematics with a shop project a student is working on.

Drawing. This can include the making of maps and scale drawings, symmetrical designs such as in window transparencies, perspective drawings, the use of straight lines to produce approximations of the conic sections, geometric ruler and compass constructions, and use of mechanical drawing tools.

Making Graphs and Presenting Data. Considerable mathematical judgment is needed to decide on the best way to present a given set of data. Teachers should provide pupils with opportunities to make these decisions and evaluate the results. The preparation and presentation of data which the student himself has collected has the characteristics of laboratory activity. This involves the construction of tables, bar, circle, or line graphs, the preparation of titles and labels, the use of color.

Drawing Conclusions from Measurements, Constructions, or Drawings. The nature of this activity is dependent on the type of project in which it is involved. The project of decorating a Christmas tree with colored, regular solids might lead to the group conclusion that the project was successful because the result is a pleasing effect. There is very little mathematics involved in drawing this kind of conclusion. On the other hand a project of finding out what kind of dance the student body prefers would involve considerable statistical judgment with regard to the data. Mathematics students would be engaged in a great deal of interaction while arriving at a consensus interpretation of the data.

SOME LARGER GOAL-SEEKING PROJECTS

The list of projects which follows should be considered to be only an incomplete, suggestive list. The number of such projects is probably unlimited. These projects will probably find the most use on the junior high level and in general mathematics, but their use should not be overlooked in the upper academic mathematics courses.

1. Opinion Poll. Deals with issues which the pupils select and about which they are concerned. Often pupils will confront parents with the results of such polls, resulting in adjustments of allowance inequities. Practice in percentage, the making of graphs and tables, and the drawing of inferences might be the activities involved.

2. Statistical Study of the School. Involves tables or graphs of attendance, breaking the data down by classes, by weeks or months, correlating absence with weather, with boys and girls, with distance from school, enrollment figures showing distribution of the student body geographically, scale drawings of floor plans and rooms, maps of the school grounds, budget figures of school overhead, data on library usage, fees and expenses of students, average growth curves of students by grades involving weights and heights showing adolescent acceleration. Such a study could be summarized by committees of students, duplicated, bound in a report and distributed to the faculty, administration, and parents.

3. Mapping the School Grounds. Involves the use of such field instruments as the tape measure and the transit or plane table with alidade. The concept of the scale will be operationalized in this activity.

4. Community Survey. Conducted by a mathematics class serves a real community need. Such problems as the following are attacked: What is the best date for the summer community festival? How many families would make use of a community library if one were started? How many families would be interested in weekly community movies at the school? What types of PTA programs are most needed? How many families would make use of a directory of baby-sitters compiled by the home economics classes? Of course, in larger towns and cities such surveys could be limited to school districts. Students could make their assigned contacts after school and assemble and study the data in class.

5. Study of Modern Airplanes from Physical Measurements.

6. The Physical Conditions of Interplanetary Travel.

7. Mathematics in a Track Meet. Involve metric and English units of length. Time is also included. Rates of speed in feet per second and miles per hour can be computed. Time graphs giving trends in records could be made. Averages might be computed.

8. Mathematics of Baseball. The angle mirror and tape measure may be used to lay out a diamond. The dimensions of big league bats and balls can be determined and compared with little league dimensions. The speed of a pitcher can be determined with a stop watch over a measured distance that the ball travels. The boys can determine their speed on the base paths. It can be pointed out that newspaper batting averages are incorrectly named "percentages" when in reality they show thousandths and not hundredths. Pupils can be shown how to compute the standings of teams based on their won and lost records. Lest we be misunderstood, the above two points should be developed by heuristic or questioning techniques, rather than lecturing techniques.

9. Measurement in the Home, in a Gasoline Station. A teacher once took a class for a walk around the block with instructions to list all cases of measurement. This being a business block, the class returned and listed over 100 different instances of measurement. Such a project when applied to a block, a home, or a service station impresses on the minds of children the significance of measurement in everyday life.

10. Discovery of Propositions in Geometry by Means of Experimental Measurements on Figures. Although most of these projects listed here are inductive in nature, this one dealing with the discovery of geometry propositions is particularly suitable for developing the meaning of induction and contrasting it with deductive procedures. The joint use of induction and deduction in developing a theory of space comes about as near as possible on the high-school level to illustrating the meaning of scientific method. This project and perhaps numbers 5 and 6 could be used as a setting for introducing the notion of significant figures and computation with approximate data.

11. Discovery of Physical Laws and Statement of Them by Formulas Through an Analysis of Physical Data. Suitable laws for this purpose could be the law of levers, the law of lenses, the law of falling objects under gravitational pull, and the relation between Fahrenheit and centigrade temperatures. This activity is very appropriate in beginning algebra where the phenomena investigated serve to illustrate various types of functions in algebra. The slope-intercept form of the linear equation can be used to derive from the graph of the data the following formula: $F = 9/5 \, C + 32$.

12. Study of the Merits of the Metric System Through the Use of Metric Volumes and Weights Borrowed from the Science Laboratory. Of course the full merits of the metric system cannot be realized by students until they have done analogous computations in both English and metric units. One of the chief merits of the metric system is often overlooked. This is the relation between weight and volume through water. A kilogram is assumed to be the weight of a liter of pure water, under standard conditions. This assumption produces great simplicity in computations involving density and specific gravity. This point is as important as the decimal nature of the system for its universal adoption in the scientific world. Students could be confronted with such problems as: Here is a can of apricot juice. How many kilograms of this juice would be in a full vat 10 meters high and 8 meters in diameter? After the students had laboriously measured the weight of a given volume of the juice in order to compute the answer, the students could be introduced to the simple procedure of taking the specific gravity with a spindle hydrometer.

13. Solving Solid Geometry Loci Problems by Constructing Models of the Solutions. Many of the complex, compound locus problems in solid geometry can have their solutions exhibited by models made of colored sheets of balsa wood glued with airplane glue. Of course, the value for the student lies in the visualization and construction of the solution. Other students, viewing the completed model, may receive competitive incentives with regard to their own problem, but will not experience the problem-solving of the maker. Neatness, care, and planning are some of the worthy, nonmathematical goals resulting from this project.

Radio and Television in Teaching Mathematics

WALTER CARNAHAN

DURING the first half of the present century in America the greatest educational experiment of all time was undertaken, the education of all the people without regard for social background, interests, or ability. The experiment brought such problems as educators had never faced and for the solution of which they were almost hopelessly unprepared. New mediums for instruction were needed. We are fortunate that with this need come new educational resources—field work, slides, motion pictures, cartoon books, radio, and television. These new mediums in their turn present new problems of effective use. It is the purpose of this section to offer some suggestions based on experience with using radio and television in the teaching of mathematics. What principles are to guide us? What experimentation has been done? What evaluation is available, and what conclusions have been reached? What facilities are available for the mathematics teacher who would like to try out the new mediums?

There are two very different postulates that are applied by different persons in an attempt to evaluate radio and television as educational resources. One postulate asserts that these resources are valuable only if they can do what it is impossible for the classroom teacher to do, or if they can do what the teacher can do but do it better. The other postulate asserts that the new resources are valuable because they supply the need for a different kind of teaching whether or not they teach better than the classroom instructor or present matter that she cannot present. It is in the nature of a postulate that one accepts it or rejects it but does not try to rationalize it. If we should here accept the first of these postulates, we would be driven to evaluate the offerings of radio and TV on the basis of their success in surpassing the effectiveness of the classroom teacher. Obviously that would be difficult to do. Hence it seems simpler in present conditions to accept the second postulate and consider the program offerings as variations of the educational experiences of learners, and avoid any discussion of their merits in comparison with traditional teaching mediums.

There are certain obvious limitations on radio and TV as mediums of instruction. They cannot develop a concept by means of questions and pupil responses; they cannot supervise practice experiences; they cannot test and examine; they cannot delay instruction and wait for the assimilative processes of learning to occur. They can tell, they can dramatize, they can stimulate interest, they can provide sidelights and historical facts, they can suggest applications, and they can furnish models of good instruction that should stimulate better classroom teaching.

The positive statements, the *can* statements of the preceding paragraph seem to the writer to constitute a reasonably complete summary of what radio and TV at present can be expected to contribute to education when these mediums are functioning at their best. Further planning and experimentation are much needed, and into this program of improvement can be fitted the ideas and labors of all seriously interested persons.

Each subject in the curriculum presents its own peculiar limitations in the employment of radio and TV. What are some of the things that these mediums can and cannot do in mathematics education? The answers to these questions must take into consideration the list of needs and benefits that a study of mathematics involves.

In the first place, mathematics is a subject that calls for and cultivates the habit of clear thinking. Perhaps the clear thinking does not extend beyond the subject in which it is directly cultivated, but clear thinking is involved. Thinking is a personal activity. It is not possible to cultivate the ability to think by any amount of telling. Development of thinking ability demands a constant discipline by exchange of ideas between the unskilled and the skilled. Hence the limitations of radio and TV as means for developing clear thinking are at once obvious. In the second place, mathematics is a skill subject. So far as its uses are concerned, mathematics is of no value if one cannot do its operations readily and accurately. This calls for directed and corrected practice. Again it is obvious that radio and TV unassisted can do little to develop the skills of mathematics. This does not mean that these mediums have no contribution to make to the cultivation of power in thinking and skill in using mathematics, but that they must be co-ordinated with the work of teachers in the classrooms.

However, the needs of mathematics education are by no means limited to power of thinking and skill in using. Mathematics is one of the ancient cultures of the human race, and as such it demands the attention of every person who has any aspiration to general culture. The subject has beauty and power; it has a long and fascinating history; it has applications in every field of human interest, in physics, in biology, in economics, in sociology, in finance, and in astronomy. Furthermore, mathematics has possibilities for worthy use of leisure that make it second to no subject in the curriculum. It is in these various fields where radio and TV seem to have their greatest possibilities. Often the classroom teacher is very little aware of the cultural possibilities of mathematics and has little time or opportunity to introduce to her classes such cultural materials as she is acquainted with. Radio and TV could make a great contribution to mathematics education by presenting the cultural phases of the subject. Some of this has been done, and successfully done. Much more should be done. It would require careful study and much work by persons who know this phase of mathematics thoroughly and are enthusiastic about its benefits. The present writer did some pioneering in the field of presenting cultural phases of mathematics by radio station WBAA, and the results were gratifying. However, one result of the experiment was the realization that a successful program of this kind is not a one-man undertaking. It calls for trained and skillful writers and for professional talent in presenting the programs. It would seem that the time and circumstances are now here for this next step.

Some Suggestions for the Use of Television in Teaching Mathematics

Phillip S. Jones

THE planning and presentation of two series of mathematical television broadcasts constitute the writer's experience in this area and hence the basis for most of his notes and suggestions. The newness of educational television may justify one's writing on the basis of such a limited background. The closeness of television to radio requires some introductory comments on the latter in spite of a lack of personal experience in this area.

Effective use of both radio and television for educational purposes involves planning based on considerations of *the nature of the expected audience, the objectives to be achieved,* and *the peculiar advantages and disadvantages of the media.*

Radio made it possible for outstanding authorities and expositors to be heard by persons who might otherwise never, in or out of school, have met their ideas or their field of interest. Sound effects and the human voice can add liveliness and reality to the conciseness and timeliness wherein radio may excel books. Further, radio, in its early days at least, drew or motivated listeners in out-of-school hours to nonrequired "assignments" by the intrinsic interest and variety of offerings of the medium itself.

Pedagogically, the increased resources and motivation it offered were offset by its lack of personal contact and adaptability. The listener could turn off a radio speaker but could neither question nor talk back to him. Radio's inability to use charts, diagrams, or visual materials was a further handicap to mathematics teaching on the air. These shortcomings made it unsuitable for day-to-day instruction in the normal mathematics curriculum for secondary-school pupils, although some experimentation, chiefly in the teaching of arithmetic, was carried on (2, 5). However, there were occasional efforts to use the radio to supply enrichment materials and supplementary classroom instruction. The most comprehensive program of this type, that sponsored by the Association of Mathematics Teachers of New York City, was considered by them to have been successful (4). The broadcasts in the series were publicized in advance to the schools, classroom discussions were held both in preparation for listening and as follow-ups to the broadcasts.

There have also been efforts to use the radio to reach a second type of audience—adults. Here the objectives were chiefly "cultural"—the spreading of information about mathematics, its history, and its uses—although a secondary objective was propaganda for the place of mathematics in the school program and in the guidance of children (4, 5, 6).

In at least one instance an experiment was conducted in in-service teacher training by radio. This latter series was planned especially for adults teaching or preparing to teach mathematics, a rather limited audience. Raleigh Schorling of the University of Michigan in the fall of 1936 taught "Education D135, The Teaching of Mathematics" as an experiment for undergraduate credit by a combination of 18 weekly Saturday morning broadcasts over WJR, Detroit and by correspondence work. L. C. Karpinski and Norman Anning of the Mathematics Department and Joseph Cannon of the College of Engineering gave talks on various aspects of mathematics, its history, and its uses as guests of Dr. Schorling.

In all but two of these instances a strictly narrative-lecture procedure was used. Two programs were staged as dialogues.

Television adds visual appeal to all the advantages of radio. However, it also adds problems of designing visual equipment and timing and organizing a presentation in a situation more complicated, mechanically at least, than is presented by either the radio or the classroom. Even with technical assistance in the actual construction of charts and devices, and advice on the writing of the script, the writer invested over 20 hours in preparing for each one of his series of seven, 18-minute broadcasts. Although this included the writing of supplementary material for distribution to listeners and some travel time, and although the needed time would decrease some with experience, it remains true that planning, designing equipment, writing scripts and rehearsals require *much* more time than the actual presentation.

The broadcasts referred to above were presented on the University of Michigan television hour over WWJ-TV, Detroit in 1952. They were scheduled at 1 PM Sunday and were aimed at an adult audience with a high-school education in accord with the data available on the audiences for earlier University broadcasts. *Understanding Numbers: Their History and Use* was used as a title for the series. Our chief objective was cultural, to broaden the insight into *why* numbers behave as they do and to increase the viewer's *appreciation* of the nature, use, historical development, and varieties of numbers. Secondarily, we also hoped to interest and entertain the audience, as well as to teach so that there would be some incidental improvement in the viewers' ability to select the appropriate arithmetic process, avoid errors, and find errors once they had been made.

Since the cultural aim was considered here to outweigh the entertaining and utilitarian objectives, the presentation emphasized the nature, historical development, and uses of such concepts as the elements of a system of numeration (base, place, symbols, zero "point"), fractions, exponential notation (this was related to "scientific notation" and the stories and puzzles about large and small numbers as well as to logarithms and the slide rule), and even, on the last program, transfinite, irrational, and transcendental numbers.

Although our chief aim was cultural, there was a mathematical end in view in even our humorous anecdotes. As an example, the paradox of the wise sheik was used to introduce fractions and the need for a common denominator in adding them. The sheik distributed 17 camels to three sons who were to get $\frac{1}{2}$, $\frac{1}{3}$, $\frac{1}{9}$ respectively by adding his own camel to the 17, distributing the camels (now 18) as directed but with one (his own) left over. The check by nines and the bookkeepers' device of dividing the amount of an error by nine as a test for a mistake due to transposition of digits were shown to depend upon the use of 10 as a base in our number system. The mathematical aim was always pointed out, emphasized, and applied in several ways.

A later series of two longer programs had for its title *Mathematics Around Us*. Its chief objective was the display of some of the often unrecognized occurrences of mathematics in simple and familiar situations. Here, too, an emphasis was placed on underlying ideas, unifying relationships, and applications or occurrence in life situations. For example, the conics were introduced with a dissectible cone and the importance of the ellipse as a projection of a circle in both mechanical drawing and art work was associated with the "visual cone" of rays of light from a circle to the eye. Next the ellipse was generated by a pin and string construction. This latter was then used to derive the property of the constancy of the sum of the focal radii which in turn was demonstrated at once to be the principle behind elliptic gears. These were represented by a movable model showing two ellipses rotating about fixed points but in contact with each other. The fact that the model was made from automobile brake pedal pads was pointed out as a further example of the occurrence of the conics in life around us. Finally, the constant sum principle was also shown to give the solution of the radius of action problem for an aircraft carrier if there is no wind. A sort of chalk-talk procedure was used, showing the cone, drawing the ellipse with pins and string, diagramming on this drawing the focal radii and their constant sum, demonstrating the gears, returning to the drawing easel to sketch and explain the radius of action problem, and similar problems. On television all these shifts should be planned and scheduled in advance and preferably discussed with the director who commands the cameras and determines the picture which goes on the air.

Some of the principles on which we operated were as follows: (a) use visual materials a large share of the time, but with variety, (b) capitalize on the use of motion wherever possible—moving models are superior to static ones in general, (c) show both everyday occurrences and more abstract and less familiar situations, but always take care to point out the common mathematical elements in apparently diverse situations.

Additional principles which were important in planning the seven-broadcast telecourse were: (d) always display the reasons for and the meaning of the mathematical processes as well as the source of the problem or use of the technique, but (e) do so first with elementary, concrete, numerical illustrations, and special cases before generalizing, (f) interject humorous, recreational, and puzzle material at the beginning of a new topic as an introduction or at the end of a program as a "teaser" to hold over until the next broadcast, but take care to clarify its mathematical significance, (g) don't neglect to associate each broadcast and new topic with that which has gone before, but plan also in each successive broadcast to gain the understanding and interest of a person who is viewing the series for the first time.

Teachers need not be told the necessity for avoiding too technical a vocabulary, too pedantic a manner, too long an excursion into abstraction. We occasionally felt, however, that some new and some old semitechnical words and phrases would actually help lead to the understanding and insights which we sought to teach. In these cases we posted signs bearing these words on a "word board" as the terms were explained and used. Such words as *base, place, binary, duodecimal, sexagesimal, pars minuta prima, pars minuta secunda, minutes, seconds,* appeared on this board at various times. The word board was a sheet of iron covered with light cloth and resting on an easel. The words were printed on cardboard strips on which were mounted little magnets.

Since the outlines of several programs which are appended to this article will further illustrate these principles, let's now turn to some comments on the possible educational implications of these experiences.

Station surveys indicate that the University of Michigan's Sunday broadcasts had an audience of 80,000 to 100,000 persons. Persons who chose to enroll in the "telecourse" sent in a dollar for which they received a supplementary lithoprinted syllabus (more nearly a text). At the conclusion of the series those of the enrollees who took an "open-book" objective examination were sent a "certificate of participation." There was no academic credit. It is a remarkable testimonial to the appeal of mathematics that over 600 persons enrolled, more than in other supposedly more popular courses in political parties—it was a convention year—and astronomy, presented the same semester.

There was no attempt to design the broadcasts to correlate with school programs; however, in one junior high school, students were given extra-project credit for reporting back to classes about the broadcasts and in particular for catching any boners made by the television instructor. In a senior high school students were encouraged to watch, then to criticize, and to discuss the broadcasts in class. In a senior high school for girls one teacher reported that several students themselves suggested that they prepare an exhibit for the hall cases based upon materials in the broadcasts. Several elementary-school teachers sent for the supplementary materials with the comment that they saw materials and ideas which they could adapt to their own teaching.

The two longer programs, *Mathematics Around Us*, presented over WOOD-TV in Grand Rapids brought forth the comment from one geometry teacher that he wished he could have seen the program because he found, following it, that his students were bringing to class observations about mathematics around them which they had never noted before.

As for adult interest, the enrollment in the "telecourse" alone was a pleasant surprise. Further pleasures included exchanging letters with a lawyer about reasoning in law and mathematics. He also displayed an interest and an insight in a criticism of the concept of transfinite numbers which were very stimulating to the teacher. So also, in a different way, was the offer of a free steak by a butcher in a nearby town who wrote of his interest! Not many wrote adverse criticisms—such critics probably tuned in a different program. One young student commented rather scathingly that Milton Berle was much better! A few thought we were too elementary; more thought the program too advanced, abstract, or speedy.

The conclusion seems to be that television has fine potentialities for stimulating interest, for broadening horizons, insights, and appreciations on both secondary-school and adult levels. It certainly will not replace any teacher but it may aid teachers by both its interest-getting stimulus and by making suggestions directly to students and teachers of enrichment projects beyond routine classroom assignments. Close co-operation between teachers and broadcasters would increase the effectiveness of such programs. This co-operation could cover the planning of the programs as well as the distribution of supplementary materials, references, solutions to problems, suggestions for related exhibits, club programs. Close school-broadcaster relations might even lead to the participation of students on the program as a recognition of their achievements.

Time schedules and the distribution of television receivers are obvious problems in any extensive or required use of television in teaching.

At least one attempt[1] has been made to teach a complete unit of subject matter via television (3). It is too soon to evaluate the possibility or desirability of teaching whole *bona fide* courses such as trigonometry for small schools or scattered adult groups. At the moment the difficulties seem very great and such alternatives as correspondence courses seem much more feasible, perhaps even more effective. However, a combination of television broadcasts and correspondence work might be a really valuable teaching team, and broadcasts for elementary school classes could be made during school hours and viewed with the teacher's presence and assistance.

Technical details of script writing and production—such things as the use of black on gray (not white) for chalk-talks, keeping one's eye on the right camera, prompt sheets and timing signals—can and will be worked out with the technical staff of the station. Some help with both general philosophies and technical details may be obtained from books on educational radio and television[2] rapidly coming on the market (8, 10, 11).

---

[1] Lessons on "Teaching the Slide Rule by Television" were given in six fifteen-minute weekly broadcasts over WGAL-TV, Lancaster, Pennsylvania.

More recently (October 5, 1953–January 25, 1954) Professor Marguerite Lehr has presented fifteen half-hour programs titled "Invitation to Mathematics" on WFIL's "University of the Air". Further, the seven-program "telecourse" described in this article is soon to be put on film via the Kinescope for the use of other educational television stations. The University of Michigan has been commissioned by the Educational Television and Radio Center, to do this.

[2] *Teaching Through Radio* (19) page 61 describes a series of "Talks for 5th Forms" on "Mathematics and Life" giving an outline of "The Aeroplane and Its Navigation" as presented by the British Broadcasting Company.

The writer would like to add his personal recognition of the debt he owes to Garnet Garrison, Director of Television, Hazen Schumacher, Jr., Supervisor of

AN OUTLINE OF THE "TELECOURSE"—UNDERSTANDING NUMBERS: THEIR HISTORY AND USE

LESSON	MATHEMATICAL TOPICS —OBJECTIVES	ILLUSTRATIVE, HISTORICAL, INTEREST MATERIAL	VIDEO
1. The Earliest Numbers	To discover and illustrate essential elements of a system of numeration (base, place, symbols, zero point)	Numbers in pre-history. Egyptian numbers. Babylonion sexagesimal system and modern time and angular measure as an inheritance. "Tangible" arithmetic: abacus, tally sticks, reckoning on lines	Abacus. A counting board used to add and subtract and to illustrate "carrying" and "borrowing." A "word board" (see text). Easel, cardboard and cargo pen for writing numbers in decimal and sexagesimal form
2. Bases and Places	To teach the meaning and role of the base and place value idea	The binary system among savages, generalized by Harriot and Leibnitz, used today in electronic computation and business filing systems. Finding errors due to transposed digits. The check by nines	Writing easel, plain and prepared charts. "Keysort" cards, punch, and needle, and a large scale model of the cards
3. Big (and small) Numbers	To define and explain the uses of exponents and scientific notation	Archimedes' "Sand Reckoner"; Hindu interest in numeration (poem); Kasner; googols, and the googolplex. Puzzles and recreations involving large numbers. The difference between a trillion here and one in England	Writing easel. Prepared charts. Posters with sliding panels

| 4. Fundamental Operations | To teach an understanding of the fundamental operations by showing roles of the system of numeration, the distributive and commutative laws in giving the real reasons for the algorithms taught in arithmetic. Subtraction and division as inverse operations; division by zero | Austrian method of subtraction and making change. Proof that $2 = 1$ Finger multiplication | Addition and multiplication tables. Writing materials. Prepared charts |

A limited experience with teaching by television leaves this writer feeling that it has tremendous potentialities which need careful exploration. This exploration will require much time and money for production—including kinescope for rebroadcasts—co-ordination, evaluation. Here is an opportunity for a fascinating research and development project with tremendous possibilities if some organization or foundation would organize and finance it. Let's hope it can be done!

Lessons 5, 6, 7 were titled *Short Cuts and Computing Devices, Fractions,* and *New Numbers.* In these lessons the nature of logarithms and the basic construction and operation of a slide rule were taught, as well as the meaning of fractions and fundamental operations with them, incommensurables, irrationals, transfinite numbers, and even a brief mention of complex numbers. In addition to related anecdotal and historical material some of the visual aids used were Napier's bones, log tables, Gunter's scale, slide rule, models of candy bars to be divided among several persons, a map, a pair of baskets from which numbers were picked to illustrate a one-to-one correspondence.

The following outline is a typical final outline—for Lesson 5—prepared by the University's script writer, Robert Newman, and production supervisor, Hazen Schumacher, for the use of Station WWJ-TV's director in rehearsing the final show, timing it, and planning his camera locations and shots.

THE DIRECTOR'S OUTLINE FOR A TYPICAL BROADCAST— UNDERSTANDING NUMBERS

VIDEO	*AUDIO*
JONES	INTRO AND REVIEW
TC[3]: MULTI TABLE TO 5	FINGER METHOD
FINGER MULTIPLYING	9 TIMES 7
WRITE ON PAD	LIGHTNING METHOD
	436
	123
	———
	53628
MULTIPLY WITH BONES AND WRITE	NAPIER'S BONES

Production, and Robert Newman, Script Editor, of the University of Michigan, whose aid made the programs described here possible and who taught the author most of what he knows of television techniques.

[3] TC stands for "title card" and warns the director that one camera should be focused on a visual chart or display to be used at this stage of the talk.

TC: NUMBERS AND POWERS (WRITE)	LOGARITHMS
	SUMMARIZE
WORD: LOGARITHM	DISCUSS LOGS
TC: LOG TABLES (WRITE)	WORK LOG PROBLEMS
WRITE CORRECT FORM OF LOGS	CORRECT WRITING
	SUMMARIZE
RULER AND COMPASS	GUNTER SCALE
INSERT SLIDE RULES	EXPLAIN SLIDE RULES
JONES	CONCLUSION

Review of the Literature on Radio and Television in Education

Louis F. Scholl

IN REVIEWING the literature on the use of radio and television in the teaching of mathematics, one salient fact emerges—how little has actually been done as yet throughout the country in the use of these media by teachers of mathematics. At the same time, this fact points up the tremendous opportunities which await mathematics teachers with vision and foresight. In those places where educational radio and television have been tried, the results have consistently amazed even their most rabid supporters. The reason for their popularity can be found in that attribute of human nature which is usually overlooked by professional broadcasters and telecasters—that man is always searching for knowledge, and finds keen enjoyment in the acquiring of new information. The present popularity of quiz shows attests this fact. Why should not mathematics teachers harness this trait of human nature by the use of the newest methods of communication provided by science?

For many years, education through radio progressed very slowly. Immediately after World War II, however, two new advances in radio communication opened new horizons. These were the development of FM radio, and the development of facsimile broadcasting. Without going into technical details, the advantages of FM radio are that it operates on very low power, and it is relatively static free (33, 34, 38, 39, 40, 41, 42). At the present time only New York State and Wisconsin seem to be taking advantage of FM radio for educational purposes. New York has established a statewide educational network called the *Empire State FM School of the Air*, composed of 18 commercial stations which donate time for classroom programs prepared by the schools, libraries, and universities (35, 43, 44). The *Wisconsin State Radio Council* is active in establishing a state system of radio broadcasting for the presentation of educational, informational, and public-service programs. Another development which may have great implications for the future, is the *National Association of Educational Broadcasters Tape Network*, with headquarters at the University of Illinois. This network, which is composed of about 75 participating stations, provides for the mutual exchange of the best programs among its members. All of the stations are noncommercial and many are directed by educational institutions.

Facsimile broadcasting is the development of transmission of printed material by means of radio waves (36, 38, 45). A special receiver is necessary to receive the printed material on special paper. Little has been done with this up to the present time, but a mathematics teacher can see how this would overcome one of the big handicaps in teaching mathematics by radio—figures could be drawn, and examples worked out on this special paper in the receiving set just as on a blackboard. It is unfortunate that the birth of television retarded the growth, at least temporarily, of this valuable tool.

In general, radio and television broadcasts of mathematics programs can be classified under two general headings—those intended for an adult audience for adult education, including cultural as well as the more purely subject-matter programs, and those which are beamed into the classroom. A review of the literature seems to indicate that radio has been used very little for the first type of program, but that there have been a few attempts to teach arithmetic programs of the second type, notably in Cleveland (30, 32, 36). Such a program requires careful preparation by the teacher from material distributed well in advance. It is usually required that certain drawings be made on the blackboard which are then referred to in the radio broadcast.

Television seems to offer great possibilities for education, both for adult education and for classroom viewing. On April 14, 1952, the Federal Communications Commission announced that 242 broadcasting channels in the ultra-high frequency band were being reserved for noncommercial uses (58, 61). Many educational organizations from various states have made application and been granted licenses to construct and operate educational television stations in this UHF range. The first of these stations actually to go on the air was KUHT, at the University of Houston in Texas, which began televising on June 8, 1953. Mathematics teachers should prepare to take advantage of this new medium which from all indications will soon have facilities in all parts of the country.

The literature indicates that an excellent start has been made in the field of adult education through television, especially by colleges and universities. In fact, many universities are giving full credit courses through television, among them being Western Reserve, Michigan, Washington, New York, Omaha, Toledo, Butler at Indianapolis, and Wayne at Detroit (31, 32, 33, 34, 35). Although few of these courses involve mathematics, the door is being opened. Since programs of this type are so new, it cannot be said that any pattern has been set, but a few basic principles seem to be emerging. Television, to a much greater extent than radio, depends upon the human equation. Teachers who are interesting and absorbing in the classroom will be just as excellent on television. The subject itself must be presented in such a way as to arouse interest. In the field of mathematics, this should not be difficult, for most people have a natural curiosity concerning mathematics. The same principles which guide good teaching hold true in a television presentation. There is no substitute for the creative art of a good teacher, whether in the classroom or on television. Persons and personalities attract. The program itself must be prepared with great care, and should be set up with the highest standards of excellence. It will be found that often the teacher becomes a better teacher for having presented a television program, because of the careful self-analysis which is part of the preparation for the program.

School systems in a few cities among which are Buffalo and Pittsburgh, have presented programs which can best be classified as public relations programs ranging from kindergarten through Grade XII (59, 60, 65, 66, 67, 68). These programs are designed to acquaint the community with their schools, and to present a picture of what happens in a modern school on an ordinary school day. In Buffalo, a local commercial television station, WBEN-TV, donates the time and puts the full facilities of their technical staff at the disposal of the school system for a half-hour each Saturday during the school year. The program is planned by teachers and administrators of the school system, and is taken as a package and presented over the commercial station. The usual program will show a typical classroom situation with from 12 to 16 pupils and a teacher. An unrehearsed lesson is then taught. The first time that the pupils see the studio is when they come in about an hour before they go on the air. Ideally, the material taught should be completely new to the pupils, but should be based upon previous experiences of the pupils and fundamental principles which they have already learned. A commentator—an experienced teacher—with an open microphone, cuts in from time to time, to explain and interpret to the viewer what is happening in the classroom. In one program, on arithmetic, a teacher presented to a group of first-graders, the concept of five. As props she had tiny plastic toys purchased in the ten-cent store. These consisted of five baby carriages and five small baby dolls to fit in them, five ironing boards and five irons, five lamp tables and five lamps, and several other groups of fives. She then developed the lesson by letting the children experiment by counting and matching up the various groups. She also developed the concept of more than five and less than five, by supplying an extra toy, or removing one on occasion. The key to the absorbing interest of the viewer in this program, was that the program was completely unrehearsed. It is a fascinating thing to watch small children learning a new concept. While these programs are unrehearsed, this does not mean that they are not carefully planned. It is estimated that it takes on the average about 100 man-hours of work to prepare for one of these half-hour programs, exclusive of the pupils' time. A different teacher and a different group of pupils are used each week.

If educators are to take advantage of television, a start should be made by developing a working relationship with the local commercial station or stations. In most cases, they are only too glad to work with the local school systems, and to donate time and the facilities of their station to a worthwhile educational program. Only in this way can educators gain the experience and know-how, so as to be ready when full-time educational stations are made available.

Television programs beamed directly in the classroom are being successfully used in many cities, notably New York City and Philadelphia (53, 54). Experiments carried out by Fordham University and by the Washington, D. C. public-school system, seem to indicate that instruction given over television is equally as effective as regular classroom instruction (62, 63, 64).

In planning a classroom lesson to be given on television, there are certain basic principles to be observed. The teaching must be related to the curriculum, which means that objectives must be examined. Careful advance plans must be made, and the class should also have some advance preparation for the lesson. The presentation should be varied as much as possible—the straight lecture method can be deadly dull. The lesson itself should be kept simple. Trying to cover too much only results in confusion. Visual aids should be used wherever possible. When pupils are used in the lesson on the screen, their purpose should be to put the lesson across. Probably no more than two children should be used, since a greater number tends to distract the viewer from the objective of the lesson. Experience indicates that better results are obtained when there is a television receiver in each classroom rather than having several classes assembled in an auditorium to view one large screen.

I believe that educational leaders should look forward to setting up central programing facilities. The best programs must be preserved for future use by means of Kinescope recordings of live television shows, or produced as motion pictures for use over television. While original costs are high, the wide usage which can be made of such films, as well as their convenience, make such central programing facilities practical and necessary.

Handmade Materials for Teaching Arithmetic—Materials for Kindergarten Through Grade III

IDA MAE HEARD

IT IS easier for a child to understand the meaning of a basic fact, such as 3 + 5 = 8, if he has manipulative material, such as disks or some other kind of marker, to objectify the grouping of numbers than if he has only abstract symbols with which to deal. Both markers and symbols are essential materials in a program in arithmetic which stresses understanding in learning. Materials of this kind may be designated as *manipulative* and *symbolic* (21).

Manipulative materials are objects which can be moved. These materials may have social significance, such as that suggested by a pint or a quart bottle used for measuring liquids. On the other hand, manipulative materials may be useful to objectify some characteristic of our number system. An abacus may be used to show the meaning of place value which is the distinguishing characteristic of our number system.

Symbolic materials deal with symbols as found in a textbook or a workbook.

Each kind of material may be used to represent numbers at different levels of abstraction. A pupil who uses manipulative materials to objectify a quantitative situation operates at a low level of abstraction. On the other hand, a pupil who uses symbols to represent a quantitative situation operates at a very high level of abstraction.

The next few pages describe some manipulative materials useful for teaching arithmetic in the first six grades. The writers wish to emphasize the fact that mere manipulation of objects, either made commercially or by the class, does not assure meaningful learning by the pupil. The teacher must have the pupil use these materials to discover facts and principles which he would not discover by use of symbols. The discovery of principles, procedures, and relationships among numbers is the step which lifts learning from the low level of manipulation to the desired level of abstraction.   J.E.M.

For the past five years the author and her students have been busily engaged in creating manipulative devices to use in teaching children arithmetic. This co-operative venture has been a most rewarding experience.

THE CHALLENGE

One day toward the end of the semester the writer brought to class 100 spools all the same size and asked the prospective teachers if they saw in them the possibility of a teaching aid to be used by little children in studying arithmetic. These future teachers were familiar with current practices in teaching arithmetic. They had already examined modern textbooks, manuals, workbooks, and well-known courses of study. They were familiar with a number of commercial aids and their uses. They had the necessary background to create some teaching aid that might be useful to them when they did their student teaching the following semester.

THE FLOUNDERING PERIOD

There lay 100 lifeless looking spools. Could they be transformed into a valuable aid to learning? The students accepted the challenge. They formed several small committees and started to work. To guide the committees in producing their teaching aids, the following criteria were set up:

1. The aid should be inexpensive and easy to make.
2. The aid should help children in one of these ways:
    a. To understand the decimal nature of the number system.
    b. To understand the processes.
    c. To see relationships between numbers.
    d. To master facts.
3. The aid should be easy to manipulate.

THE FINISHED PRODUCT

Within one week each committee was ready to share its creation with the rest of the class.

The String of 100 Spools. Perhaps the simplest aid was one made by dyeing 50 spools yellow and 50 spools blue. These spools were then strung on heavy cord in groups of 10 with the colors alternating. A loop at the ends of the cord made it possible to hang the string on two hooks at the front of the room so that the children and their teacher could take turns in manipulating the spools which were hung at the right height to be seen by all. There was enough space left on the cord beyond that taken up by the 100 spools to allow room for sliding the spools freely along the cord.

How might these spools be used?

1. In counting by 1's, 2's, 5's, and 10's to 100.

2. In representing 2-place numbers as so many 1's or as so many 10's and so many 1's toward another 10. For example, the number 34 is seen as 34 separate spools, i.e., as 34 ones. The alternate groups of 10 blue and 10 yellow spools show 34 also as 3 tens and 4 ones. It is thus possible to picture two meanings of all 2-place numbers.

3. In appreciating the relative positions of the numbers in their respective decades. Five comes in the middle of its decade just as 25, 45, 85, and 95 do. Two is the second number in its decade just as 22, 42, and 62 are. Eight comes toward the end of its decade like 18, 38, and 78.

Knowing the relative positions of the numbers is a great aid in transferring the addition and subtraction facts of the first decade to those of a higher decade. If a child locates the second spool in any decade, say 2, and moves up 3 more spools, he will be on the fifth spool in that decade. Adding 3 to the second number of any decade gives the fifth number in that decade. When the principle is applied a whole group of related facts is found:

$$2 + 3 = 5$$
$$12 + 3 = 15$$
$$22 + 3 = 25.$$

In a similar way subtraction facts may be transferred from the first decade to other decades. The child moves down the string of spools to find his answer instead of moving up as in addition.

4. In appreciating the concept of bridging. Suppose a child

has 29¢ and his uncle gives him 5¢ more. Twenty-nine is represented as 2 tens and 9 ones. In adding five more, the child sees that one of the five must complete the decade and so his answer becomes 3 tens and 4 ones or 34¢. The meaning of addition where a full ten is completed and some ones "spill" over into the next decade is dramatically demonstrated.

The reader no doubt will think of other possibilities for this simple device.

The Racks of Spools. Perhaps the most flexible device was one that made use of 100 spools glued together in groups and painted to represent the numbers from 1 to 10. Fifty-five spools were glued together in 10 groups and painted with red enamel to picture the numbers 1 to 10 and the other 45 spools were glued together in 9 groups and painted with white enamel to picture the numbers from 1 to 9.

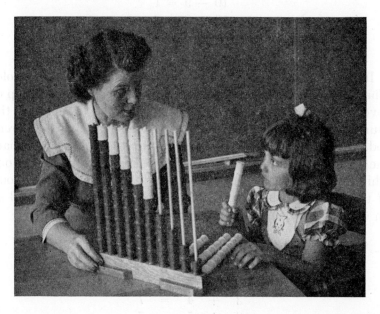

Nine separate racks were made to hold all the combinations that made two, three, four, and so on to ten. It was then possible to analyze the component parts of any of the numbers. The rack which holds the complete story of 10 is shown in the photograph. The two colors make it possible to show the facts and their reverses. When the story is completed the child can tell and then write the story as he has seen it grow, thus:

Red		White		
9	+	1	=	10
8	+	2	=	10
7	+	3	=	10
6	+	4	=	10
5	+	5	=	10
4	+	6	=	10
3	+	7	=	10
2	+	8	=	10
1	+	9	=	10

By removing one group of spools, say the white ones, the corresponding subtraction facts are discovered. (See photograph.)

$$10 - 9 = 1$$
$$10 - 8 = 2$$
$$10 - 7 = 3$$
$$10 - 6 = 4, \text{ and so to } 10.$$

In like manner the stories for the other numbers may be told. The rack for seven contains seven rods the height of the group of seven. The child first picks up enough red spools to represent the numbers from 1 to 7. Each group of spools is placed on a different rod. The rods are close enough together for the child to appreciate the sequence of the numbers as they increase by one. Then one white spool is added to the six red ones to make seven. The group of two white spools is next added to the five red spools and so on until this moving picture is completed:

Red		White		
6	+	1	=	7
5	+	2	=	7
4	+	3	=	7
3	+	4	=	7
2	+	5	=	7
1	+	6	=	7

One outstanding feature of this aid is that the same groups of spools used in telling the story of 10 can be used in telling the story of the other numbers as well.

The author has found this particular aid most helpful in getting mastery of the 45 addition facts and their corresponding subtraction facts. In brief:

100 spools + a desire to teach children effectively + a bit of imagination = some dramatic experiments in arithmetic.

Materials for Grade IV Through Grade VI

FOSTER GROSSNICKLE

THE chief content of the arithmetic curriculum for Grade IV through Grade VI consists of the operations of the three basic processes, common and decimal fractions, and area. Some courses of study call for the introduction of per cent. A wide variety of materials may be used to show some phase of the topics mentioned. Many teachers find it more profitable to use a minimum number of materials which are effective for showing the topic than to use a wide variety of materials. Three materials considered as basic for teaching arithmetic at the intermediate grade level are:

1. Place-value pocket chart
2. Flannel board
3. Fractional cut-outs.

Manipulative materials in arithmetic may be designed for demonstration purposes by the teacher or for pupil use. The two kinds of material should be used to supplement each other. To illustrate, the teacher should have large fractional parts which may be displayed on the flannel board. At the same time each pupil should have cut-outs to objectify any fraction which the teacher demonstrates on the flannel board.

A place value pocket chart is used for class demonstration purposes. This chart may be made of wood or of oak tag. The teacher may use the chart to show how to multiply or divide a two-place number by a one-place number. A chart of this kind should not be used to objectify multiplying or dividing by a two-place number. A pupil should discover the meaning of the process from the use of a one-place multiplier or divisor.

Each pupil should have material to use to represent the first three places in our number system. Material of this kind can be made from a piece of oaktag 15″ x 30″ ruled into ¾-inch squares. This material provides enough squares from which to cut 1 hundred, 24 tens, and 30 ones. The cards to represent ones are 30 separate squares. A card to represent a 10 is a strip of 10 squares and the card to represent 100 is a square containing 100 small squares. The pupil should group the cards according to value and label each group. After cutting the parts mentioned, the spare part from the large sheet provides enough material to make the labels for 1's, 10's, and 100's.

The pupil uses his material to discover how to perform a given operation, such as dividing a two-place number by a one-place number, as in the example, $2)\overline{36}$. He objectifies the number with his materials as three 10's and six 1's. He will discover that it is not possible to divide the 10's as 10's into two equal groups. He must regroup three 10's as two 10's and ten 1's, making a total of two 10's and sixteen 1's. Then he divides the number into two equal parts.

After the pupils have discovered different ways to divide 36 by 2, the teacher gives a demonstration of the method to follow by representing the numbers in the pocket chart. If a pupil has used a different procedure in his solution, he now sees the best method to use. He uses this method to find the solution of other examples until he is able to divide without the use of objective aids.

A teacher can make a pocket chart from a sheet of black tag board stock about 20″ x 26″. Draw a line 5½ inches from the top edge along the length of the sheet and fold along this line. Then measure down 2 inches from the line you drew before, then fold under at this point as before and staple the part folded under. This folded part should make the first row of pockets for the chart. Measure down 4 inches from the bottom of the lower edge of the first pocket and repeat the process. Continue the process until three or four rows of pockets have been formed. Then divide each row of pockets into three equal parts by taping at the points of division a retainer of heavy cardboard so as to keep the pockets open. Now with white ink label the pockets as 1's, 10's, and 100's, respectively, beginning on the right. The chart then may be attached to a wire coat hanger (23).

A pocket chart can be adapted for teaching decimal fractions by giving the appropriate label to the pockets. The three pockets should be labeled 1's, $\frac{1}{10}$'s and $\frac{1}{100}$'s, respectively, beginning on the left.

A flannel board can be used to advantage in the intermediate grades in teaching common fractions. The size of a flannel board should be approximately 20" x 30". Heavy cardboard or ply-board covered with durable black flannel stretched taut over the board makes a flannel board for class demonstration purposes. Other materials which have a nap may be used instead of flannel.

The teacher should make fractional cut-outs to be shown on the flannel board. These fractional parts should be lined with red, green, or some other bright colored flannel. The cut-out should be made of heavy tag and should include wholes, halves, thirds, fourths, sixths, and eighths. There should be at least 12 whole circles so that two circles can be cut to represent each of the parts indicated. Each circle should be approximately 10 inches in diameter.

Each pupil should have fractional cut-outs to parallel those used by the teacher. A pupil can trace a circle on tag or heavy drawing paper by using a $2\frac{1}{2}$-size can. He should cut 12 circles of the same size and then divide them among the fractional parts mentioned. He will need help from the teacher to measure a third. The fractional cut-outs should constitute the pupil's Fraction Kit.

The pupil uses his cut-outs to find the answer to a problem involving the use of fractions. If the pupil does not know the sum of two fractions, such as $\frac{1}{2}$ and $\frac{1}{4}$, he uses his cut-outs to find the answer. The teacher uses the flannel board to demonstrate to the class the steps in finding the sum. The pupil uses the manipulative material in fractions until he is able to make progress with symbols.

The pupil uses his cut-outs to discover relationships among fractions. If the object of a lesson is to teach the meaning of reduction in fractions, the pupil uses his cut-outs to show the equivalence of such fractions as $\frac{3}{6}$ and $\frac{1}{2}$. The teacher should question the pupil about the number of equal parts into which the whole is divided in each case. Then she should direct the pupil to compare the size of the equal parts. The directed use of the manipulative material should enable the pupil to generalize about the meaning of reduction. The writer saw a fifth-grade teacher using fractional materials in a similar circumstance. After a few illustrations, one pupil said, "We reduce fractions by making bigger parts but not as many parts." This pupil discovered the change which took place in reduction of fractions. Then the pupils were ready to learn how to reduce a fraction by dividing both of its terms by the same number.

A few hand-made materials, such as a place-value chart, an abacus, and a flannel board with fractional cut-outs, represent the minimum number of manipulative materials needed in the classroom to make arithmetic meaningful to the pupil in the intermediate grades. A flannel board may be used to show the meaning of per cent if the teacher has 100 disks to place on it. These disks need not adhere to the board. The reader will find a discussion of the use of materials for teaching per cents in another publication (21).

As mentioned previously, it is not the manipulation of material as such, but the use of the material which vitalizes instruction in arithmetic. If a pupil is able to make discoveries and generalizations in quantitative situations by use of symbols, he should not use manipulative materials. On the other hand, if he cannot deal understandingly with quantitative situations by use of symbols, he should use objective materials to discover relationships among quantities. The pupil should be encouraged at all times to operate at the highest level of abstraction at which he understands the work.

Aids for Junior High Mathematics

ALLENE ARCHER

PUPILS in junior high school are at that stage when they are no longer children nor are they adults, and yet one minute they resemble the former and the next, the latter. They need help and guidance to bridge the gap between elementary and secondary mathematics. Visual aids, which create interest or help to develop concepts in junior high school mathematics, make the study of this subject enjoyable for both pupils and teachers. Those described here are some easy ones which my pupils have made for themselves.

AID I. MATH-TIC

Materials: 6-ply cardboard in different colors.

Pupils love games and Math-Tic is a very delightful one for reviewing fundamentals of arithmetic and algebra. Different sets may be made for whole numbers, fractions, decimals, percentage, and positive and negative numbers.

Cut 6-ply cardboard 6 inches by 4 inches for the pupils' cards and $2\frac{1}{2}$ inches by $1\frac{1}{2}$ inches for the tickets. Lay four tickets one under the other on the left side of the large card. Write an example on each ticket and the answer opposite the ticket on the large card. Be sure that the same answers occur on several cards. Each pupil is given a large card with the answers and the teacher keeps the tickets. The teacher reads an example and the pupils who have the correct answer on their cards raise their hands. The first one to raise his hand should be allowed to answer first. If he misses, the next pupil is called on. When a pupil tells the correct answer, he is given the ticket to put on his card. When his card is filled with the four tickets, he calls "Math-Tic", and drops out of the game. After three pupils have stopped playing, the pupils exchange cards and all start playing again. If a teacher wants to add zest to the game, a candy Lifesaver or a Chiclet may be awarded as a prize when a pupil fills his card. The award greatly increases the interest and fun of playing the game. This is an excellent game for the day before a holiday.

AID II. LINKS

Materials: 6-ply cardboard.

Like Math-Tic, this is a game for reviewing fundamentals of arithmetic and algebra. It is particularly useful for pupils who are weak or who have been absent.

Cut 6-ply cardboard in pieces, 3″ x 1″ and 2″ x 1″. Cut a slot at the top of the larger piece ¾ inch from the right edge and ½ inch long. Cut a similar slot at the bottom of the smaller piece ¾ inch from the left edge and ½ inch long. Fasten the pieces together at the slots. Write an example on the large piece of cardboard and its answer on the smaller piece.

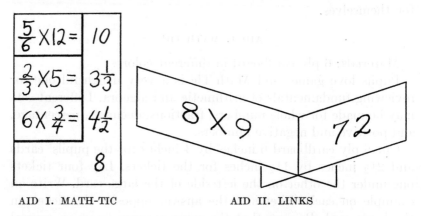

AID I. MATH-TIC   AID II. LINKS

This game may be played by one child or by a small group, not over five children. Put the pieces with the examples in one box and those with answers in another. The pupil picks out an example and hunts through the other box for the answer, then links them together. The aim is to see how many correct links can be made in a certain time. The time may vary, but do not have it too long. A good student or the teacher can check the links.

AID III. THE ROVING DECIMAL POINT

Materials: Large cards with a number, 0 to 9 on each card. Two cards each with a decimal point.

Divide the class into two teams. Each pupil should have a card with a number or a decimal point. Only one pupil on each team should have a decimal point. When the teacher reads a number with a decimal, the pupils on each team with the digits of the number and the decimal point try to see which team can go to the front of the room and make the number first. The cards should be exchanged frequently so that the same pupils will not participate too often. The team with the highest score wins.

AID IV. AREA OF A PARALLELOGRAM

Materials: 14-ply cardboard, corrugated cardboard, masking or cellophane tape.

Draw a rectangle on a piece of 14-ply cardboard and mark lines to show its area in square inches. Draw a line (not a diagonal) from one vertex to make a triangle. Cut out the rectangle and cut off the triangle. Cut a large piece of 14-ply cardboard of another color and mount it on corrugated board with masking or cellophane tape. (Cellophane tape disintegrates after a few years.) Paste the part of the rectangle which is a trapezoid to the large cardboard, allowing room for the triangular piece to be placed on the board.

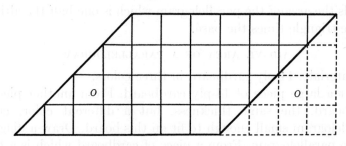

Use a thumb tack with a short pin and fasten the triangle to the board so that a parallelogram is formed. Move the triangle and place it to form a rectangle, so that the pupils can see that the area of the parallelogram is the same as the area of the rectangle or the base times the altitude.

AID V. AREA OF A TRIANGLE

Materials: 14-ply cardboard, corrugated cardboard, a thumb tack.

Mount a large piece of 14-ply cardboard on corrugated board with masking or cellophane tape. From 14-ply cardboard of another color cut a triangle small enough to fit on the board. Mark off lines to show its area in square inches. Draw the altitude of the triangle. Draw a line which bisects any two sides of the triangle and cut along this line. Paste the piece of the triangle which is a trapezoid on the board. Allow room for the other piece of the triangle to be placed to form the original triangle and to be moved so that a parallelogram is formed.

With the thumb tack, fasten the small triangle to the board to
form the original triangle. Move this triangle and place it to form
a parallelogram with the same base as the original triangle and

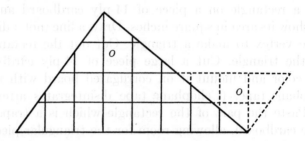

with half the altitude of the triangle. The area of the triangle
equals the area of the parallelogram which is one-half the altitude
of the triangle times the base.

AID VI. AREA OF A PARALLELOGRAM

Materials: 14-ply cardboard in three colors.

Cut a large piece of 14-ply cardboard. From another piece of
cardboard, the same thickness, but a different color, cut a
parallelogram small enough to fit on this board. Draw a diagonal
of the parallelogram. From a piece of cardboard which is a third
color, cut a triangle which is congruent to the triangles formed
by the diagonal of the parallelogram. Draw an altitude of the
triangle and one of the parallelogram. Fasten the triangle to the
board with a pocket behind it so that the parallelogram can be
slipped into the pocket and only one of its triangles shows. This
pocket can be made by pasting a strip of paper on the back of
each side of the triangle which equals a side of the parallelogram
so that the paper protrudes ⅝ inch beyond the sides of the tri-

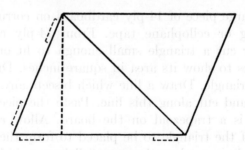

angle. Fold the paper back along each side of the triangle and
⅛ inch from the side. Paste the paper which is ½ inch wide to
the board. The triangle projects out ⅛ inch from the board to
form a pocket into which the parallelogram can be placed.

Place the parallelogram on the triangle and show that their
altitudes and bases are equal. Put the parallelogram in the
pocket and show that the triangle equals one triangle of the
parallelogram. Take out the parallelogram and turn it around
and put it back in the pocket to show that the triangle equals the
other triangle of the parallelogram, and thus it is one-half the
parallelogram. Since the area of a parallelogram equals its altitude
times its base, the area of the triangle equals one-half its altitude
times its base.

AID VII. AREA OF A TRAPEZOID

Materials: 14-ply cardboard, corrugated cardboard, a thumb
tack.

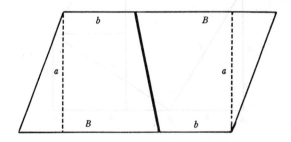

Cut two congruent trapezoids from 14-ply cardboard. Draw
an altitude on each and label both altitudes a. Cut a piece of
14-ply cardboard of another color large enough to hold both
trapezoids side by side and mount it on a piece of corrugated
cardboard with masking tape. Paste one trapezoid on the board
with the longer base down. Label its bases, b and B. Hold the
other trapezoid with its shorter base down and label its bases,
B and b.

Show that the two trapezoids are equal in area by placing
one on the other, mentioning the facts that their altitudes and
bases are equal. With a thumb tack fasten the movable trapezoid
to the board with the longer base on top so that two equal non-

parallel sides of the trapezoid will coincide. A parallelogram is formed with an altitude equal to the altitude of the original trapezoid and a base equal to the sum of the bases of the trapezoids. The area of this parallelogram equals $a(B + b)$. Since the area of the original trapezoid is equal to one-half the area of the parallelogram, the area of a trapezoid is equal to $\frac{1}{2}a(B + b)$.

AID VIII. PYTHAGOREAN THEOREM

Materials: 14-ply cardboard, two thumb tacks.

As shown in the figure, draw two squares side-by-side on 14-ply cardboard. Label the side of one square, a, and the side of the

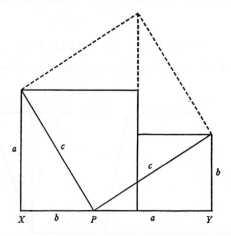

other square, b. Cut out the squares, but leave them joined together. Mark off a point P which is at a distance a from Y and a distance b from X. With a as the altitude and b as the base, draw a line c which will be the hypotenuse of a right triangle. With b as the altitude and a as the base, draw another line which will equal c and is also the hypotenuse of another right triangle. Cut off these triangles. To a piece of 14-ply cardboard, paste the part of the two squares which is left, then fasten the triangles to the board to form the two original squares. Finally, move the squares and place them as shown in the figure where one square is formed with c, the hypotenuse of the right triangles, as its side.

MEASUREMENT

AID IX. MAGNIFIED RULERS

Materials: 14-ply cardboard, colored construction paper cut in ¼ inch strips or colored cellophane tape ¼ inch wide.

Take two pieces of 14-ply cardboard, 28″ x 11″, and lay them so that two short ends will coincide. If a dark color is used, it will not show soil. One inch from the left-hand edge, paste a ¼ inch strip, 5 inches long. This is the zero strip. Since 16 inches will represent 1 inch on the magnified ruler, paste one of the strips every 16 inches. Paste a strip 4 inches long of another color every 8 inches to represent the half inches; then using another color, paste a strip 3 inches long every 4 inches to represent the quarter inches. With two other pieces of cardboard, 28″ x 11″, make another ruler like the first one. Midway between the strips representing the halves and quarters of inches, paste strips 2 inches long of a fourth color to represent eighths of inches. Use two other pieces of cardboard, 28″ x 11″, to make a ruler like the last one. Paste strips, 1 inch long of still another color and 1 inch apart to represent sixteenths of inches.

It is best to start with the ruler showing the quarters and halves of inches. Place it at the back of the room and do not allow the pupils to look at it when they are drawing lines of various lengths. After they have drawn the lines on their papers, have them exchange papers. Each pupil should find the required length of a line on his ruler, compare it with his partner's ruler, then compare it with the length pointed out by a student on the magnified ruler. When he is sure that he knows the length of the line, he measures the line on his partner's paper and checks it right or wrong. After the pupils have mastered the measurement of quarters and halves of inches, that magnified ruler should be put away and the one with eighths of inches displayed. Later the ruler with sixteenths of inches can be used. These rulers create interest in measurement and help the teacher to check to see if pupils have learned to measure lines accurately.

AID X. MEASUREMENT OF ANGLES

Materials: filing cards or pieces of 6-ply cardboard, 6″ x 4″.
On each side of pieces of thin cardboard, draw two angles.

Make at least one a right angle and one an obtuse angle and draw them in different positions. Number each card and label the vertices of the angles, A, B, C, and D. On a separate card write the number of each card and the size of each angle.

These cards are to be used after the measurement of angles has been taught so that a teacher can quickly determine which pupils need more help and practice in measuring angles. Give each pupil one of the cards and tell him to measure $\angle A$. When this has been done, ask each pupil to tell the number of his card and the degrees in $\angle A$. Allow a tolerance of one degree in the answer given. The teacher can jot down the names of pupils who do not know how to measure angles and help these pupils while the others measure the rest of the angles.

It is handy to keep a box of polygons, all shapes and sizes, with the sides and angles labeled. A pupil who finishes measuring the angles on his card quickly can measure the sides and angles of some polygons, then exchange polygons with another pupil and check the other's measurements. In this way the pupils obtain practice not only in measuring angles, but also in measuring straight lines in inches and centimeters.

Illustrative Aids for the Senior High School

FRANCES M. BURNS

ONE of the significant emerging practices in mathematics is the increased use of the laboratory method in classes at the junior and senior high-school levels. The term laboratory method is used here to indicate the practice of providing the opportunity for independent pupil investigation and discovery through the use of individual models, devices, or materials.

Effective results from the laboratory method are related to three simple principles: (a) the device or material should be *simple* and, wherever possible, flexible or dynamic as opposed to a static piece; (b) there should be *tactual activity* on the part of the pupil; he must be a *doer* and not an observer only; (c) pupil activity must be *guided* by the use of investigation sheets which direct the pupil during his search for relationships.

The purpose of this article is to give specific illustrations of the method at the senior high-school level. Space limitations prevent detailed directions for construction of the devices; investigation procedures are given in full.

MEDIAN OF A TRIANGLE

Description of the Pupil Device. A piece of wallboard 7″ x 12″ is covered with colored cardboard on which the base AB of a triangle has been drawn in ink. Points A, B and the midpoint

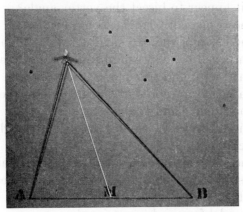

M are lettered and small holes for elastic drilled at these locations. The remaining two sides of the triangle are formed by a black elastic which runs through an eye screw inserted in a small dowel peg. Holes large enough to seat this peg are bored at the vertices of acute, obtuse, right, and isosceles triangles. A white elastic connects point M with the eye of the screw (vertex of the triangle) to form a median.

Pupil Investigation Sheet. It is suggested that the pupils work in groups of two during these investigations. This facilitates handling the model, reading directions, and provides exchange of ideas.

1. Insert the peg in a hole on the model so that an acute triangle is formed; an obtuse triangle; a right triangle; an isosceles triangle.

2. On the model, M is the midpoint of the base AB. Repeat step 1 and note that the white elastic always connects the vertex of the triangle with the midpoint of the opposite side.

3. If a line always connects the vertex of a triangle with the midpoint of the opposite side, it has been agreed to call such a line by the name *median of a triangle*. This is the *definition* of median of a triangle.

4. Insert the peg so that an acute, but not isosceles, triangle is formed. Answer the following questions:

    a. Does the median bisect the base?

    b. Is it perpendicular to the base?

    c. Does it appear to bisect the vertex angle?

    d. Are the two small triangles congruent?

    e. Are the bases of the two small triangles equal?

    f. Hold a pencil to represent the altitude to the base AM of the small left-hand triangle.

    g. Hold a pencil to represent the altitude to the base MB of the small right-hand triangle.

    h. Are the altitudes of these two small triangles the same identical line?

    i. Are the areas of the two small triangles equal?

    j. Is this median equal to, more than, or less than the altitude from the same vertex?

5. Set the model for an obtuse triangle.

    a. Does the median bisect the base?

    b. Is it perpendicular to the base?

    c. Does it appear to bisect the vertex angle?

    d. Are the two small triangles congruent?

    e. Are the bases of the two small triangles equal?

    f. Hold a pencil to represent the altitude to the base AM of the small left-hand triangle.

    g. Hold a pencil to represent the altitude to the base MB of the small right-hand triangle.

    h. Are the altitudes of these two small triangles the same identical line?

    i. Are the areas of the two small triangles equal?

    j. Is this median equal to, more than, or less than the altitude from the same vertex?

6. Set the model for a right triangle.
    a. Does the median bisect the base?
    b. Is it perpendicular to the base?
    c. Does it appear to bisect the vertex angle?
    d. Are the two small triangles congruent?
    e. Are the bases of the two small triangles equal?
    f. Are the altitudes of these two small triangles equal?
    g. Are the two small triangles equal in area?
    h. Is this median equal to, more than, or less than the altitude from the same vertex?

7. Set the model for an isosceles triangle.
    a. Does the median bisect the base?
    b. Is it perpendicular to the base?
    c. Does it appear to bisect the vertex angle?
    d. Are the two small triangles congruent?
    e. Are the bases of the two small triangles equal?
    f. Are their altitudes equal?
    g. Are the two small triangles equal in area?
    h. Is this median equal to, more than, or less than the altitude from the same vertex?

8. How many medians can a triangle have?

9. Tell whether each of the following statements is sometimes true, always true, or never true.
    a. A median of a triangle bisects the base to which it is drawn.
    b. A median of a triangle falls outside the triangle.
    c. A median of a triangle is perpendicular to the base.
    d. A median of a triangle forms two congruent triangles.
    e. A median of a triangle is equal to the altitude from the same vertex.
    f. A median of a triangle is longer than the altitude from the same vertex.
    g. A median of a triangle forms two triangles equal in area.
    h. A median of a triangle is shorter than the altitude from the same vertex.

10. By using the model, but without looking at questions 1–10, organize your knowledge about *median of a triangle*. Do this orally with your partner.

SLOPE OF A STRAIGHT LINE

Description of the Device. A rectangular graph chart 9″ x 11″ with ⅜-inch sections is mimeographed on oak tag paper and fastened to wallboard with Scotch tape. The X and Y axes are scaled in units to the edge of the paper. An 8″ straight, narrow round wire, in which a hole large enough to admit a pin has been

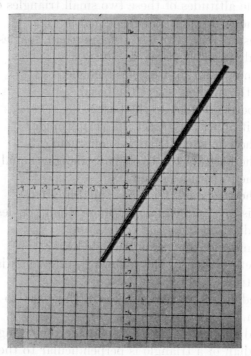

drilled, serves as a line. If wire is not available, a sucker stick or a narrow stiff cardboard strip may be used.

Pupil Investigation Sheet.

1. Insert a pin through the hole in the metal line.

2. Put the pin containing the metal line near enough to the point (4, 3) so that the *edge* of the line goes through this point.

3. Note that the line will turn freely about this point.

4. Turn the line so that it *rises toward the right.*

5. Pivot the line so that it makes a *steep* slope upward to the right.

6. Pivot the line so that it makes a *gentle* slope upward to the right.

7. Turn the line so that it has the *greatest possible slope upward*.

8. Turn the line parallel to the *x*-axis. The line now has *no* slant.

9. Pivot the line so that it slopes *steeply down to the right*.

10. Pivot the line so that it slopes *gently down* to the right.

11. Turn the line so that it has the *greatest possible down slope*.

12. Turn the line so that it again has *no slant*.

13. Pivot the line so that it again slopes *up* to the right in any position *except* perpendicular to the *x*-axis.

14. Notice that the line makes an acute angle *and* an obtuse angle with the *x*-axis and with any line parallel to the *x*-axis. From here on in this investigation, have the longer segment of the line cut the *x*-axis and consider only the *acute* angle it makes with the *x*-axis.

15. Slope of a line is expressed as a *ratio*. We shall see how to do this in the following steps.

16. Keep the line pivoted at (4, 3). Have the longer segment of the line cut the *x*-axis. Put a second pin very close to the point (6, 4) and turn the line so it also passes through point (6, 4).

17. Note that at the second point (6, 4) the line is one unit higher up than it was at (4, 3). This is called its *rise*. At the second point the line is two units farther to the right than it was at (4, 3). This is called its *run*. The *ratio of rise to run* is 1:2. *Slope* of a line can then be expressed as *ratio of rise to run*. The slope of this line is 1:2.

18. Since a straight line has the same steepness throughout, this 1:2 slope could be detected between *any two* (convenient) points. We shall try this in step 19. Do not remove the two pins on the model.

19. Put another pin near where the line goes through (0, 1) and another pin near where the line goes through (8, 5). Consider the line as it passes through the points (0, 1) and (8, 5). How many units does it *rise* between these points? How many units does it *run* between these points? Will the ratio of rise to run reduce to 1:2? Keep all pins on the model. Put other pins near where the line passes through (−4, −1) and (−2, 0). Is the slope 1:2?

20. Take out all pins except the pivot point (4, 3) and turn

the line so that it has a slope of 3:2; a slope of 4:1; a slope of 1:1.

21. Turn the line so that it has a slope of −2:1. (Did you note that a negative rise would be a fall?) Make a slope of −3:1; of −3:2.

22. Between any two points on the line such as R and S, a right triangle could be used to find the ratio of rise to run. From this ratio the number of degrees in angle S could be found. With respect to $\angle S$ in this right triangle

$$\frac{\text{rise}}{\text{run}} = \frac{2}{3}$$

or

$$\tan \angle S = \frac{2}{3}$$

$$\tan \angle S = .6667$$

$$\angle S = 34°$$

To say that the line has a slope of ⅔ and to say that it rises at an angle of 34° are two different ways of talking about its steepness.

23. Turn the line to any position except a 0° slope. Now hold another line (pencil) parallel to the first one. Does it have the same slope or a different slope? Complete the statement which follows. If lines are parallel then their slopes _____ .

24. Form the converse of the statement you wrote in No. 23. Do you believe that the converse is true?

25. Turn the original line to any position except 0° or 90° slope. Hold another line so that it will intersect the first one. Is the slope of the second line the same or different from that of the first line? Complete the following sentence. If two lines intersect then their slopes are _____ .

26. Form the converse of the statement you wrote in No. 25. Do you believe that the converse is true?

27. A line passes through the points (4, 5) and (10, 7). Try to determine the slope of this line without a graph.

THE AMBIGUOUS CASE OF THE LAW OF SINES

Description of the Pupil Device. White cardboard 8″ x 13″ is fastened to wallboard with Scotch tape. On this cardboard are drawn a base line, angle A, and side b. Five dowels of various

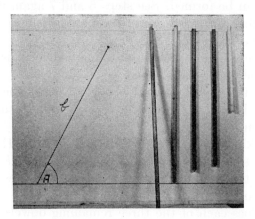

lengths and colors are provided. Near one end of each dowel a hole large enough to admit an upholstery nail is drilled.

Pupil Investigation Sheet.

1. We shall try to determine how many triangles can be formed if the arrangement of the three given parts is two sides and the angle opposite one of these sides. We shall consider angle A to be acute.

2. Two of the three given parts are fixed on the model. These are angle A and the *adjacent* side b. The third given part (the side *opposite* angle A) will be formed by the various painted dowels.

3. How does the length of the *red* dowel (side opposite angle A) compare in length with line b (side adjacent to angle A)?

4. Put the nail through the hole in the red dowel and insert it at the upper end of line b.

5. Pivot the dowel until the lower end contacts the base line to the right of angle A. Note that this triangle contains the two given sides and the given angle.

6. Continue to pivot the red line toward the left until it again contacts the base line.

7. Does the triangle which is now formed contain the *three* given parts?

8. If the side opposite the given angle is greater than the side adjacent to the given angle, how many triangles containing these parts can be formed? See steps 5 and 7 again if necessary.

9. How does the *green* dowel compare in length with side *b* (the side adjacent to angle *A*)?

10. Put the nail in the hole near one end of this dowel and insert it at the upper end of line *b*.

11. Swing the dowel toward the right until the lower end contacts the base line. Does the triangle thus formed contain the *three* given parts?

12. What kind of a triangle was formed in step 11?

13. If the side opposite the given angle is *equal* to the side adjacent to the given angle, how many triangles containing these parts can be formed?

14. How does each of the three remaining dowels compare in length with side *b*?

15. Fit the *pink* dowel at the upper end of line *b*.

16. Pivot it to determine if it will contact the base line.

17. If the pink line contacts the base line, what relationship does it seem to have to the base line?

18. How many triangles can be formed using the pink line?

19. If the side opposite the given angle is *less* than the side adjacent to the given angle but equal in length to the perpendicular from the vertex then _____ triangle(s) can be formed.

20. Fit the *yellow* dowel at the upper end of line *b*.

21. Can a triangle be formed using this yellow line?

22. Complete: If the side opposite the given angle is less than the side adjacent to the angle and _____ than the perpendicular from the vertex then _____ triangle(s) can be formed.

23. Remember (from step 14) that the *blue* dowel is less than the side adjacent to angle *A*.

24. How does this *blue* dowel compare in length with the *pink* dowel? (Remember that the pink dowel was the length of the perpendicular from the vertex to the base.)

25. Insert the *blue* dowel on the model. Pivot it until it contacts the base line. Does the triangle so formed contain the three given parts?

26. Continue to pivot the *blue* line. Will it contact the base at *any other* point than that of step 25?

27. Does the triangle formed in step 26 contain the *three given* parts?

28. Complete: If the side opposite the given angle is less than the side adjacent to the angle but _____ than the perpendicular from the vertex, then _____ triangle(s) can be formed.

29. Summarize the results of this investigation.

30. Given side $AB = 10$, side $BC = 9$, angle $A = 40°$. How many triangles can be formed?

Suggestions for Making Slides

LAUREN G. WOODBY

TEACHERS in general are aware of the trend toward improving learning experiences in schools, and teachers of mathematics in particular are familiar with the illustration of this trend in the Eighteenth Yearbook (7), which contains many suggestions and ideas for vitalizing mathematics through the use of multisensory aids. Most specialists in audio-visual education agree that the individual classroom teacher is the primary factor in determining the effectiveness of these multisensory aids to learning. A good teacher has the ability to select or prepare the appropriate learning aids for a given situation, as well as the ability to use these aids wisely.

Although the use of handmade slides is usually found in the literature among the means suggested for vitalizing mathematics instruction, teachers of mathematics ordinarily do not make extensive use of this aid to learning. Perhaps, that is as it should be, since there is always the danger of overexploitation of a teaching technique with the result that the means become confused with the end. However, there are distinct possibilities for the effective use of handmade slides in communicating some ideas peculiar to mathematics. The information and suggestions that follow may help the teacher in the use of this communication technique.

2″ x 2″ SLIDES

The simplest type of slide to make is a photographic transparency made from 35 mm. or bantam color film. Its simplicity arises from the fact that the processed film is returned in 2″ x 2″ cardboard mounts ready for projection. The cost of processing is included in the purchase price of the film, so each resulting slide costs a little less than 20 cents. Of course, a suitable miniature camera is required, and, for indoor use, adequate lighting is necessary. Photofloods are much less expensive than flash equipment and are entirely adequate for most pictures useful in mathematics classes. An exposure meter is desirable but not essential. Many schools have the necessary photographic equipment available. Pupils having their own photographic equipment are usually eager to contribute their knowledge and ability. However, it is emphasized that the teacher or student who is interested in making color slides need not be an expert photographer; by following a few simple directions, anyone can achieve satisfactory results.

Black and white 35 mm. film likewise can be used to make the convenient 2″ x 2″ slides. Although the photographic processes are simpler, it actually becomes more involved for the user because a positive transparency must be made from the original film. There are some pictures that produce striking results by projecting the mounted negative. Considerably more skill is required to make a positive contact print on film than on paper primarily because positive film is much more sensitive than paper. Then, too, the large magnification of the projected image requires a minimum of such defects as dust spots and fingerprints. These difficulties are not insurmountable, but they do offer a real challenge to those interested in photography.

Anything that can be photographed can be made into a slide of this type. Thus, an unusually good bulletin board display, printed material from a rare book, the class at work on a field exercise, a model solution of a problem, a construction exercise in geometry, or different types of graph paper can be preserved on film and converted into readily available teaching material.

Because of the extremely small working space, at most $1\frac{1}{2}''$ x $1\frac{1}{2}''$, the $2''$ x $2''$ slide is not recommended for handmade slides other than the photographic slides just described. The larger lantern slides are well suited for making both photographic and nonphotographic slides.

$3\frac{1}{4}''$ x $4''$ SLIDES

Standard $3\frac{1}{4}''$ x $4''$ black and white slides can be made photographically by projection from an enlarger. Sensitized glass plates are used, and the process is essentially the same as that used in making a projection print on bromide paper. Although photographic skill is required in order to achieve a slide of high quality, the work is fascinating for those whose interests are in this area.

For uses in mathematics, slides of the nonphotographic variety are generally better suited than those made photographically. The usual size is $3\frac{1}{4}''$ x $4''$ with a working space of at least $2\frac{1}{4}''$ x $3''$, and the materials used include clear glass, etched glass, cellulose acetate, carbon paper, and cellophane. An excellent instructional film, *How to Make Handmade Lantern Slides* (13), demonstrates in detail the preparation and utilization of several types of these nonphotographic slides. This 21-minute color film stresses sources of picture material and special production techniques. Another instructional aid that has been found helpful is the low-cost booklet with the same title, available at the Keystone View Company (13).

Etched glass slides are the easiest and simplest to make. Any ordinary pencil can be used, but a 3H to 6H drawing pencil is preferred for fine clear lines. India ink improves the contrast. If a color slide is desired, either special colored crayons or special slide inks can be used.[4] The crayons are much easier to use, but more brilliant colors can be obtained with slide inks. One feature of the etched glass slide is that the material can be cleaned off with hot soapy water and the glass reused. This feature is important because each etched glass plate costs about 16 cents.

---

[4] The Craftink Manufacturing Co., Cleveland, Ohio; and the Keystone View Co., Meadville, Penn.

Teachers as well as students are usually surprised to find how easy it is to prepare cellophane slides. Either clear or colored cellophane (usually amber) is sandwiched between folded carbon paper cut to size and inserted in the typewriter. These cellophane slides are ideally suited to the drawing of geometric figures or graphs. Ready-cut cellophane carbon paper and masks, such as Radi-O-Mat,[5] are recommended because they are convenient to use and are relatively inexpensive.

Many different grades and thicknesses of plastics are available in both clear and frosted materials. Prepared mats, such as Slidecraft,[6] are unbreakable, are easy to use, are cut to $3\frac{1}{4}''$ x 4″, and have a convenient opaque mask. It is considerably less expensive, however, to purchase large sheets of acetate or lumarith and cut them to the size desired. The thickness should be at least .009″ to minimize warping due to the heat of the projection lamp. If thinner material is used, it should be bound between clear cover glasses. One disadvantage of the translucent plastic material is that it cannot be cleaned well enough for reuse.

In many schools the ancient—or perhaps modern—lantern-slide projectors are collecting dust in a storeroom because of the lack of commercially prepared slides of recent vintage. Distributors of audio-visual equipment report that sales of $3\frac{1}{4}''$ x 4″ projectors, slides, and slide-making materials are negligibly small. This is most unfortunate because there are many possibilities for effective use of this medium of instruction. The enterprising teacher can likely have the continued use of such a projector if it is requested.

5″ x 7″ SLIDES FOR OVERHEAD PROJECTOR

The principal feature of the overhead projector, one of the improvements in visual instructional devices that grew out of World War II, is the large size of the projection stage. While both 2″ x 2″ and $3\frac{1}{4}''$ x 4″ slides can be shown, 5″ x 7″ slides are often used, and some models will handle a 10″ x 10″ transparency. In addition to the benefits due to the larger sizes of

---

[5] Radi-O-Mat Slide Co., Daytona Beach, Fla. 3¢.
[6] The Slidecraft Co., South Orange, N. J. 8¢.

slides that can be used, the overhead projector has the unique feature that the user faces the audience while making the transparency or pointing out detail on the horizontal projection stage. Transparencies can be built up in successive layers and the combination projected as one image. For example, in teaching graphs of quadratic functions, a parabola can be superimposed in various positions over a cross-section transparency to illustrate changes in the effect of the constant terms in the equation.

Another interesting technique that is possible with the overhead projector is "blackboard writing," in which the image is projected on the chalkboard. This is done with an ordinary pencil on a special film to give white figures on a black background. The plastic slide thus prepared can be placed in a 5″ x 7″ cardboard mount or can be covered with a second plastic sheet and bound with masking tape if the teacher wishes to keep it for future use. This dynamic technique is ideally suited to many problems in graphic representation. There is a unifying effect that results in the classroom because the instructor works at the projector in the front of the room. With the projector only 6-feet from the chalkboard, the image from a 10″ x 10″ slide is more than 3-feet square.

Because of the large size of the slides, special supplies are needed. These materials include plastic sheets, special film, tracing carbon paper, backing sheets, masks, mounts, and rolls of cellophane. A china-marking pencil works very well on clear plastic or cellophane, and it can be erased easily with a cloth if desired. Drawing instruments work well with the special film and carbon paper. The manufacturer of one type of overhead projector also distributes a complete line of accessories and slide-making supplies.[7] As with materials for the 3¼″ x 4″ slides, it is much less expensive to purchase large sheets of cellulose acetate or lumarith and cut them to size. Thin sheets of cross section acetate with an adhesive backing are available and can be applied to the under side of a clear plastic sheet for use where needed.[8]

---

[7] Charles Beseler Co., 60 Badger Ave., Newark 8, N. J.

[8] Zip-A-Tone No. 62, available from H. A. Rogers Co., 815 Marquette Ave. Minneapolis. 8″ x 12″ sheet, 50¢.

SOME SUGGESTIONS FOR CONTENT

The criterion proposed by Harrell (14) that "almost any teaching material worth preserving for successive sections of students or successive years of teaching justifies the work of putting it on slides," seems defensible as a general basis for selection of content.

An excellent example of the application of this criterion is the group of slides prepared by Cell to illustrate unusual graphs of common functions.[9] These $3\frac{1}{4}''$ x $4''$ slides were photographic copies of graphs of a few functions carefully drawn on various types of co-ordinate paper. It was interesting to note the favorable reaction of the group of mathematics teachers to the skillful use of the overhead projector.

Another unusual graph that could be preserved in slide form for use by the enterprising teacher is the condensation of the cartesian plane on the interior of a circle.[10] In this transformation the plane is projected onto the lower half of a unit sphere tangent to it at the origin by means of rays through the center of the sphere. This mapping is then projected orthogonally onto the interior of the unit circle.

In either plane or solid geometry, there is a wealth of material suitable for slide presentation. Students respond to the change of routine offered by the projection of a figure for a problem. Most teachers have special problem resource material such as unusual methods of construction of tangents to a circle from an outside point, fallacious "proofs," or applications of the Pythagorean Theorem.

The use of slides to visualize some ideas in the history of mathematics is well illustrated by the fascinating collection of hand-made colored slides prepared by Agnes Herbert, Baltimore, Maryland. Although most teachers do not have such artistic skill, it is often possible to capitalize on the special skills possessed by students in providing purposeful learning experiences, and at the same time to produce good instructional materials. Enthusiastic group participation can be achieved in a class project of making slides on a topic such as "Origins of Our Units of Measure" or "Development of the Metric System."

---

[9] Presented by John Cell at the Duke Mathematics Institute, August 12, 1952.
[10] From a paper, "Condensed Graph Paper for the Cartesian Plane," presented by Kenneth O. May at the Minnesota Section of the MAA, May 9, 1953.

Another example of material that has been found worthy of preserving in slide form is the graphs of trigonometric functions carefully drawn by students. The use of colored slide inks is

HYPERBOLIC LINE OF POSITION

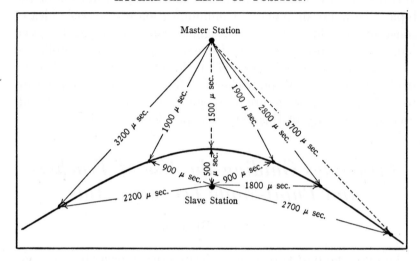

TWO LORAN PAIRS WITH COMMON MASTER STATION, P

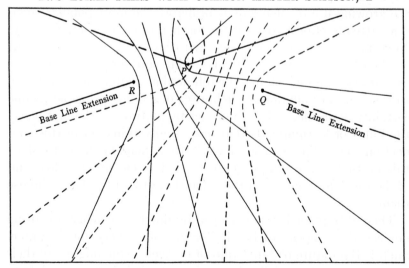

especially recommended. As a variation in method of presentation, it is suggested that 5" x 7" (or larger) slides be partially

prepared beforehand so that the teacher can produce the graphs
and project them at the same time with the overhead projector.
The two slides shown in the figures on page 157 illustrate an
interesting application of the hyperbola. Certainly a chart or
drawing of some kind is a necessary aid in a presentation of the
topic, "How Loran Works." Communication of the basic idea of
constant time differences of the signals from a loran pair has been
found to be most effective if discussion of the slides is followed
by construction of a hyperbola at the blackboard and then by
study of some actual loran charts. Thus, the slides are a means
to an end and, as such, are only one of several multisensory aids
used in the study of this very real problem in navigation.

Principles Guiding the Use of Teacher- and Pupil-Made Learning Aids

EMIL J. BERGER

DURING the past two decades the practice of using teacher- and
pupil-made learning aids has gained wide acceptance. In fact
the growing use of such aids is probably the most popular trend
that attends efforts to improve mathematics instruction today.
Nevertheless, there does not seem to be any general agreement
on the precise function of such materials in the teaching situation
nor on principles which may be followed as a guide in using them.
In fact, the formulation of such a set of guiding principles, while
certainly desirable, seems somewhat premature. In the first place,
the kinds of learning aids that one usually thinks of in this connection—i.e., "homemade devices that may be used to show
this or that"—are unique in that what is meant by "this kind
of devices" does not mean the same thing to all teachers who use
them.

Then also, procedures developed by different teachers for using
devices that appear to be similar are often very much unlike.
Such is the nature of "this kind of devices." One might say their
use represents an undefined technique. So it is hardly possible to
arrive at a statement of principles on procedures of usage by

looking for agreement among the informal opinions advanced by teachers who are acquainted with the technique.

There is another reason why the statement of a set of principles may be somewhat premature. Enthusiasm for the technique is still gaining momentum and there is no way of telling at this stage in its development what ramifications of procedure are likely to be accented next. The consequence of this situation and the facts explained above are that there are no specific procedures that have been isolated for evaluation in an educational study.

Obviously then, this exposition does not rely on the results of an educational experiment for what is presented. Nor is it a composite of the opinions of fellow teachers who use the technique in question, but rather it is this writer's interpretation of opinions he has heard voiced, demonstrations he has observed, and personal classroom experiences.

It is for the foregoing reasons that we hesitate exceedingly to be so bold as to announce anything offered in this section as a principle. Specific suggestions that are made will simply be referred to as suggested procedures.

As a simple measure of expediency for introducing some order in this discussion we propose the following fourfold classification of teacher- and pupil-made aids:

1. Demonstration aids   3. Analysis aids
2. Developmental aids   4. Projects

This division is both arbitrary and somewhat artificial, and in many instances it would probably be quite difficult to decide under which category to list some particular device, but the classification given does have the advantage of differentiating between possible uses that may be made of teacher- and pupil-made learning aids. Probably the most numerous of the devices used in classes are demonstration aids. These are what one would expect: models, mock-ups, and dynamic devices—those having movable or adjustable parts. Devices used for this purpose may be either teacher-made or pupil-made, and demonstrations performed with such devices may be co-operative ventures conducted by both teacher and pupil or the individual work of one or the other. While this article deals specifically with teacher-

and pupil-made aids, it should not be overlooked that there are commercial devices available which can also be used as demonstration aids.

Occasionally it is claimed that using pupil-made demonstration aids is superior to using ones made by the teacher or those obtained commercially. Experience tends to indicate that this is sometimes true when the device being used is one that has been produced by a member of the class in which it is used. The fact that a fellow classmate designed the device used in a lesson certainly does enhance interest and enthusiasm among class members, and this is especially noticeable when the student who produced the device also gives the demonstration. For best results in following such a plan the pupil should be coached beforehand so that he will not be learning how to demonstrate while he is trying to present something to the class. At first thought this last suggestion may appear to be a wrong approach, but a little reflection will show its wisdom.

However, one must not be misled on the point made above. It is not always true that student-made demonstration aids are superior to others. A teacher-made device must of necessity be fairly respectable mechanically, and commercial devices are generally well-finished, so these types make an appeal to pupils which, while certainly somewhat impersonal, are nonetheless highly effective. This is especially true in the case of boys; a nicely finished commercial device is apt to get much more attention from them than a poorly made one produced by a classmate.

Demonstrations in mathematics that call for the use of equipment differ somewhat from the usual conception of demonstrations as carried on in the natural and physical sciences. For one thing there is less equipment available and very often a particular device can only be operated by the person who produced it. Then also those concepts which lend themselves to a demonstration at all are often not very easy to construct in the first place. Another difference is that the equipment used in a mathematical experiment is generally some home-made or adapted contrivance, as is certainly true with the type of aids discussed here, and so its structure must be fairly well understood before it can be used at all. Finally there are few organized laboratory outlines available for mathematics demonstrations so one must rely largely on his own ingenuity in preparing for lessons of this type. Because demonstrations in mathematics, relatively speaking at least, are still somewhat of a pioneering idea, the following suggestions on procedure may be found helpful:

1. To insure the workability of a demonstration it should be planned in advance and rehearsed if possible. Demonstrating concepts with the aid of concrete materials is not the usual mode of approach to some of the topics of mathematics; hence familiarization with the plan of procedure may help one avoid the feeling of being "all thumbs."

2. If a demonstration is to be successful, students must understand what is going to be attempted. The habit of writing leading questions on the board will be found helpful.

3. Do not attempt too much. Many devices can be used to illustrate a whole series of related concepts, but yielding to the temptation to do so may not only becloud a student's understanding of the main concept being pursued but even destroy what meager insight he may have acquired initially. Also, the person in charge of the demonstration must not allow himself to be led too far afield by one or two alert students who wish to examine some remote detail of the main concept. The demonstration should be performed for the whole class at least the first time through.

4. Keeping up a running summary as the demonstration proceeds will help the slower student keep the details of the work in mind.

5. Repeat the demonstration for the slower student if it appears that such repetition will help him organize his thinking.

6. When the demonstration proper has been completed, opportunity should be provided for the members of the class to manipulate the demonstration device individually if they desire. Occasionally a student is able to clear up some detail for himself in this way even when he is unable to formulate a question concerning his particular difficulty. Handling a device by oneself is quite different from observing someone else perform a demonstration with it.

7. Finally follow up the demonstration with shrewd questioning, or possibly even a short quiz, to insure that the concepts demonstrated were actually communicated.

The term, developmental aid, as here intended may be roughly defined as a class activity in which each student is given the opportunity to develop a thought model or illustration of some concept from simple raw materials placed at his disposal for that purpose. Typical examples include such activities as paper folding to effect common geometrical constructions, building triangles from sets of given parts, building the different quadrilaterals from a given set of sticks, plotting points on Celotex squares with map pins to discover loci, cutting out figures with equal areas from squared paper, curve stitching, illustrating superposition with dress patterns, giving concrete geometric interpretations to factoring problems, building polyhedrons, and other such activities.

The use of this procedure is time consuming but it is also one of the most direct methods that can be employed to assist students in experiencing the feel of what it means to make a genuine discovery. The main problem encountered in using this technique is organizational. What preparations must be made in advance? How shall a lesson be motivated? Can the plan be employed in the typical classroom? Answers to these and similar questions are incorporated in the following suggestions:

1. Of necessity every student must be equipped with some simple tools, and as a measure for avoiding confusion, each student's materials should be stored individually somewhere in the classroom. If individual drawer space is not available, then shoe boxes—or some other sort of boxes that are uniform in size and shape—should be used. Uniform size and shape makes storage easy. Each student's laboratory kit should contain such simple tools and materials as a pair of scissors, paper punch, razor blade, ruler, compasses, map pins, push pins, corkboard or Celotex square, mucilage, elastic, protractor, color crayons, pick-up sticks, fruit jar covers, dress patterns, road maps, Scotch tape, and whatever else the teacher thinks may be useful.

2. Select only tools and materials that everyone can use, and that can be stored in the container selected. Students should equip their own kits if this is feasible.

3. Raw materials such as construction paper, squared cross-section paper, and precut items such as cardboard strips should be distributed to students only as needed.

4. For best results the classroom should be equipped with tables—preferably two-chair tables. Desks with large tops are superior for this type of work to lecture room armchairs.

5. If exercises attempted involve more than two or three steps, an outline of key steps should be duplicated or placed on the blackboard.

6. If the activity calls for building a model, mimeographed pattern sheets with instructions will be found helpful.

7. Do not attempt too much.

8. A problem can be set up by posing questions whose answers

suggest activity to the student. For example suppose students are given a set of precut cardboard strips and are asked to decide which sets of three each may be combined to form triangles. As another example, suppose students are directed to place two map pins on their Celotex squares three inches apart, and are then asked to locate all points that are two inches from each pin.

9. Resist the temptation to tell more than is absolutely necessary to motivate a student to action.

Student activity interspersed by questions that help direct further activity in the direction of the goal desired is the secret of this method of teaching. The entire design of the technique is to provide the student with opportunities that will lead to discovery experiences, so the teacher must be careful that he does not give directions, offer suggestions, or provide hints faster than the majority of the members of the class can assimilate them. The experienced teacher will have no difficulty regulating himself in this respect because he will know the signs at which individual students arrive at the discovery point—sudden smiles of satisfaction, scarcely audible sounds, a nod of the head, or other signs.

Consider Now Analysis Aids. In reality these are a special kind of demonstration aids, but they also have some of the qualities of the type referred to above as developmental aids. All of us have at sometime stopped in front of a department store to watch a sidewalk barker selling cooky presses, soapstones, needle-threaders, coffee-makers, or some other household gadgets. Consider for a moment the demonstration put on by such a barker when he sells cooky presses. In order to attract as much attention as possible he assembles the whole gadget piece by piece with ostentatious deliberateness. As each part is put in place he makes a special play for attention. Finally he puts dough into the tube, turns down the screw and squeezes out star shaped cookies. "Step right up, only one dollar!" Even the 100 per cent sales proof onlooker feels compelled to buy one of the gadgets.

This little anecdote may not seem to have much in common with the use of learning aids, but it is included here because it helps explain what is meant by an analysis aid. If we sift out the element of overdramatization on which the barker depends and analyze what his act really is we have what this writer calls an "analysis aid"—namely developing a concept through the act of assembling the constituent elements of a projected thought model in some logical order.

Suppose we desire to develop the concept that an angle is an amount of rotation of one line away from a second line around a point called the vertex. To develop this concept three separate elements need to be introduced and related. Suppose we begin by introducing an ordinary nail and identifying it as the vertex. Next, identify a white-colored stick with a hole near one end as the initial side of the angle and place it on the nail. Finally, identify a red-colored stick, also prepared with a hole near one end, as the terminal side and put it in place. Then show what is meant by rotation of the red line away from the white line around the vertex. The deliberate isolation of the three elements on which this concept is based is what makes this procedure effective. The parallel which exists between this example and the anecdote given above is not hard to see. Is the expression "analysis aid" appropriate?

The effectiveness of this technique depends of course on how well the demonstrator can combine the building process with an appropriate commentary. Both are essential. The example offered above implies that the materials needed in the building process must be prepared in advance. This is true, but it is simply amazing how many different demonstrations can be developed by using Makit Toy, a colorful, sturdy building set manufactured by the W. R. Benjamin Company of Granite City, Illinois. The teacher who has such a set at his disposal will find that he can perform a great many analysis type demonstrations with it.

An area in which this particular technique may be used extensively is solid geometry. The idea is especially adaptable for developing proofs of theorems involving lines and planes in space and polyhedrons, and of analyzing original problems in order to discover proofs.

We come now to the fourth classification of teacher- and pupil-made aids listed above—namely projects. In general, the word project implies some preplanned activity which may be carried on over a period of time. In this broad sense the project technique may involve many different kinds of activity, but since this section is concerned primarily with teacher- and pupil-made aids we shall limit our discussion of projects to this special phase of the technique.

The value of the project method in this connection is twofold. For one thing the method can be employed as a means for making demonstration type aids available for use by the class. Lacking other means for providing a class with suitable demonstration devices one cannot completely discount this particular function of the project technique. However, if procurement of a stock-pile of devices is allowed to become the main objective of project assignments, then the value of such activity to the students who are individually concerned is certainly questionable. Some type of co-ordination with class activity would certainly seem to be an essential part of any program in which the project technique is employed.

Fortunately the collection aspect of the project method is minor compared with the real values which accrue to students who develop models, dynamic devices, and other materials as project assignments.

In general, individual assignments work out more satisfactorily than do assignments made for groups. This is one of the strengths of the project technique. The experienced teacher will recognize in it a really practical means for dealing with the problem of individual differences. Any teacher who would use this plan should fortify himself with a card file of possible projects from which students can choose assignments or get ideas for developing projects of their own. Each entry in this file should carry a brief description of the project, a simple drawing, suggested references, and a note concerning its difficulty. This last bit of information will assist the teacher in helping students make appropriate selections. One way of using such a file is for the teacher to engage a student in an informal discussion of a project in which the student seems interested up to the point at which the teacher senses that he has touched off enough interest to motivate the student to action. No precise formula can be stated for this procedure, because the success of such an approach depends almost entirely on the skill of the teacher who uses it.

As another suggestion a teacher may find it helpful to work out direction sheets for specific projects which will be sufficiently complete to get students started and to help them over some of the hurdles, but which do not solve the problem for them.

Helping students select projects which will be appropriate for them in terms of their interests, previous training, and ability is undoubtedly the most difficult phase of the entire project assignment. No general suggestions appear to be consistently helpful, except possibly these two. For beginning students individual project assignments should be quite closely related to the actual classwork in progress. However, for the more advanced student, this is not an essential restriction. In fact, two of the purposes of the project method are to enrich the regular course work pursued by the class and to provide students of good ability with opportunities for extending their information about special topics.

The building of a device by a student provides him with an exceedingly fine opportunity to develop desirable thinking abilities. In building a device to aid his understanding of some concept, the student must organize the information which he brings to the situation and decide in what respects his knowledge is inaccurate or incomplete. At first thought it might appear that an immature student cannot be expected to organize a problem with which he has had little or no previous association in sufficient detail to be able to analyze it. Experience has been encouraging in this respect, however. It is occasionally almost unbelievable how quickly a student is able to decide independently of outside assistance on what facts he is ignorant or on what points he is confused. After a student has had experience with several project assignments his requests for information become increasingly direct and to the point. All this is stated as a prelude to the suggestion that the teacher who plans a project assignment must be careful to outline the problem clearly but not to give up on the result too easily. A rule of thumb is to tell only what a student needs to know in order to get started. If the motivation is well executed the student will of his own accord either find the result by himself or ask for what he needs to know. Also, when a student does ask for information the teacher must be careful that he does not, either deliberately or otherwise, direct the student to follow a plan to which the teacher has become attached because of years of successful experience. When students are thus directed, they often develop constructions which while not standard by the teacher's experiences are in many cases far more stimulating in terms of class reception than are ideas that have become sacred through usage. It is worthwhile to follow this suggestion even when a student's questions clearly indicate that he may be in error. Errors made in this way provide excellent material for class discussion and in the end help the entire class develop a deeper insight into the actual facts than is sometimes the case when a student's work is over-directed. In this connection it seems appropriate to make mention of one of the immediate consequences that invariably appears when an individual student has completed a project assignment. If the student's handiwork is displayed in the classroom—as indeed it should be—his classmates will have the opportunity of examining his work and discussing it with him. An untold amount of learning often takes place in this rather informal way, and it is not uncommon to find that what one student has discovered through a project assignment may never have to be treated formally by the class.

Earlier in this section, in the discussion of demonstration type aids, it was pointed out that the commonly held opinion that student-made devices are superior to teacher-made or commercial devices was not entirely true. Occasionally it is also claimed that a student will learn most from a device if he makes it himself. One must be careful about the real meaning of this statement. If taken at face value it would contradict the whole thesis that the project method may be used as a means of providing for individual differences. Actually it often happens that a student learns a great deal from a device which he couldn't possibly produce by himself. It is only necessary to point out the fact that usually only the better students can produce a complicated device, but that once the device is a reality the majority of students in class are able to profit from seeing it used in a demonstration or by having it explained to them by the person who made it.

The main objective of the project method as here described is to develop in a student both the desire and the capacity to think independently. When project assignments are employed in this way independent thinking replaces learnings that are formal and artificial.

The discussion and suggested procedures presented on the preceding pages have been an attempt to answer the questions: What is the nature of teacher- and pupil-made learning aids, and how may they be used? The reader will recall that we openly admitted at the outset of this section that we were on uncertain ground with respect to answering questions like these because of the undefined nature of the technique of using such aids. The question, "When shall such aids be used in the teaching situation?" is equally perplexing and the latitude of opinion on it ranges between wide extremes. Some teachers would like to use them whenever they serve an appropriate purpose; others would use them sparingly.

The difficulty is that the answer to this question depends on a whole host of factors. To name a few: it depends on the ability and previous training of the pupil; the ingenuity of the teacher in communicating ideas; and certainly on what the objective of the moment happens to be. If visualization is the main objective then it would seem absurd for a teacher to withhold them from use; however, if the objective is to develop pupils' capacities to think in terms of abstract symbolism then dependence on their use for too long a period of time may actually impede a pupil's progress toward the goal desired. Nevertheless experience seems to indicate that there are a great many situations when devices may be used to good advantage if they are available or can be obtained. We answer our question of when to use aids by offering suggestions as before:

1. Use a device as a means of motivating work on a new concept or topic. When used in this way a device will sometimes enable a student to gather up enough of the main idea in a few moments so that he will wish to learn more about the concept in question.

2. Use a device to help concentrate interest and attention. Even when the main objective is that of developing ability to think in terms of abstract symbolism, an introductory use of devices has a beneficial effect on the learning situation.

3. Use a device to improve or speed up communication. One of the

most frustrating experiences that a teacher can have is that of not being able to "get through" to his students. Every teacher who has experienced this feeling knows that more verbalization is seldom the remedy for such a predicament.

4. Use a device to eliminate distracting details that compete for attention with the main idea in a problem situation. In planning devices to fill this need one must be careful, however, not to delete so much that actual facts become distorted.

5. Use a dynamic device, those with variable parts, to help students speed up consideration of the different positions that secondary parts of a basic figure can have, and of the variations in relations that may be implied by these different positions.

6. Use devices to help students discover and formulate generalizations. This means that the devices used must be planned to relate scattered ideas that are intrinsically the same. Developmental and analysis aids will be especially helpful in this respect.

7. Use a device to consolidate concepts that have been learned through other techniques. When used in this way the device provides a sort of climax to the learning of a concept. "Seeing is believing"!

8. Use a device as a relief from more formal classroom methods. Such variation in technique will help improve attention much as a change of menu often helps improve one's appetite.

9. Use models and mock-ups to help students in setting up relations which are necessary to the solution of problems, especially verbal problems and problems in application. A good selection of learning aids will help students with individual problems, and similar treatment with a variety of problems will give students confidence and a sense of direction when they are asked to work without the aid of devices. This is part of the idea implied in the time-honored directive, "Teach for transfer."

10. Use a model or mock-up in teaching applications when an actual object would be helpful but cannot be brought into the classroom because of its size or inaccessibility.

11. Use a device to enrich instruction. This idea was hinted at in the discussion of the project assignment technique as a means of providing for individual differences.

As a concluding note to this section it seems appropriate to state some cautions that should be kept in mind by anyone who uses teacher- and pupil-made learning aids in his teaching.

The first of these is that the use of devices is not always economical or beneficial to the learning situation. Occasionally it is much easier, less time-consuming and more effective simply to *tell* what is to be communicated about a concept. Poor selection of devices, and their misuse or over-use, may actually impede the learning process or carry confusion beyond the point of repair. So one must be careful.

Finally it should be pointed out that the use of learning aids is not something which is distinct from all other instructional activity. Devices should be a part of instruction; they are not a substitute for it.

We conclude with this remark: The teacher who would use learning aids must acquire a feeling for this sort of thing and there is *no* substitute for a little experience.

PART THREE
Teacher Education

Introduction

"As the twig is bent, so is the tree inclined" is an old proverb which applies well to the subject of teacher education in mathematics. If prospective teachers acquire real understanding of children and of the mathematics they will teach, and if they have rich preparatory experiences in the classroom, they will have progressed far toward becoming valuable members of the profession of mathematics teachers. However, the important next step is progressing on the job where the teaching problems are real and the solutions significant.

Thus this section on teacher education emphasizes both preservice and inservice work. Accounts of emerging practices are given in each area. Practices in the arithmetic preparation of elementary teachers are described in three teachers colleges—State Teachers College, Millersville, Pennsylvania; Ball State Teachers College, Muncie, Indiana; and the State Teachers College at Towson, Maryland. College preparation of secondary-school mathematics teachers is summarized by a status study of courses offered, and by descriptions of practices in student teaching at Ohio State University and Illinois State Normal University.

It has been said if one is graduated today and stops studying tomorrow, he is uneducated the following day. So it is in mathematics teaching, and most teachers are growing professionally as they work together on vital teaching problems. The section on inservice education gives descriptions of professional growth on the job, including curriculum work, professional classes, an arithmetic clinic project, excursions designed to enrich mathematics teaching, and participation in activities such as conferences, workshops, and institutes.

This section on teacher education is designed to give just a sampling of interesting practices of promise. Innumerable others could be added. But it is hoped that the ones described in this limited space will be interesting and challenging to the reader

171

and will suggest ideas for the reader's own local situation. Each of the authors would welcome further inquiry about details of any of the projects.

V. S.

Preparation of Elementary Arithmetic Teachers[1]

Lee Emerson Boyer

ARITHMETIC IS A SPECIALIZED SUBJECT

THERE was a time when it was thought the course Teaching of Arithmetic could be taught by almost any faculty member; the reason: Didn't everyone know how to recite the multiplication tables, how to do long division, how to divide one fraction by another, and even how to find the square roots of numbers? The same thinking did not apply to the courses College Algebra or the Calculus; they were always assigned to members of the mathematics staff. The course, Teaching of Arithmetic, is now regarded at Millersville as a highly specialized course because a meaningful development of quantitative concepts and a professional grasp of the applications of the Hindu-Arabic number system to the problems of everyday living are simply not comprehended by just any teacher. Today the course is always taught by an experienced member of the mathematics department.

AN ARITHMETIC PHILOSOPHY

Before an institution can go very far in its program of preparing arithmetic teachers it must be conscious of its arithmetic goals; it should have a written statement of beliefs. Since every philosophy is in a constant state of evolution the statement of beliefs is not regarded as fixed or final, or as being the same for every teacher-preparing college. But it is something which, as of today, we believe helps us at Millersville to see better what we are attempting to do in our arithmetic program.

---

[1] At the Millersville State Teachers College, Millersville, Pennsylvania.

This arithmetic philosophy needs to grow from the grass roots upward. At Millersville we have an Arithmetic Committee in whose hands is the formulation of this philosophy. The committee has a representative from the supervisors of every grade in the elementary division of the campus school and has the head of the college mathematics department as its chairman. (The junior high-school mathematics teachers of the campus school are members of the mathematics department and participate in its regular meetings. Millersville does not at the present have a senior high-school division in its campus school.) Periodically, the committee meets with the Director of the Campus School, all of the arithmetic supervisors of the elementary school, and both of the teachers of the mathematics department that give courses in Teaching of Arithmetic. This provides a means of effectively co-ordinating the entire program.

A portion of the Millersville Arithmetic Philosophy, as it stands at present, reads:

We believe that:

1. A co-operatively planned, sequential curriculum is essential.

2. The arithmetic curriculum has a social and a mathematical phase. Children should use arithmetic ideas and skills to solve their own personal problems. But the meanings and rational principles should always be presented with the aim of making arithmetic a part of mathematics. A unit in arithmetic should never be taught *alone*.

3. Since pupils differ greatly with respect to purposes, needs, desires, and interests, each pupil's curriculum should be so set that he will be likely to succeed in it.

4. Much good can come through teacher-pupil planning.

5. Learning is a growth process based quite largely on many varied experiences. The spirit of discovery is a strong motivating factor. Much of elementary arithmetic learning proceeds most readily from a recognized and accepted problem situation to a concrete representation of it, to a semiconcrete representation, to a symbolic representation, to a conclusion and, finally, to a check of the conclusion.

6. Meaningfulness should always precede practice or drill objectives.

7. An ample vocabulary and a sufficient reading ability are necessary.

8. Although it is sometimes impossible to prove one method of handling a topic to be superior to another, a school system should adopt *one* practice as *basic*.

9. Since forgetting is a concomitant of learning, judicious practice and drill work are important.

10. The success of the arithmetic curriculum, especially in kindergarten and Grade I and Grade II, depends a great deal upon the teacher's sensitiveness to recognize and alertness to use the almost innumerable arithmetic situations that can be found in the children's everyday lives.

ARITHMETIC TEACHERS NEED A "CONTENT" COURSE

For years Millersville has been concerned with the effect that the gradual, but steady, drop in the percentage of secondary-school pupils who choose to study mathematics after Grade IX may have on the mathematical competence of the prospective teachers of arithmetic who come to Millersville (8, 9). It is recognized that since no specific entrance credits in mathematics are required for admittance to Millersville it is possible that a prospective teacher of arithmetic may reach the certification stage without having studied a content course in mathematics since that of Grade IX. Since it is believed that the first requirement of a teacher is that he know his subject, Millersville has taken certain steps to promote and to insure a certain degree of mathematical competence in its prospective arithmetic teachers.

Since the tendency to require courses in college is so great and since time is so limited we have, first, segregated in our thinking the prospective kindergarten-primary teachers from the prospective intermediate teachers. We require the prospective intermediate teachers to take one three-semester hour course in content mathematics and one three-semester hour course in methods of teaching arithmetic. The first course is labeled Fundamentals of Mathematics; the second, Teaching of Arithmetic. The prospective kindergarten-primary teachers are required to take a three-semester-hour course labeled Teaching of Arithmetic but about half of the time in this course is devoted to content and the other half to methods of teaching arithmetic.

In offering this content work, there is great danger to regard it as *remedial* or *make-up* work and to establish a provision for excusing students from taking the course by achieving a certain degree of performance on a test. While we at Millersville recognize the great variations in the mathematical competencies of students enrolled for this work, we much prefer to graduate the character of the course materials and the amount of work done to secure a passing grade than to excuse any student from taking the course. Although the materials of the course are directly related to the grade area in which the prospective teacher will teach, they are kept on a level that challenges the student. They serve to *ground* the student with respect to the materials that both *precede* and *succeed* the several grades in which the student expects to teach.

An over-all view of the mathematical topics treated most frequently in this content work may be had by examining the writer's book, *An Introduction to Mathematics for Teachers* (22, 23). This book is written with a historical perspective. It assumes that the child, in learning his mathematics, should progress much as mankind did in developing mathematics from its earliest beginnings to its present highly useful stage. It is divided into four parts: arithmetic, algebra, geometry, and trigonometry.

The arithmetic section begins with substantial topics related to our number system. With this beginning few, if any, students conclude that this is the "same old stuff" they studied before; the topics are definitely on an adult's level. Then follow chapters on the fundamental operations, fractions, percentage, the influence of measurements on work with numbers, slide rule, denominate numbers, a substantial unit on the metric system, and finally problem-solving.

The algebra section begins with a chapter on the nature and meaning of algebra in which the nature of a mathematical proof is emphasized and used to relate algebra to arithmetic. The chapter on "Algebra as the Language of Science" illustrates many applications of algebra. This part of the book is closed with a discussion and numerous exercises on "The Generality of Algebra."

The geometry section opens with a fascinating historical approach explaining how Eratosthenes, by applying a bit of geometry, calculated the circumference of the earth to be 25,000 miles as early as 200 B.C.! The topic of *reasoning* is introduced early with a chapter on "Three Ways of Reaching Conclusions." This leads into—in an elementary way—the logic of geometry and simple life applications. The topic "Geometric Forms" shows the prospective teacher an excellent approach for correlating geometry and art. This part also contains an amazingly complete set of geometric theorems numbering only 37! "Applications of Geometry" is followed by a chapter on "The Educational Value of Geometry."

The trigonometry part is very short. It illustrates the trigonometric method of indirect measurement and has a chapter on logarithms with exercises illustrating applications of the uses of both trigonometry and logarithms.

At Millersville we cannot study *all* of the topics presented in this book in one three-semester hour course—essentials of the arithmetic part, however, constitute a *must* for all students—but *groups* of students, depending on their backgrounds, needs, and interests often choose to study topics here or there in the text-book. Some may never have studied logarithms and are now interested in learning about them and their uses; others seem challenged to learn about non-Euclidean geometry; still others may want to learn about Euclid as a person or about his *Elements*; they would turn to page 300 of the book and go to the college library in addition!

TEACH GOOD METHODS BY EXAMPLE

It is often observed that young teachers tend to teach as they were taught. It seems to us at Millersville, therefore, that one of the best ways of teaching methods effectively is to demonstrate them, and call attention to them, while conducting our content work. We endeavor to have the classroom atmosphere—in its broad sense—pleasant. The study of mathematics is not to be dreaded; it is really fun. Who wouldn't be interested in *inventing* a new number system, say to the base 12? Or, learning how algebra can be used to show that there is no difference in final cost whether we purchase a $300 piano at store X which offers two successive discounts, one of 10 per cent and another of 5; or at store Y which offers a first discount of 5 per cent and a second of 10? Or, discovering why *truth* depends upon the experience of the individuals doing the reasoning or upon the definitions and assumptions they choose to accept? Or, how the Egyptians determined the height of the Great Pyramid? Or, why does it happen that if we ask five students to measure, just as carefully as they can, the length of the teacher's desk and record their measurements in secret they often report five different lengths? Or, what's the magic in a magic square? Or, what is systematic about the number system? Or, how can we show that the circumference of a circle is about $3\frac{1}{7}$ times its diameter? Or, that its area is equal to πr^2? Or, what kind of problems can be solved by a scaled drawing?

Perhaps it is our laboratory approach that we like to use so that students can discover for themselves why things are as they are in this elementary mathematics (14). In addition to having inherently interesting problem material and the discovery approach we are alert to student-supplied mathematical problems that arise in the community, such as installment buying advertisements, stock market *breaks* or *rises*, reports of athletic—or other—contests using metric units, efficiency reports involving percentages, puzzle problems, and such. Sometimes we require each student to make a notebook of mathematical applications as he noticed them during the semester. The notebook begins with a table of contents and a course of study for a particular grade level. Then follow clippings having to do with topics in arithmetic. Each clipping is accompanied with a student-invented problem suitable for use in a certain grade. It is surprising to note how much arithmetic can be found in travel plans, gas bills, mail-order catalogues, fertilizer-bag analysis tags, direction sheets issued to shop workers, and many other such things.

Some objections may be raised to having prospective arithmetic teachers learn the uses of the slide rule, elementary algebra, logarithms, and the like. But we like the prospective teachers of arithmetic to be well acquainted with a certain spirit of mathematics. We want them to be curious about the arithmetical things that they meet and see around them every day and to gain confidence in elementary mathematical investigations. As they on their level probe these things and gain an understanding of them, so we hope they will have their pupils probe the things they find in their environments.

THE SOCIAL PHASE OF ARITHMETIC

It is believed at Millersville that the arithmetic program for the elementary school should be planned to contribute to the school's fundamental objective—that of developing the whole child. As such, it is clear that mere facility in computational skill cannot be its entire goal; mathematics apart from mankind's needs soon becomes stagnant. It is therefore easy to subscribe to the principle that arithmetic should supply the facts-for-life decisions of the type: Shall I purchase a 1, 2, or 2½-size can of pears? A dozen or a bag of oranges? A $1000 bond or 12 shares of stock? Shall I borrow money from the bank or from the loan company whose advertisement I read in the local newspaper? What does it cost to operate my car for one month or a year? Does it cost more to own one's home than to rent one? Shall I take a "20-year endowment" or a "straight life" insurance policy? What does it cost to raise a child to age 18? Shall I purchase a "PRR 4½s 65" bond at 104 or deposit the money in a savings account at my bank?

Naturally, there is no one answer to any of these problems that is *right* for every individual or family; and that's what makes teaching the social aspect of arithmetic challenging. To develop the willingness and patience to think carefully for oneself in applying arithmetic to one's social problems we rely on presenting the same issues in numerous varied settings. We will attempt to illustrate the procedure by describing, somewhat in detail, one class project that is well adapted for use in any grade.

The project is entitled "Comparing the Cost of Homemade Ice Cream with the Cost of Commercially Produced Ice Cream." We have a 6-quart freezer operated by an electric motor which we use for executing the plan in early fall or late spring when we can work outdoors to avoid sloppy work in the schoolroom. Groups, or individuals, are appointed by the students to bring the several ingredients on the desired day. We think of the serious consequences that would follow if the appointed person forgot to bring the salt or even the dipper! Naturally, the costs of the ingredients are considered and recorded. At about this stage of the project it arises that some students can get some supplies at wholesale prices, some can get discounts, and other such savings. Then will come an avalanche of questions: Shall we figure depreciation on the freezer and motor? Something for labor? Overhead? Rent for the building? Can we determine the cost of the electricity used? The motor is stamped "2.5–5 amperes" and there is a formula

$$\frac{\text{Volts} \times \text{amperes} \times \text{hours}}{1000} = \text{kilowatt-hours.}$$

Also

Kilowatt-hours times price per kilowatt-hour = cost.

Other typical questions are: What is the cost of commercially made ice cream of this brand? Of that brand? Packaged? Bulk? Do you have a deep-freeze? A 75-pound freezer compartment in your refrigerator? It may be that dry ice will solve the storage problem. Anyway, for what event are we planning to use the ice cream for which we wish to compare costs?

In addition to the cost we can't neglect, in a project of this type, to study the effect of the use of salt. We use a centigrade thermometer to determine the coldness of the brine. But what is this in terms of the Fahrenheit scale? (Fahrenheit reading = centigrade reading × ⅑ + 32°.) Denominate numbers, too, are not overlooked: Is one pound of sugar equivalent to two cups of sugar? And many other such questions.

The main thing we wish to emphasize is that *talking* about these things has its necessary point, but it can become aimless. The remedy is to require *written* reports, comparisons, tables, and such things, and then grade them for soundness of analysis. This takes time but we feel that there is no substitute for its teaching effectiveness. Another "trick" is to discuss the problem rather adequately but not to stipulate any particular set of conditions to be observed in the written report by any one student. This is altogether reasonable in that some families will have different electricity rates, different qualities of ice cream at different prices may be available to different families, the farmer may buy rock salt in 100-pound bags while someone else buys it in 5-pound bags at different prices.

Since no stipulated form of report was made some pupils will take pains to consider quality of product, an amount for incidentals—enumerated, of course—labor, delivery charges, packaging, and such things, for which one may grade with an "A;" those who give less detailed—and therefore misleading—reports may be given a "B," and so on.

SUMMARY

We have seen that our study of arithmetic, at Millersville, is as comprehensive as life itself. Nevertheless, it is a specialized school subject with specific educational goals that can be set forth in an arithmetic philosophy. It has a specialized vocabulary, certain basic topics, and numerous rather technical processes. To teach arithmetic competently we believe that a teacher needs to be professionally and thoroughly acquainted with the *content* of arithmetic. To this end we have organized appropriate course materials on a level challenging to our prospective arithmetic teachers. While teaching this content material we attempt to exemplify, through deed and word, good methods of teaching. This three-semester-hour content course is, however, supplemented with the more usual course, Teaching of Arithmetic.

We feel that arithmetic has two phases, the mathematical and the social. To make prospective arithmetic teachers conscious of the social phase we rely heavily upon current problem material found in the local community. To acquaint our students with the uses of arithmetic in such life problems we frequently employ the laboratory technique. We also encourage an attitude of discovery as we deal with the many varied problems that children —and adults—actually meet. During the study of these problems considerable leeway is allowed, indeed encouraged, to permit consideration of factors peculiar to particular situations. Written reports and notebooks are relied upon to bring sound conclusions from the possibly hazy beginning materials.

Background Mathematics for Teachers of Arithmetic

FRANCIS MUELLER AND HAROLD MOSER

FOR a number of years there has been much discussion at all educational levels about the need for improving the quality of instruction in mathematics. At present the most promising signs of large scale dividends are to be found in the elementary school. There are at least three reasons for this enthusiasm:

1. Teachers are energetic about doing something to improve the teaching of arithmetic. The meaning approach to the teaching of elementary arithmetic is gathering momentum each year. There is evidence to indicate that teachers are losing faith in a program that begins and ends with drill procedures. There is increasing agreement that the educational product of mechanical instruction is likely to be competent only in the rote aspects of number work.

2. The emerging point of view fits into the long-range mathematical point of view. The primary objective of number instruction is generally described as the ability to think quantitatively. Furthermore, the newer courses of study seem to have accepted the implications of this objective because they acknowledge that arithmetic must be taught as a structured system of related ideas, principles, and processes. The implication is that only as the pupil sees number relationships imbedded in the social applications of number can he hope to understand the situation and deal with it effectively.

3. This movement for better instruction in mathematics is resting on the broadest base possible. Any reorientation of instruction that begins in the elementary school will not only involve the greatest number of teachers and pupils but it will begin with the concepts essential for providing a solid foundation for later mathematical learning.

It seems hardly necessary to caution the reader that no sudden metamorphosis in instructional practices is likely to occur. Development is certain to be uneven. Some of the obstructions to progress are even now beginning to take shape. One of these is especially important. Reports from consultants working with the inservice training of teachers indicate that the biggest single barrier to a more effective implementation of meaningful arithmetic is the inadequacy in the mathematical background of the teachers themselves. Teachers cannot do a creditable job teaching that which they neither practice nor understand.

It is at this point that the teachers colleges should be prepared to make a positive contribution, if they are to accept the responsibility for initiating a more effective preparation for teachers of arithmetic. Traditional course offerings and time-honored instructional procedures clearly need to be reevaluated in the light of the newer needs of prospective teachers. Grossnickle's study (17) shows the limited extent to which this is being done, and Newsom's thoughtful article (21) suggests the direction such revision might take.

The present report has been prepared to describe the efforts of one college to meet the need for a special kind of mathematical background. The program discussed here is in no way meant to be a prescription of what background experiences are essential or best designed to do the job nationally. Perhaps it may best be described as a way of attacking an instructional need. The report is offered in the hope that others may be encouraged to attempt what has been tried here and that they may profit by our experience.

The State Teachers College at Towson, Maryland, has an enrollment of about 850 students. One-third of the students are male. The college prepares teachers for the kindergarten-primary, elementary, and junior-high areas for the public schools of Maryland. The mean score of entering freshmen on the ACE test of scholastic aptitude falls in the 50–60 percentile bracket and so the students may be considered as fairly representative of the national average. The standard deviation for the local group is usually somewhat smaller than for the normative population, however, and so the students may be described as somewhat more homogeneous, intellectually, than is true for freshmen of the nation.

When general ability is factored into quantitative and linguistic scores, the L-Score is found to be about 10 percentile points higher than the Q-Score. Two possible explanations may help account for this interesting variation: (a) The presence of a selective factor in that the college offers few inducements to students interested in becoming teachers of mathematics and consequently few students with strong interests in this area come to Towson. (b) The large number of women students may exert a depressing influence on the Q-Score since women generally score lower on this subtest than men.

Almost all of the entering students have had one or more years of high-school mathematics. The exceptions are the students who enroll by passing general equivalence examinations. About one student in four will enter with a marked weakness in the basic fundamentals of arithmetic. Fraction, decimal, and percentage relationships are poorly understood by at least 40 per cent of the students.

The test instruments currently available do not adequately describe many of the deficiencies which must be taken into consideration in designing a mathematics program to equip these students to teach arithmetic in the public schools of the state. Classroom experiences, student interviews, and incidental observations provide additional data of importance. Generalizations from these sources are summarized in the following list. Each statement represents a deficiency estimated to be characteristic of 50 per cent or more of the freshmen enrolling in the college.

1. The number system is seldom thought of as related to the development of culture. For most freshmen number either seems unrelated to the development of culture patterns or it is viewed as a kind of constant for all peoples in somewhat the same sense that hydrogen is a constant in the natural environment. The number system is thought of more frequently as a discovery than an invention. The Roman number system is the only system, other than the one currently used, with which the average freshman is remotely conversant.

2. Except for the obvious rhythmical pattern suggested by the number words the freshmen do not see structure in the number system. Positional number can't really be a principle of organization for those unable to conceive of a positional number system using a base other than 10. The idea of expressing the values of the orders in a positional number system as exponents of the number base is almost always a new idea.

3. The approach to quantitative computation is almost completely stereotyped. Rarely would a student attack an example, such as

$$5\tfrac{1}{2}$$
$$6\tfrac{3}{5}$$
$$+ \ \ 2\tfrac{3}{4}$$

by changing the addends to mixed decimals. Likewise, to cite another example, the division $6 \div 1\frac{1}{2}$ is uniformly solved by reducing the divisor to an improper fraction, inverting it, and then multiplying. And yet, most of the freshmen performing this lengthy operation are able to state—in other circumstances —the principle that multiplying the numerator and denominator of a fraction will not change the value thereof.

4. The students are exceedingly dependent upon the written algorisms. Few have been trained to compute mentally. It is not unusual to see the use of paper and pencil to divide a number by 100. When mental arithmetic is attempted the procedure employed is an attempted visualization of the written algorism. The results are seldom satisfactory because of the inordinate demands upon the memory span.

There is no way of knowing how unique this portrait of the mathematical shortcomings of an average teachers-college freshman is to the local college community, but it is a fair assumption that many aspects of the picture are experienced generally. Obviously, teachers with so little knowledge of the number system can do little toward teaching children to think quantitatively. At best they can only pass along to another generation the performance stereotypes inherited from the preceding generation.

The curricular framework at Towson provides facilities for attacking the problem that are somewhat better than is found for the country as a whole according to Grossnickle (17). Background mathematics is required of all students in addition to training in the teaching of arithmetic. Students electing the kindergarten-primary or elementary areas are required to take one three-hour course in mathematics and one two-hour course in the teaching of arithmetic. Those preparing for the junior-high field are required to take six hours of background mathematics and one credit-hour of orientation to curricular practices and procedures in the teaching of mathematics.

The content of the course in background mathematics was selected to meet the specific needs revealed in our survey. Traditional courses in college algebra, trigonometry, or analytics were rejected as not helpful in the over-all problem although concepts or processes from these fields were used as the occasion arose. Electives in the standard college courses were retained for students wishing special training in these areas.

The following paragraphs contain a brief synopsis of the general background course as it is now evolving. Some of the understandings expected as outcomes have been cited to show the relationship between the materials of instruction and the specific deficiencies in the mathematical background of entering students.

The Historical Development of Systems of Number. By tracing the evolution of number in the Egyptian, Greek, Roman and Hindu-Arabic systems of notation there is an opportunity for students to gain an insight into the fact that peoples of different cultures have produced different systems for counting. Just as different nations have developed different forms of government, some of which have worked better than others, so it is that some systems of notation have worked better than others. By comparing and contrasting the advantages of each of these four systems the student may better appreciate his own. The important outcome the student may gain from this consideration is that the number system he uses is not a product of nature but that it is a man-made device, that it is an evolving thing and that it is not necessarily the best possible system which could have been devised.

The Principle of Structure in Number Systems. In the study of the various systems of notation particular emphasis must be placed upon distinguishing between what philosophers term the *essence* and the *accidental* aspects of a thing. Applied to various counting systems, the essentials would be that structure peculiar to a given system, its principles, its basic design, while the accidentals would be those modifying elements which afford detail in the expression of the essentials. These latter superficial elements are the symbols themselves and the choice of a base or compounding point in a given system.

The daily and almost automatic use of numbers, unfortunately, produces such a familiarity with the superficial aspects of our system that there is small wonder that number is readily thought of in terms of these accidents alone. As a result, the number system for most people becomes only a sequential order of symbols—few are aware of the basic structure of their system. Since personal control over any system is obtained not upon mastery of its superficialities but upon mastery of its fundamental principles—when its basic structures are clearly perceived—it follows that true understanding of our system of counting is indicated not by the ability to count correctly to a given value, but rather by the extent to which the underlying principles of that system are clearly recognized.

By introducing number bases other than 10, additional emphasis is placed upon this structure concept. As the student learns to express numerical magnitudes in other bases he begins to distinguish between that which is unchanging in his system of notation (the principle of place value) and that which does change—the sequential order of the symbols. Another fruitful line of attack on the structure of the number system is opened up with a discussion of exponential notation. The ability to express the values of all orders in a positional system as powers of the number base often permits a brief excursion into the principles of scientific notation. Thus in current social usage one mechanically reads all numbers in terms of ones (10^0); theoretically however, there is no reason why any number cannot be read in terms of any power. Example: 125 (ones) is also 1.25×10^2 or 12.5×10^1, and so on. This is the principle behind scientific notation. There are other social applications of this principle. Example: Changing the decimal 1.35 to a per cent really means to rewrite a number ordinarily read in terms of ones to a value expressed in hundredths, or, $1.35 \times 10^0 = 135 \times 10^{-2}$.

The Fundamental Processes. As presently constituted, about half of the course is devoted to a study of the fundamental operations. The processes are studied in groups. Two general classifications may be distinguished according to the services they render. First there are the synthesizing processes which include the operation for putting together like groups—multiplication—and the more general operation—addition—which makes no distinction between the likeness of groups. The second set of processes are analytical in action. They include a specialized operation for dividing a given quantity into a number of equal parts—division—and a less specialized operation—subtraction—which can separate a group into two subgroups without distinction in the matter of the evenness of the division. In studying these four operations the student's attention is directed toward distinguishing between that which is accidental to the operation —the system of counting, the symbols, the particular algorism employed to perform the act of regrouping—and that which is essential, the fundamental processes described above. Each of the four operations is considered in detail and the student is pressed to abstract, to search out the unchanging principles of the operation. Application of the operations to systems employing an unfamiliar number base has been found to be an extremely useful approach to this objective.

Fractions. Up to this point in the development of the structural frame of reference, number has been identified solely with a system of integers. Fractions are introduced as a particular class of numbers employing a new arrangement of symbols. In the operations with fractions there is no change in essentials—changes occur only in the accidentals—the symbols and the algorisms. Students discover a variety of ways in which these accidentals may find expression. Symbolically, they may be written as common fractions, as decimal fractions, or per cents. Each is accompanied by a variety of algorisms.

When all fractions have been found to possess the same essential attributes, the students are ready to trace out the relationships among the forms of expression. Per cents are found to be highly specialized with the denominator held constant and the numerator allowed to vary. Decimal fractions are somewhat less specialized since they utilize a set, or class, of denominators related to the base in a particular way. Common fractions are unspecialized since any divisor-dividend relationship may be expressed as a common fraction.

Evaluation. The specific content in the course has changed in detail from year to year. We have learned not to attempt too much. The learning pace must be slow, especially in the beginning because the students feel insecure in the unfamiliar surroundings. When reasonable provision is made for range and pace, the interest level runs high. At the outset we had hoped to employ algebraic explanations in rationalizing many of the procedures in arithmetic but we abandoned the attempt because too many of the students were unable to follow the development. There is tested evidence that students are gaining power to think out relationships without the complete dependence upon the mechanical assistance of a written algorism but perhaps the biggest promise of success comes from the increasing number of students who are beginning to question arithmetical procedures formerly accepted without challenge.

The Use of Professional Laboratory Experiences in a Methods Course

CLARENCE ETHEL HARDGROVE

A METHODS course in the teaching of mathematics can be made meaningful through the use of professional laboratory experiences. The experiences provide an opportunity for college students to relate the theory of the college classroom to practice by giving them a responsible role in an actual teaching-learning situation in a secondary school and by guiding them in the defining and study of the problems involved in teaching boys and girls the content of mathematics. Professional laboratory experiences are defined by the American Association of Colleges for Teacher Education to "include all those contacts with children, youth, and adults . . . which make a direct contribution to an understanding of individuals and their guidance in the teaching-learning process (1)."

The methods course in the teaching of mathematics in the education of mathematics teachers at the Ohio State University had for several years provided professional laboratory experiences on a limited scale (18). A study (18) in 1949–50 explored the further use of such experiences in the methods course. This study continued for two quarters. Involved in the program were 102 college students, 17 schools, 49 supervising teachers, and several thousand boys and girls. It is the experiences of that year which are described here.

The methods course in the teaching of mathematics was a five credit-hour course required of all students who declared mathematics as a major or minor teaching area in the College of Education at the Ohio State University. The class met on campus three days each week for lectures, demonstrations, discussions, and student reports. Each student acted as a teacher-helper at least two class periods each week in a secondary mathematics classroom of the schools of the greater Columbus area.

The professional laboratory experiences in the public schools began the second week of the quarter and continued throughout. Arrangements for these experiences were made with the school administrators and teachers prior to the opening of the University. The classroom teachers were asked to allow the college students to enter their classes with the agreement that the students were to assume the responsibility for finding ways to help the teachers and the boys and girls. The quality of the professional laboratory experiences which each student had as a teacher-helper depended to a large extent upon the initiative he displayed and the amount of responsibility that he assumed for the learning experiences of the boys and girls.

The instructor of the methods course helped the student as he worked with the teacher and the boys and girls in creating effective teaching-learning experiences. Ideas for consideration in the college classroom had their source in either the college class or in professional laboratory experiences. The ideas from professional laboratory experiences were enlarged, reenforced, and integrated through study and class discussion. The instructor acted as a guide in helping the students define and study problems, in challenging the students to follow up the study of problems defined, and in helping them integrate the total course experiences.

The campus class meetings of the first week were used to introduce the program of participation as a part of the general plan of the course and to help orient the students for the experience.

AIMS OF PROFESSIONAL LABORATORY EXPERIENCES

The values of the direct experiences in a classroom were recognized to be those of determining the problems of teaching mathematics to boys and girls, of studying these problems, and of being able to test the hypotheses formulated.

The class with the guidance of the instructor defined specific aims for the professional laboratory experiences and planned and evaluated their experiences in terms of them. These aims were as follows:

1. To define and study problems arising in a teaching-learning situation
2. To study boys and girls as groups and as individuals
3. To relate concepts developed in the professional program to those which exist in practice
4. To become effective in relationships with the boys and girls, the teacher, and the school staff
5. To become familiar with planning for teaching-learning experiences
6. To stimulate the boys and girls to think critically
7. To become effective in securing and using to advantage material for teaching-learning situations.

GUIDANCE

Guidance of the students, both formally and informally, to aid them in planning in terms of their needs helped them relate the theory of the college classroom to their participation experience, and helped them intellectualize their experiences for the greatest meaning for themselves. Communication with the students for the purposes of guidance was achieved by the following procedures: class meetings, student anecdotal records of direct experiences, special written reports of students, conferences with the college instructor, small discussion groups, information bulletins, and self-evaluation.

The students were encouraged to schedule short informal *conferences* or just come in at frequent intervals. A few of the conferences were requested by the instructor, but the majority were sought by students because they needed help, were anxious to share an experience, or were in need of a little reassurance.

The purpose of the conferences was to plan experiences with the student in terms of his needs and goals and in relation to the situation in which he was participating, to help the student evaluate his progress in terms of his own purposes and in terms of the aims of participation, and to help the student relate his professional experiences on the campus to those of his participation.

Discussion groups that were small enough for each member to have an opportunity to state his ideas and problems and yet large enough to have a number of ideas and problems presented for sharing were useful in helping the student plan for his experiences. Many small discussion groups were informal and unplanned. Two planned coffee hours were held early in the quarter so that the instructor could get acquainted with the students, but more important so that the students could get to know each other for the sharing of experiences.

Student daily logs or anecdotal records were important to guidance. They were daily records of a student's experiences with the boys and girls in the classroom and his reaction to them. They contained such things as (a) what the student, the class, and individuals in the class did, (b) ideas regarding the teaching-learning process, (c) ideas regarding the role of a teacher, (d) problems which arose in the class that the student believed needed study, and (e) remarks about the significance of any part of the experience. In general they were statements of what the college student did, what the secondary class did, and the reactions of the college student.

The student records kept the instructor in touch with the experiences so that help could be given to those who needed it. The greatest resulting value was to the students as it helped them to rethink the experiences; that is, to draw out of the experiences, meanings for use in their own teaching. Data from the records were also used for evaluative purposes by both the students and instructor.

It was found from reading the early daily anecdotal records that the students lacked some necessary information regarding the program and that there were items on the *logs* of such value that they could be profitably shared. Therefore, a mimeographed *participation bulletin* was planned to provide this information. It was of such great value in giving direction to participation that three other bulletins followed. They were also of value to the supervising teachers in planning with the participants as well as sources of information regarding the program. The bulletins also contained quotations from the students' daily logs, ideas that the students were asked to consider, description of some of the experiences of the students in the class, and suggestions for planning future experiences.

Continuous evaluation was a principle of operation which the students were encouraged to use at all times. All the procedures of guidance used, such as conferences and small discussion groups, were aimed at helping the student to evaluate himself in terms of his personal goals and in terms of the aims of the participation experiences.

Two formal self-evaluations by the students were made and followed by conferences. The self-evaluation form asked the participant to check whether he had made "no progress," "some progress," or "much progress" toward the realization of each of the seven aims of participation, and to furnish evidence from his participation of experiences which contributed to such progress. The student self-evaluation was then discussed in a conference with the student to help him plan for further experiences.

TYPES OF EXPERIENCES

The professional laboratory experiences in the secondary classrooms were many and varied as the college student went into the classroom situation, learned to know the boys and girls, studied the plans for the class, and found ways of helping the teacher and the boys and girls. Participation began as observation with an early acceptance of some responsibility, led to an increase in responsibility during the term, and culminated in an exploratory teaching experience. The experiences of each student were different but followed a general pattern. Generally the students' activities followed this pattern:

1. Observed the class
2. Had conferences with the supervising teacher
3. Became acquainted with the boys and girls
4. Kept attendance records
5. Planned a test
6. Checked written work
7. Helped an individual
8. Helped a small group
9. Helped during supervised study

10. Diagnosed student difficulty
11. Provided resource material
12. Planned work for an individual needing special help
13. Planned for a teaching-learning experience
14. Had charge of the class for a short time
15. Had charge of the class for the greater part of the period
16. Had charge of the class for all of the period.

These and other teacher activities in which the college students engaged were not important as mere activities. But they were important to the college students in proportion to the meanings which were formulated as a result of the activities. The real value came from rethinking of their experiences for the defining of problems and the formulation of hypotheses.

These experiences and resulting meaning can best be described by citing typical examples from the students' anecdotal records.

A First Day of Participation: Since this was my first day in class, the supervising teacher felt that I should spend it observing. I did not ask for a seating chart but constructed one of my own by putting down the first name of the boy or girl called upon. . . .

I have no complaints, saw no real problems and could not offer any suggestions to improve the class.

Problem of Working with Individuals: One boy gave me a bad time. He seemed bored by the procedure. I kept asking him questions trying to get his interest. If he answered correctly he acted as if he had solved the problem of developing an atomic-powered aircraft engine; if he didn't answer correctly he just smirked so much as to say, "So what if it is wrong?"

After checking his homework on which he got a perfect score, I decided he could do the work if he wished. But getting him to do it, will be my problem.

Value from Helping During Supervised Study: For most of the period, the class worked. I assisted the teacher in giving the boys and girls help when help was needed.

This is a wonderful experience to make me think of the basic ideas underlying a simple operation. It is also valuable to be able to work with boys and girls and see what makes them tick.

A Short Teaching Experience: Then the teacher turned the class over to me for an introduction of ratio. It was an extremely interesting experience for it was the very first time I had ever had charge of a class. I had often wondered how I would react to a situation like this. So far as I know everything went fine.

I realized that my time was short. I did most of the talking in the beginning so I would be able to finish. I would have preferred to have gone slower and had the boys and girls participate. I used the last few minutes for class discussion and was pleased with the spontaneous response. . . .

I amazed myself by not being the least bit nervous for I wasn't afraid in the least. In fact, on the contrary, I enjoyed myself immensely.

The supervising teacher and I had a conference after the class and discussed the happenings. He agreed with me that I talked too much.

Studying the Boys and Girls: October 13—At least one member of the class is not being reached. I say one, because I've noticed the girl who sits beside me. There may be others but I have observed her closely for several days. Mary is rather quiet in class. Silent, in fact, when it comes time for class to begin.

I do not believe that Mary is bored from knowing the things being discussed, for her test papers and daily papers show that she needs help. I believe that one of her difficulties is that she does not know how to do her work and therefore dislikes it. I want to talk with her to see if I can determine her interest. Perhaps I will be able to help her.

October 26—During class Friday, Mary gave the answer to a problem . . . the teacher asked her to explain it. She was very hesitant, at first, with her explanation. So hesitant, in fact, that I thought she really did not understand what she had done. The teacher knows that I am helping her in an extra class period and I believe he wanted to see what she could do. Finally she explained the problem as though she knew what she was doing. Needless to say, I was very relieved and pleased that she could explain the problem. My work with her has been of some help.

Understanding Boys and Girls: I can see that as a teacher you take a personal interest in the boys and girls as you get to know them. . . . You begin to see each one as a personality.

I have noticed that there are no really bad boys and girls in the class. Those few with unusual behavior are really among the most intelligent and need only to be helped to find the best way of acting in a way that seems reasonable to their level of development.

Gathering Resource Material: In preparing for a class period on automobile insurance, I contacted an insurance company and obtained literature from them. The manager gave me copies of three different pamphlets and loaned me a collection of photographs of accidents which he used in exhibits for safety campaigns. One of the photographs was taken at the school corner which made the whole problem realistic to the boys and girls. The class session was very good. Class interest is much higher on a day when resource material is used.

Studying a Problem: The problem stated: Is the use of the number scale in teaching directed numbers an efficient method? Are there other methods?

October 25—I intend to refer to several references to see what I can find. I feel that it is wise to have several good methods at hand for teaching each concept and to experiment whenever possible.

November 1—I introduced the multiplication of directed numbers by using some historical facts which stimulated interest. . . . I attempted to impress on the boys and girls that mathematics is a consistent system upon which we can rely. I then presented a system of numbers to be multiplied that fall in a consistent system. From this argument the generalizations were evident to the class.

My method of last Tuesday was fairly successful, however, after hearing in class of another method based on the number scale I feel that method may be more efficient. The boys and girls have used the number scale so the method could be used.

Maybe a combination of these methods would be best. I shall discuss this with my supervising teacher and find out what she thinks of the relative value of the two methods.

These quotations from the student records not only illustrate the type of experiences but show their integration with other course experiences and their resulting meanings to the students.

EVALUATION

Evaluation of the course experiences was continuous and was a responsibility of the student as well as the instructor. Evidence for the evaluation of student progress was obtained from the records of participation, which revealed what the students did, what they considered important in the situations, and what they thought of their experiences. The sources of such data were student anecdotal records, student self-evaluations, and an anecdotal record which the instructor kept.

Data from these sources were used to give evidence of the following: (a) kinds of experiences, (b) involvement, (c) significance of problems defined, (d) problems studied and hypotheses formulated, and (e) progress toward realization of the aims of participation.

The experiences of the students were varied and were progressive in character. Progressiveness of experiences means that the experiences involve a steady increase of responsibility for the learning experiences of boys and girls and that the experiences culminate in the assumption of responsibility for an entire class period.

The students were greatly *involved* in the learning experiences of the boys and girls of the secondary class. They attended more than was required; they found many ways of helping; and they showed through action and in their records that they were a part of the group of boys and girls with a concern for the learning of the group; and they assumed responsibility for that learning.

Many significant problems were defined by the students for individual or class study. The following problems were a few of those defined:

1. How to help boys and girls develop an understanding of the fundamental concepts of mathematics
2. How to evaluate individual progress
3. How to obtain and maintain the interest of the class
4. How to teach to all levels of understanding within the class
5. How to teach percentage
6. How to plan within the time allotted for the class
7. The place of the textbook
8. How to encourage students to make their own discoveries.

These problems were of great value in the methods class because they were the problems of the students. Evidence from the records indicated that the students studied these problems because the hypotheses formulated had a definite relationship to the problems defined.

The great variety and number of hypotheses formulated indicated that there were many problems considered and studied that were not stated verbally in the records. The hypotheses which appeared most often in the student records were as follows:

1. The work of the class should be related to the problems and interests of the boys and girls.
2. Boys and girls should be led to make their own discoveries, i.e., to think for themselves.
3. Good teachers guide the boys and girls to an understanding of the *why*.
4. The work of the class should be on the level of the learner.
5. Boys and girls should be evaluated in terms of their progress.
6. Variety in class work helps to stimulate and maintain interest.
7. Boys and girls must see the sense of what they are doing.
8. Boys and girls show more interest when they actively participate in a class.
9. Each lesson must be carefully planned.

10. Plans should be flexible.
11. An emotional disturbance blocks learning.

The experiences of the college students and the problems defined and the hypotheses formulated by them indicated that the students showed an effectiveness in relating the educational concepts of the professional program to those in practice. They were effective in their study of boys and girls as well as in their relationship with boys and girls and with the supervising teacher. They were effective in planning for teaching, in stimulating boys and girls to think critically, and in securing and using materials for teaching.

The participation experiences cannot be separated from the total course experience. Their purpose was to help the student define and study the problems involved in the teaching of mathematics. The ideas that had their source in experience were enlarged and integrated through study and through class discussion. They were an important and vital part of the course but did not replace it.

The methods course was vital to the students involved because it gave each student an opportunity to identify himself with a problem of teaching mathematics and to become vitally concerned with its solution. The theory of the college classroom acted as a stimulus for further study and provided data to consider with that gathered from actual experience. The direct experiences of the students in the schoolrooms vitalized the professional course by providing real problems for study. The integration of all the course experiences made a great contribution to the education of resourceful teachers.

Student Teaching in Secondary School Mathematics at Illinois State Normal University

T. E. RINE

ILLINOIS State Normal University is a teacher-education institution whose primary purpose is the education of teachers. It is accredited by the National Association of Colleges and Secondary Schools and by the National Association of Colleges for Teacher Education. Its laboratory schools are maintained to give prospective teachers an opportunity to have actual teaching experiences under competent supervision. This institution also has access to the facilities of various public schools for the purpose of giving student teachers an opportunity to teach in schools similar to those in which they will teach after graduation.

The department of mathematics at Illinois State Normal University is composed of teachers who have all had experience in teaching in the public schools. All have at least a master's degree; approximately half of the members of the department of mathematics have a doctor's degree. All are members of the National Education Association, the Illinois Education Association, the National Council of Teachers of Mathematics, the Illinois Council of Teachers of Mathematics, and the Mathematical Association of America, Inc. All of the members of the department of mathematics participate directly in the student-teaching program.

A study of course offerings reveals much of interest regarding the mathematics courses prerequisite to student teaching in secondary mathematics. If the student has not completed a third semester of algebra and a course in solid geometry before entering Illinois State Normal University, he must complete these requirements before he may do any further work in mathematics. Then before he may begin his work in student teaching, the student must complete courses in plane and advanced trigonometry, analytic geometry, college algebra, differential and integral calculus, as well as all of his requirements in professional education. Also work in college geometry and history of mathematics must either precede his student teaching or be taken concurrently with student teaching.

In regard to professional courses in mathematics, Illinois State Normal University offers several: Foundations of Arithmetic, primarily for elementary teachers; Special Problems in Junior High School Mathematics; Field Work in Mathematics, a course in the outdoor use of instruments; and a course in Survey of Mathematics. The course in survey of mathematics includes many of the concepts frequently included in professional courses in the teaching of mathematics given in other teacher-education institutions as well as an analysis of secondary mathematics from an advanced viewpoint. Although a course in the teaching of mathematics, named as such, is not offered, yet, in connection with the work in student teaching, many of the concepts are actually not omitted. This work is part of the biweekly seminars, in which all student teachers and faculty in the department of mathematics participate. These seminars are excellent in that the group considers the problems of the classroom as experienced immediately by the student teachers.

At Illinois State Normal University a student is eligible for student teaching if, among other requirements, he has earned at least as many grade points as semester hours credit. On a five point grading scale of A, B, C, D, and F, this standard is equivalent to a grade of C. It is evident then that at least a fair degree of scholarship in the total program of studies prior to student teaching is required. To be admitted to student teaching in any teaching field, students are required to offer the same amount of preparation in the subject as is required by the North Central Association for teaching in the high schools of the state.

The ability to speak effectively is considered essential. Work in speech is required prior to student teaching. Each student must take a speech test in the freshman year and corrective work is provided for those who need it. In the junior year another speech test is given. At this time members of both the department of speech and the department of mathematics are represented. In this speech test the student presents materials of the nature that he would use in the high-school classroom.

This speech test must be passed before the student is allowed to do student teaching.

At Illinois State Normal University, student teachers are encouraged to appraise their own work. In their seminar meetings all student teachers and members of the faculty in the department of mathematics—the same faculty members are also the supervisors—discuss and appraise the entire student-teaching program in order to make such changes as will give the student teachers those experiences that are most helpful to them.

Besides the regularly scheduled seminars, where all of the supervisors and student teachers in secondary mathematics meet to discuss the common problems of the classroom, the supervisors meet in individual conferences with student teachers to discuss the particular problems associated with daily lesson planning, testing, organizing units of instruction, collecting and selecting materials of instruction, and assisting with the detailed application of methods to the particular subject matter of mathematics.

Student teachers have access to files of information concerning the pupils whom they are teaching and are urged to make full use of all available records. Also the psychological testing service is available for remedial cases or in any case where this service is needed.

Films for classroom use are available through the office of the Director of Audio-Visual Aids. The supervisor has an excellent opportunity to give the student teacher much assistance in this respect.

Little work is done in regard to carrying on experimental work for the improvement of instruction with student teachers; however, in the total teacher-education program much work is done in this area by the faculty and graduate students. Lack of time makes experimentation somewhat difficult, and in some instances, the supervisors feel that the student teachers are not quite ready to participate in this type of work.

At Illinois State Normal University, the supervisors do much to encourage the professional growth of student teachers through recommending attendance at mathematics and other educational conferences, membership in professional organizations, and the reading of professional literature, and also through discussing problems related to professional ethics.

In the department of mathematics, the student teachers do some practice teaching in practically all of the subject areas of secondary-school mathematics. There is a tendency to place all student teachers first in one of the traditional courses, usually algebra or geometry. After about 12 weeks of practice teaching in this initial area, the student teacher is shifted to do his observing and teaching in some other area of secondary mathematics. In this way the student teacher is given the opportunity to become familiar with the teaching-learning situations in most of the teaching areas of secondary-school mathematics.

In the beginning stages of his period of student teaching, the student teacher studies all the available records of the pupils who are in his classroom. The following data record sheet illustrates the kind of diagnosis he is expected to make.

STUDENT TEACHING IN SECONDARY MATHEMATICS
INDIVIDUAL DIAGNOSIS

Each student is requested to complete each of the following, in order to secure an understanding of the pupils in the class assigned:

1. Secure some measure of the pupil's ability to learn mathematics.

2. Describe each pupil in terms of his adjustment to the demands and opportunities of the classroom.

3. As a result of classroom contact and test scores select two pupils who indicate potentialities of superior achievement; select two pupils who indicate average achievement; and select two pupils who are experiencing difficulty in comprehending desired concepts.

4. Determine genesis of, and interest in, or apathy for mathematics.

5. Devise a remedial program for two students who find mathematics difficult.

6. Devise some challenging activities for two talented pupils to supplement the regular assignment.

Each student teacher is expected to use the following forms to collect required information, record generalizations, and to indicate recommendations for increasing the teaching effectiveness. If any part of the following form does not provide sufficient space, the additional information may be submitted in acceptable written form.

Conferences with pupils are to be arranged after consultation with critic teacher. All contacts with pupils should endeavor to render service to pupil and not conflict with scheduled classroom activities.

Name _____

Describe this pupil in terms of:
1. Vocational ambitions.
2. Intended use for or recognized value of mathematics
3. What kind of mathematics has proven to be interesting? dull? easy? difficult?
4. Suggestions for making mathematics more meaningful to him
5. Challenging activities to supplement regular assignment.

Describe the average and remedial pupils in the same manner as was done with the superior pupils.

PROGNOSIS OF ACADEMIC SUCCESS AND ADJUSTMENT

Academic Achievement

| | I.Q. | Math. Apt. Percentile | Reading Percentile | Date of Reading Test | Grade in Mathematics | | |
					Gen. Math.	Alg.	Geom.
1.							
2.							

Adjustment—place check in proper column

| | Co-operation | | Initiative | | Leadership | | | Work to Capacity | | | General Eval. | | |
	Selfish	Acceptable	Helpful	Apathetic	Acceptable	Eager	Follower	Acceptable	Others follow	Below	Av.	Above	Remedial	Av.	Sup.
1.															
2.															

These records are discussed at the seminar meetings of all student teachers and supervisors of student teaching in secondary mathematics. Such questions as the following are discussed: How should the data be used? What data should be kept confidential? How are the data collected? To whom should the data be made available?

During this early stage of student teaching, the student teacher is *learning about* his pupils and observing the teaching of the supervisor. Gradually the student teacher takes on more and more responsibilities. First he is giving pupils individualized instruction, then several pupils are working with him at a time, and finally he takes over all the responsibilities of the classroom. While teaching, he is confronted with numerous problems; and these problems are discussed either with his supervising teacher alone or in the biweekly seminars, which are a required part of his student teaching and for which credit in student teaching is given.

After a period of about 12 weeks, the student teacher is shifted to a different group of learners under a different supervising teacher. He is informed of this shift about two weeks in advance. Previously he has made observations in this classroom so that he already knows most of the pupils there and they know him. The student teacher knows the supervisor in this classroom also, since he has already discussed numerous teaching problems with him and all of the other supervisors during the biweekly seminars. He now does only a few more days of observing in this classroom situation and very soon again takes over the full responsibilities of teaching, the decision being left to the supervisor as to how soon he should take over the full responsibility. The supervisor in this classroom has discussed the work of the student teacher with his previous supervisor and so attempts to give the student teacher experience in those areas where his need is the greatest. The individual conferences and biweekly seminars continue throughout the entire semester. If the student teacher's program permits and the supervisor feels that he is ready, or if there is a particular need for him to teach in still another area, he is given this opportunity.

The student teacher has opportunities to participate in many activities outside of the classroom: the activities of the mathematics club, assembly programs, noonhour activities, supervision of study halls, assisting with plays, assisting in sponsoring parties, and still other activities. He is encouraged to participate in many of these activities.

Illinois State Normal University sponsors an annual mathematics conference for both elementary and secondary teachers. Student teachers are given some duties in connection with this conference, and all student teachers in mathematics are expected to attend the general and group meetings. Membership in the National Council of Teachers of Mathematics and other professional organizations is encouraged.

The department of mathematics gives a few students an opportunity to do off-campus student teaching. In this program the student teacher lives in the public school community where he does his student teaching for a period of nine weeks. There he is given the opportunity to participate in most of the activities of a teacher of secondary mathematics in the kind of a position which he is likely to have after graduation. The student electing to do this type of teaching has his program of classes arranged so that he can do full-time teaching, with no other college class responsibilities, for a period of nine weeks. This program has the disadvantage of not allowing close supervision. Nor does the student teacher have the opportunity to take part in the individual conferences and seminars in which those who are on the campus can participate. However, it has the advantage of giving more experiences in the out-of-class activities of the community as well as in those experiences that are associated with the problems of full-time teaching.

The supervisors and student teachers feel that both the on-campus and off-campus student teaching offers much for the students and would like to have each student given the opportunity to participate in both programs. It is hoped that more time and credit will be available for student teaching in the future. Many of the supervisors and students also feel that greater opportunity for laboratory experiences in the junior year should be made available.

After the student receives a position, he is invited to the campus to discuss with the mathematics supervisors and student teachers the immediate problems that face the teacher in his first year of teaching. This informal meeting, a coffee hour, is held during homecoming, at which time many graduates return to the campus. The purposes of this meeting are to aid the new teacher in solving the problems that he is facing in his new teaching position, to orient the present student teachers to the problems faced by the first-year teacher of secondary mathematics, and to aid the department of mathematics in the improvement of its practice teaching and professional program.

As part of the program of the evaluation of the student teacher himself, many of the competencies, including subject matter proficiency, understandings, skills, abilities, attitudes, appreciations, and personal and professional qualifications are discussed co-operatively with the student teacher in the early stages of his student-teaching period. He is made aware of goals toward which he will need to strive during his participation period of student teaching. Objectives of teaching secondary mathematics are discussed in individual conferences and in the biweekly seminars. The growth of the pupils under the student teacher's guidance toward the mutually agreed upon objectives is considered as part of the evaluation of the student teacher. In frequent individual conferences, the student teacher discusses with the supervisor his own growth in teaching. His growth in classroom situations and in participation in the seminar meetings, his work with his own pupils outside of the classroom, his willingness and ability to assume responsibilities of teaching, both in and out of the classroom, are also considered in his evaluation. This continuous evaluation during the student-teaching period is intended to aid the student teacher in his growth as a professional teacher.

The faculty of the department of mathematics, working in close co-operation, discuss with one another the needs, strengths, and weaknesses of the various student teachers.

The student teachers themselves, meeting in closed session, are given an opportunity to evaluate their total experiences in student teaching in secondary mathematics. At this time they discuss with one another what they believe to be the strengths and weaknesses of their total student-teaching experience. This discussion is held after the student teacher's grade has already been determined, so that he is under no pressure of having his comments influence his own final evaluation. A student chairman and secretary are elected by the group for this discussion, and a written report of this meeting is turned in to the faculty member who is in charge of the student-teaching seminars in mathematics. This report is utilized in helping the supervising teachers determine the nature of the student-teaching experiences for the following year.

The mathematics faculty also meet in closed session to discuss the final total evaluation of each student teacher. Each supervising teacher is given the opportunity to discuss the progress of the student teachers who have been under his guidance. The strengths and weaknesses of each student teacher are discussed to aid in the formulation of a written report of each student teacher's final evaluation and also to help the student teacher in his future growth. The supervisor to whom the student teacher was assigned originally is responsible for writing up his final evaluation. This total evaluation, even though written up by a single laboratory teacher, is the responsibility of the academic and laboratory teachers as a group.

This emerging practice in student teaching in secondary-school mathematics is not, perhaps, the most idealistic one that theorists might describe. It is, however, a practice that does actually exist. It is a practice that is changing year after year in accordance with the changing needs of the student teachers. The unique feature of the seminars is based on the principle that the supervisors must be able to do those things that are expected of the student teachers. The writer firmly believes that the strength of the student-teaching program in secondary mathematics at Illinois State Normal University is based on the co-operative efforts of all of those who participate in the program.

The Contribution of the Laboratory School Prior to Student Teaching

ALICE ROSE CARR

A VERY important part of the preservice education of teachers of mathematics, as well as of all teachers, consists of professionalizing experiences with children in an actual teaching situation. At Ball State Teachers College, the initial laboratory experiences are provided at Burris School, a campus school in which are enrolled all the children of a given district of the city[2] from preschool through high-school levels. The general practice is not to have student teaching at Burris. The functions of the campus school as we consider them are: (a) to provide the student an opportunity for seeing some of the best educational practices in operation, (b) to afford him early contact with children, and (c) to furnish a setting for research and experimentation with new ideas. The consensus of opinion has been that one school cannot provide this opportunity for experimentation, for laboratory experiences with children, for observation of good teaching practices and at the same time permit students to do full-time student teaching.

We who teach at Burris School feel that we make an important contribution to the education of teachers by having in our classes college students designated as "participating" students. These are usually juniors who are enrolled in a college class entitled Principles of Teaching and Classroom Management, a course which is a prerequisite for student teaching. The college instructor meets the members of the group once a week and each student attends a Burris class five days a week for a full quarter. Students are assigned to the areas of their choice, and, insofar as possible, at the grade level they choose, although some adjustments have to be made so that there will be not more than two participants in any one class. Thus a mathematics major who expects to teach algebra and geometry may find himself in a seventh-grade mathematics class. Such a situation usually promises more benefit than is apparent at first glance.

The very fact that this course is not called Student Teaching has a good psychological effect upon the prospective teacher. It allows him to be inducted gradually into the teaching situation. Since this is the student's first experience of any length in which he sees the pupils from the teacher's point of view, the first task of the Burris teacher is to make the participant feel that he is not an observer but rather an integral part of the class, and one who contributes to the teaching. In my mathematics classes, it is easy to get the students on their feet the first day, for there are

---

[2] Muncie, Ind.

always compasses to be distributed, papers to be collected, or problems to be written on the board. As the student moves about the classroom among the Burris pupils he begins to lose his sense of strangeness and forgets himself in the task he is performing.

Participants are expected to be prepared to help pupils with all assigned work, to move about the room during work periods, and to give individual help just as I do. It is through such active participation that they begin to realize what is meant by saying that it is not enough for a teacher to know how to work a problem. It is not at all unusual to find that a mathematics major who can easily solve a problem in calculus has difficulty explaining some simple process of arithmetic to a 12-year-old. He sees that he must not only know how to do the problem but also know how to present it in a way the pupil will understand; he learns to teach by helping pupils to help themselves.

Although teaching, as it is usually understood, is not the major emphasis of this course, we try to give the student an opportunity to take full control of the class for at least a short period of time just as early in the quarter as possible. This gives him a chance to see what he can do by himself and results in a greater appreciation of the problems involved. After his first experience, which may be from one to three class periods in length, he is much better able to profit from what he sees the regular teacher do. Later in the quarter, he teaches again at least once. *When* he teaches and *how long* he teaches are questions which depend upon the individual.

During the quarter, we make an effort to give the student a wide variety of experiences with many phases of teaching. He learns what mathematics materials are available; he examines courses of study; he constructs visual aids for mathematics; he checks papers and records scores; he brings in supplementary material; he takes charge of small groups for remedial work. He is having firsthand experiences with teaching, yet he is not faced with full responsibility for any length of time. Several times during the quarter I find it "necessary" to be out of the room for a short period of time so that he may feel really "on his own"; occasionally, I have been away for several days while participating students carried on the classes in my absence. The evaluation sessions which were held after these absences have proved especially fruitful, sessions involving Burris pupils, participants, and myself. Discipline is one of the great worries of beginning teachers and it is one with which it is difficult to help a student directly. Burris pupils have been very helpful to college students by their criticisms. Even in cases where they knew their own behavior was not blameless, they have helped the young teacher by a frank discussion of what they thought caused the trouble, often pointing out that good discipline depends on good teaching.

In addition to his experience in a mathematics class, the prospective teacher participates in many other activities of Burris students in order to have a better understanding of children as they appear outside the classroom. He attends convocations; he eats in the cafeteria occasionally; he helped to plan "fun-nights"; he visits other classes; he attends basketball games; and he observes behavior at the corner drug store. All of these experiences contribute to his education as a teacher and all of them will be of value to him when he begins his student teaching and later when he is a full-fledged member of the profession.

It may seem that in all of this program there has been very little emphasis upon mathematics itself. It has been my experience that insofar as actual knowledge of mathematics is concerned, the student is usually well-prepared by the mathematics department. This does not mean, however, that he will not profit from this experience in a classroom where he must bring his knowledge of subject matter into a new focus, centering on the learner, not on the subject. Here he no longer teaches plane geometry, but rather teaches plane geometry to specific 15-year-old high-school sophomores. Herein lies the real value of the course for training teachers of mathematics. It is not a question of education courses *versus* mathematics courses or of content *versus* method, but rather a synthesis of the two. We at Ball State feel that our students go out from this course confident of their ability to meet the situations which will arise in student teaching and that they will be better teachers as a result of this gradual induction.

The Laboratory Method in Mathematics Education

Daniel B. Lloyd

Most of us started our mathematical careers by counting wooden blocks when we were quite young. The second age of man, mathematically speaking, witnessed his weaning from counting of concrete objects to the counting of pictured objects; and the third stage was the symbolized number, or digit. With increasing mental age more complete abstraction is achieved and the concepts of one-ness, two-ness, and three-ness emerge more purely as ideas. But the gradual steps taken in teaching these relatively simple concepts should guide our judgment in teaching more complicated ones.

Dealing with things as an approach to ideas is the essence of the laboratory method of instruction. Inductively, physical experiences lead to generalization, expressed as an idea or principle. Deductively, we utilize and combine known principles to discover new ones, either general or specific, and apply them to the solution of our problems. This is typical of mathematical thinking and its daily utilization. But, regardless of whether it is the *formulation* of principles or the *application* of principles, in either case, conceptual learning is nurtured by perceptual experience, and we are eager to provide all helpful multisensory stimulation to assure this growth.

Pictorial thinking has presaged abstract thinking throughout history. The logical geometry of the Greeks was preceded by the practical surveying of the Egyptians; and the lack of further illustrative patterns delayed for many centuries the extension of geometry beyond its classical Euclidean forms.

It is sometimes forgotten that the rapid strides made by modern scientists in explaining the nature of matter and its manifestations were preceded by attempts largely pictorial to illustrate and interpret existing relationships. Leaning on such imagery, Lord Kelvin, some 70 years ago, devised a model of the molecule. It was based on Newtonian mechanics and consisted of a thin rigid shell, to whose interior masses were attached by springs. He was heard to make the following statement, which showed that his conviction in his hypothesis had been strengthened: "I am not really satisfied until I see a model of it."

Thomas Jefferson, who was an educator, as well as a statesman, once wrote in a letter to George Wythe:

> I have reflected on your idea of wooden or ivory diagrams for the geometrical demonstrations. I should think wood as good as ivory; and that, in this case it might add to the improvement of the young gentlemen that they should make the figures themselves.

Confucius, ancient and learned Chinese philosopher and religious leader, said: "One picture is worth a thousand words." We should like to add that a three-dimensional model might well be worth several thousand words. Robert C. Yates, professor of mathematics at the U. S. Military Academy at West Point, once made the following pointed statement: "I never learned anything that did not come up my arm."

Of the concrete approach to ideas, Eric Bell has the following to say: "Thinking in terms of mechanical models is inherently no less respectable than translating everything into mathematical abstraction. Both methods yield purely symbolic representations of nature, and it does not follow that one is more *realistic* than the other. It is all a question of who is doing the thinking" (6). Or, we might say *"trying* to do the thinking," if we are thinking of the modest mental age of some of our students today. Dr. Bell goes on to opine that the visualizing ability of most mathematicians is no better than that of the average man.

In 1947, Howard Fehr said:

> The mathematics laboratory should be used to create a spirit of research and discovery. Field work should be a part of every mathematics course from Grade III through Grade XII and perhaps in junior college. It should not be play, but must consist of planned experiments and testing of desired outcomes. There is not a single topic in grade or high school that cannot be exemplified and put to work in a mathematics laboratory (16).

Although it is not sound pedagogy to substitute things for thinking, or models in place of ideas, still the fact that any virtue carried to an extreme becomes a vice does not vitiate the virtue.

The immature student acquires new mathematical concepts and understandings more readily through experimental activities, in which he collects and uses quantitative data in concrete situations, such as in measuring, reading instruments, drawing, mapping, weighing, counting, estimating, comparing, classifying, and checking data. Much of the work can be done in the classroom, but some may be done outside, such as surveying and measuring, with more or less simple field instruments. Also, it is believed that more interest and better mastery of mathematical principles result when acquired in a functional setting and seen in relation to actual applications.

However, laboratory methods should be used with restraint and only as an *adjunct* to the teaching of mathematics. Mathematics is a discipline in its own right for which there is no substitute. With this proper perspective in mind, the laboratory method, when well-planned, becomes a valuable supplement to the teaching process.

The laboratory method has been increasing in favor for many years in mathematics education. This has been due to a number of causes. The first strong influences date back to John Perry in 1901, and to E. H. Moore of Chicago, in 1902, who advocated a shift from the purely abstract teaching of mathematics to the graphic approach and the use of models and equipment to discover the principles as well as portray the applications of the subject. Again, John Dewey's pragmatic philosophy of "learn to do by doing" has afforded it a sound psychological foundation. Also, our changing student body has demanded curricular changes. It has brought the need for more variety in pupil activity, and, in fact, more actual *physical activity*. This is inherent in the philosophy of the *junior* high school, particularly. It has had an impact on all the courses of study, even the more abstract ones, such as mathematics. Also, the tendency to correlate and integrate subject matter fields, has resulted in stressing the applications of mathematics along with the teaching of its principles. The wider use of mathematics in modern applications heretofore unknown has further increased this trend in teaching the subject.

Decreasing enrollments in secondary schools in recent years have resulted in smaller classes in some places, and correspondingly more attention to individual needs. A double-track curriculum in many schools has been adopted. Even a triple-track in some larger schools has been started. These moves toward more differentiated instruction have made possible a wider use of laboratory methods.

Let us take a look at the attitudes of leaders in mathematics education. We note the statements made by national committees: The Joint Commission Report of 1940 devoted 3000 words—some 7½ pages—to the topic of teaching aids and equipment; the Commission on Post-War Plans, 1945, stressed laboratory methods in three theses out of their total of 34, and implied its importance in five others; other reports have done likewise.

A recent, 1945 Yearbook, the Eighteenth, of the National Council of Teachers of Mathematics was devoted entirely to *Multisensory Aids*; the Seventeenth Yearbook dealt entirely with *Applications of Mathematics*; the Nineteenth was on *Surveying Instruments*; and the Twentieth was on the *Metric System of Weights and Measures*. Professional journals, such as the *Mathematics Teacher*, and others, are devoting more space to teaching aids and laboratory techniques than formerly, thus reflecting an increased interest throughout the profession.

As is usually the case, the advocacy of progressive practices has far exceeded their implementation. National policy-making committees on the one hand and actual classroom practices, on the other hand, remain somewhat separated. But both of these *ends* are far out in front of the *center*, or at least what should be the central stimulus for implementation, namely the teacher-education institutions.

During the past decade numerous teacher workshops, summer institutes, and similar vacation groups have made notable contributions toward training teachers in the laboratory method. But in general they have not carried college accreditation or recognition. It is inevitable, however, that these work-study groups should help pave the way for more formally organized college courses with the same coverage. Such is beginning to be the case in a limited number of teacher-education centers.

Within the purview of this discussion, the laboratory method will be considered to mean activity by the students with material aids other than blackboard, paper, or library reference materials. It will involve the use of materials, models, instruments, or equipment, with the aim of deducing and abstracting therefrom certain mathematical concepts and understandings.

For the purposes of teacher training, a methods course in the laboratory procedure is presumed to provide actual experience with a wide variety of such laboratory materials. These materials should be of a type appropriate to future teaching needs. The average students enrolling in such courses are woefully unfamiliar with such materials and equipments and require basic training with them. As the variety of such materials is so broad, and yet the limitations of time generally so exacting, the problems of choice and relative emphasis are of primary concern in the designing of these courses. Considerable lack of uniformity among such courses in different training schools would be expected.

A recent survey by the author, of professional methods courses in mathematics (see page 219), indicates that very few colleges are offering courses dealing primarily with the laboratory method. Such courses are at present limited to about a dozen institutions in the country. They are given names such as "Mathematics Laboratory," "Field Work in Mathematics," "Measuring Instruments," "Mathematics of Measurement," "Applications of Mathematics," and similar names.

Courses entitled "Mathematics Laboratory," were listed by only four institutions. These did not include outdoor field work. Courses entitled "Field Work," in which outdoor measurement predominated, were listed by six colleges; while two colleges give a combined field work and laboratory course. As indicated by the questionnaire survey, these courses were first offered from two to 15 years ago. They are elective only, except for one college, which requires such a course for its mathematics majors. Enrollment ranges from seven to 35; goodly per cents of inservice teachers are enrolled, most of them taking it for graduate credit, wherever this was granted, which is in about half of the places offering it. Notebooks are required in two-thirds of the courses; assignments are generally rather uniform. The above survey does not include summer school short courses and workshops.

The survey indicated that laboratory methods were used only incidentally in the *basic* methods courses for secondary-school teachers. Of those replying to this question, 10 per cent said that they used such methods therein; 50 per cent said occasionally; and 40 per cent said they did not use them. Such methods were reported less frequently in elementary and other miscellaneous methods courses.

Below are described several actual courses which are being currently offered and which are fairly typical of present practice.

IOWA STATE TEACHERS COLLEGE, CEDAR FALLS, IOWA

An elective course for mathematics majors and minors has been given for several years, entitled "Mathematics of Measurement." Three quarter-hours of credit are given for four hours of work per week. Actually, nearly every mathematics major and minor takes the course. The textbook, *Field Work in Mathematics*, by C. N. Shuster and F. L. Bedford, is rather closely followed.

Instruments studied include: steel tape, angle mirror, hypsometer, plane table, sextant, transit, verniers (circular and linear), dumpy level, stadia tubes and rods, calipers, and slide rules. Scale drawings and blueprints are studied. Each student makes a measuring instrument of some kind. The slide rule is taught by the method of Keppers and Chapdelaine (18). Each student is required to write a paper on some phase of measurement. Outdoor projects are worked on unless the weather is inclement. Formal reports on these are required, using Reinhardt lettering. The following are typical field projects:

1. Pacing—standardization of the pace
2. Chaining over uneven ground, going around buildings by 3-4-5 triangles
3. Heights by shadows—various objects on campus
4. Lay off rectangular plots—basements, courts, athletic fields, and such
5. Distance across body of water by triangulation
6. Heights by angle mirror, hypsometer, and transit—checking one result against the other
7. Lay out a circle with angle mirror
8. Mapping an island by angle mirror, and finding its area
9. Mapping by plane table method
10. Differential leveling by transit or level
11. Profile leveling; laying an underground pipeline

12. Solar observation for latitude
13. Distance by stadia
14. Contour mapping.

Effort is made to limit the class size to 15. Field parties work in groups of three or four students. Equipment is checked out and in carefully for each party.

WILSON TEACHERS COLLEGE, WASHINGTON, D. C.

There is offered at Wilson Teachers College a senior course, bearing the following catalogue description:

Mathematics 492—Laboratory Experiences in Secondary-School Mathematics. This is a practical course for inservice and preservice secondary-school teachers. It provides a broad coverage of special techniques for enriching instructional content and diversifying teaching methods. Topics include mathematics laboratory, use of measuring instruments, (verniers, surveying instruments, etc.), computing instruments, projecting machines, and other equipment and procedures designed to meet varying class situations. Individual projects may be assigned in accordance with the needs and interests of those enrolled.

Prerequisite: One methods course, or teaching experience.

This is a semester course, one-hour lecture, and two two-hour laboratory periods per week, for a total of three semester-hour credits. A laboratory fee of one dollar is charged for materials. It is scheduled in late afternoon, from 3:45 to 5:30, to accommodate inservice teachers in the area. Most inservice teachers attend only once a week, on Tuesdays; the undergraduates of the college attend all three days. This results in differentiated assignments, although the inservice teachers generally accomplish more, in proportion to the time they are there, than the college students. Some of the experienced teachers audit instead of registering for credit.

The list of topics covered varies from year to year. The following list is representative, although all of the topics listed would not be covered in any one year:

TOPICS

1. Reinhardt Lettering (used by engineers and draftsmen). Instruction and practice. Other styles of lettering are discussed and compared.

2. Making simple working drawings. Preliminary sketching and measuring of simple models, such as machine parts; using calipers and

scales. Drawing of front, plan, and profile views in orthographic projection.

3. Three-dimensional drawing and sketching. Blackboard practice. Oblique, isometric, and perspective projection—basic elements only.

4. Paper Folding, for intuitive geometry.

5. Making Aids. Flexible kinematic boards. Practice with papers, cardboards, plastics, or such material.

6. Drafting Instruments. Parallel rulers, carpenter's square, center square, pantograph, proportional dividers, and such.

7. Small measuring instruments. Astrolabe, angle mirror, clinometer, hypsometer, cross-staff, sighting tube, sextant, pocket transit. Principles, construction, and use. Ready-cut instrument kits, verniers.

8. Direct and indirect measurement projects. Field work, approximate computation. Accuracy, precision, error, relative error.

9. Surveying instruments. Operation and use. Tapes and chain; field work methods. Organization of field parties. Solar observation. Mapping, transit, plane table, surveyor's compass, engineers' transit, wye level.

10. Computing instruments. Abacus. Slide rules and such. Modern computing machines (small).

11. Projecting machines—slides and moving picture.

Differentiated interests and backgrounds of these students are a primary consideration in administering this course. At the first session the topics to be covered are chosen by group conference and questionnaire, and a tentative program is set up to include the preferences. Sometimes guest speakers are included; a trip or so, such as to the city visual education department, is scheduled. The field work is done on the campus or in a nearby park. The gaining of skill and facility in things the students can use with their own pupils is particularly stressed. The making of teaching aids from materials that are accessible and inexpensive is encouraged.

One large group project is the planning and staging of Open House Day. This comes late in the semester and is sometimes in conjunction with the meeting of the District of Columbia Teachers of Mathematics, a local affiliated group of the National Council. The students of the laboratory class present a program of mathematical topics and exhibit their instruments and other teaching aids that they have constructed. One or two of the more attractive topics may be presented after the dinner meeting which follows in the evening.

OTHER COLLEGES

Other colleges, probably even better known for such similar courses as the above include: Boston University School of Education; Eastern and Western Illinois State Teachers Colleges; Teachers College, Columbia University; Millersville and Indiana State Teachers Colleges in Pennsylvania; and the Montclair and Trenton, New Jersey, State Teachers Colleges, the last named being the one where the field work course is given by Carl Shuster, probably the pioneer of them all.

These courses do not differ a great deal as to aims, content, and procedures. Certain local differences exist, as when equipment of an unusual kind happens to be available, such as astronomical telescopes, Johansson gauge blocks, sine bar, planimeter, map projection equipment, and other equipment.

A college mathematics department need not spend a great deal of money equipping its own laboratory. Probably it would be well to own or have access to a number of surveying instruments, projecting machines, and related equipment. Vernier and micrometer calipers, drafting and art equipment can often be borrowed from other departments. An abacus, slide rules, angle mirrors, and tapes are less expensive. Other equipment can be acquired gradually. Miscellaneous teaching aids can be made by students and donated to the department. It is desirable to train student teachers to make their own aids, or have their pupils make them. This is usually necessary, as schools frequently do not have funds for expensive factory-made equipment.

Some of the questions which the foregoing discussion has endeavored to answer are:

1. Is the laboratory method of teaching new?
2. Is the laboratory method psychologically and pedagogically sound?
3. What are the teacher-training institutions now doing about it and what is the trend?
4. How should a college course in laboratory methods for teachers be designed?

Other questions to which further consideration might be given are:

1. Should *all* teachers be trained in laboratory methods and techniques?

2. If so, what should such training include?

3. Where should laboratory courses be made available?

4. What materials and equipment should be made available for this training?

5. How much time in the course should be devoted to professionalization, e.g., its adaptation to use in secondary-school classes, its evaluation for different kinds of learning situations, and such things?

6. What relative emphasis should be placed on primitive student-made types of equipment and instruments as compared with modern, factory-made types?

7. Should correlation with other departments using measuring instruments be encouraged, e.g., the science and mechanical drawing departments?

8. Would correlation with the art department be helpful in organizing a unit on the use of art in mathematics (or mathematics in art) and in decorating the mathematics classroom.

Much serious attention was given to these and other related questions at the "Workshop in Mathematical Materials" held at Teachers College, Columbia University, July 20–31, 1953.

The teacher-training institutions have been tardy in recognizing the need for laboratory training courses. Many of us look back regretfully and wish we had had such training early in our teaching careers. For those just starting to teach, it bridges the gap between their basic methods course and their first teaching experience. The importance of laboratory methods is widely accepted and yet adequate teacher training in this field is not yet available. We believe that the offering of such a course in many places would fulfill a need heretofore neglected.

PRESENT STATUS OF VARIOUS METHODS COURSES

Out of a total of approximately 1000 institutions of higher education which offer some kind of professional preparation for teaching mathematics, the author examined the published catalogue offerings of over 300 of the more promising ones. Of these, only 75 offer more than one basic methods course for the secondary field of teaching and one for the elementary field. To these 75 schools the following questionnaire was sent, to which

59 replied, answering the following questions for each course offered:

1. Title of course
2. Name of instructor
3. Number of years course has been given in present form
4. Semester hours of credit
5. Approximate average enrollment
6. Graduate credit allowed for it?
7. Approximate per cent of class graduate students
8. Approximate per cent of class inservice teachers
9. Of whom is the course required?
10. For whom is the course elective?
11. Are assignments uniform or differentiated?
12. Are special topics assigned?
13. Are laboratory methods used?
14. Are notebooks required to be kept?
15. How much field work is done, in clock hours?
16. How many trips are taken?
17. How many outside speakers are brought in?
18. Mention any other noteworthy features
19. Topics covered, in addition to those listed in catalogues.

From these sources of information, both catalogs and questionnaire, and from other standard sources, some interesting facts were learned. First, concerning the basic methods courses, for the elementary and for the secondary levels, these courses were found to be fairly uniform both in content and teaching procedure. The most frequently offered professional course was a course in Secondary-School Methods. Elementary School Methods was found only two-thirds as often, but with a total enrollment four times as large. For the former, the median class size was 12, and rarely exceeded 20. For the elementary classes the figures were about double, and more than one section taught per year in some places. The above courses are preponderantly three semester-hour courses (or four quarter-hours for the minority of schools using the quarter-term schedule).

About one-half of the schools allow graduate credit for these courses. Less than 20 per cent of the enrollment is graduate, and in fewer than a dozen schools is the enrollment 100 per cent graduate. Only in a few urban centers are inservice teachers enrolled in sizeable numbers, and even there they constitute a minority of total enrollment.

To a limited extent differentiated assignments are made, more on the secondary than on the elementary level. Notebooks are seldom required to be kept, but the majority of such students keep them. Outside speakers are seldom brought in, and class trips are very rarely taken. Directed observations of good teaching in nearby schools are frequently required. Laboratory methods are used to limited extent—10 per cent said "yes," 50 per cent, "occasionally," and 40 per cent, "no"—in the secondary course. Such methods were reported less frequently in elementary and various other methods courses. The length of time that these courses have been offered in their present form ranges from one to 37 years, according to their own testimony. The secondary courses seem to have been standardized over a longer time, whereas more of the elementary courses have been set up, or redesigned since World War II.

Features such as the following were frequently reported: preparing lesson plans and simulated teaching by the students; and less frequently, demonstration teaching by guest teacher with pupils brought in to the class; student-teacher evaluation of outcomes; and the making of teaching aids.

Besides the two basic methods courses, elementary and secondary, described above, the following courses with various differentiated aims and content are offered in this country:

General Title	Estimated Incidence
Arithmetic in the Primary Grades	2
Arithmetic in the Intermediate Grades	2
Problems in Arithmetic (clinical, etc.)	6
Evaluation in Arithmetic	1
Resource Materials	1
Teaching of Business Arithmetic	5
Teaching of General Mathematics	4
Teaching of Junior High School Mathematics	4
Teaching Algebra in Secondary Schools	2
Teaching Geometry in Secondary Schools	2
Teaching of Advanced Secondary Mathematics	4
Evaluation in Secondary Mathematics	1
Problems in Secondary Mathematics	4
Teaching Non-Academic Mathematics in the High School	2
Teaching Atypical Students (slow, gifted, etc.)	2
Math. Education for supervisors; current issues, etc.	3
Applications of Secondary Mathematics	6

The above list does not include content courses in mathematics, summer-school offerings, advanced research courses, readings in mathematical literature, foundations, philosophy, and history of mathematics, and a few courses primarily for supervisors. Neither does it include courses for nonmathematics majors, designed for general education.

Most liberal arts colleges report that a very small number of their mathematics majors choose teaching as a career, resulting in a meager enrollment in methods courses. Some of the state universities and other large colleges report less than a half-dozen students in their teacher-training classes in mathematics, although they have many times this number of requests for applicants for teaching jobs. All colleges report the need for more and better applicants for the teaching profession.

An Experiment in Clinical Procedures for Arithmetic

LESTA HOEL

FOR two weeks in the summer of 1952 the Portland Public Schools under the author's direction conducted their first arithmetic clinic. The objective of the clinic was to discover the specific arithmetic weaknesses of each child, and to determine at what stage in the development of his ability to use numbers effectively this trouble arose. For those with emotional problems resulting from confusion about arithmetic the clinic attempted to find where they could succeed, thus building a feeling of security and confidence in their ability to solve quantitative problems.

In order to isolate the arithmetic ills, students were selected whose only learning problem was arithmetic and whose lack of success in the subject was in most cases a source of emotional disturbance. Information on the pupils selected may be of interest. Twenty-two children were selected, eight boys and 14 girls, from Grades VI, VII, and VIII. The average IQ of the group was 115, ranging from 140 to 84, 17 above 100 and 5 below. Three pupils with physical difficulties were selected, a partially deaf child, one with a former eye difficulty, and one child medically diagnosed as brain injured[3].

The children were first recommended by the teacher and principal and were selected after a conference with parent, pupil, principal, and teacher. Only one child attended against his will. Discussion of his case deserves later comment. (See page 231.) The preliminary parent conference was followed with a tea for the parents on the last day. Three-fourths of them came. This represents an excellent response since several of these children were from homes in which the mother was working.

In addition to the aims stated above, the clinic was an experiment in teacher training. Seventeen teachers representing all grade levels worked with the director. The clinic gave an opportunity to demonstrate effective techniques of diagnosing and teaching. It made teachers aware of the emotional factors which affect arithmetic achievement. It familiarized them with concrete materials which can be used in a normal as well as a remedial situation and most of all, it pointed up their own weaknesses to the teachers.

Briefly, the daily program for the clinic was as follows:

8:00– 9:00—Teachers' planning period for the day
9:00–10:30—Pupil participation, usually broken down as follows:
  1. Director working with groups, either the entire group on common problems or with small groups
  2. Play period using arithmetic games
  3. Individual work—each teacher had one or two students.
10:30–11:00—Coffee hour
11:00– 1:00—Discussion of individual progress and of findings.

The arithmetic mistakes of these children were the ones usually encountered. For example, they had no idea of place value, as it relates to the meaning of *borrowing*; they borrowed one but they did not know that when they borrowed in fractions it was one whole, and in denominate numbers, one foot. Such a mistake as the following was common:

---

[3] Binet scores for 3 people, California Test of Mental Maturity—Short Form, for the others.

$$\begin{array}{r} 4\frac{2}{8} \\ -1\frac{7}{8} \\ \hline 2\frac{5}{8} \end{array}$$ or $$\begin{array}{r} 4 \text{ ft. } 2 \text{ in.} \\ -1 \text{ ft. } 7 \text{ in.} \\ \hline 2 \text{ ft. } 5 \text{ in.} \end{array}$$

What is the mistake? Our first supposition is that $\frac{2}{8}$ was sub-tracted from $\frac{7}{8}$ or 2 in. from 7 in. But why then is the answer not $3\frac{5}{8}$ or 3 ft. 5 in.? This is what actually happened at the clinic. One of the children could not take $\frac{7}{8}$ from $\frac{2}{8}$ or 7 inches from 2 inches, so he borrowed a *1* from the *4* and changed the problem to:

$$\begin{array}{r} 3 \\ \cancel{4}1\frac{2}{8} \\ -1\frac{7}{8} \\ \hline 2\frac{5}{8} \end{array}$$ or $$\begin{array}{r} 3 \\ \cancel{4} \text{ ft. } 12 \text{ in.} \\ -1 \text{ ft. } 7 \text{ in.} \\ \hline 2 \text{ ft. } 5 \text{ in.} \end{array}$$

He had learned the *borrow 1* process *well*, but he had no idea that this *1* is not 1 *ten* but 1 *whole* which must be changed to eighths, or 1 *foot* which must be changed to inches. The basic difficulty here is a *rule too well learned* and fundamental *concepts completely lacking*.

Mistakes in computation set the clinic children trying to recall the rule. They were lacking in resources of their own to rediscover the mathematical process. They were unaccustomed to, even resented in some cases, the use of concrete materials. (See page 229.) Their ability to use measuring instruments was surprisingly low. It must be recalled that these pupils were able to learn other school subjects. One of them, an eighth grader and perhaps the most extreme case, had confidence enough to become the champion speller in his school yet ranked 5.9 in arithmetic computation. (See page 229.)

The clinic staff agreed that two of the basic causes of trouble were emotional rather than mathematical. In the first place, these children were afraid. Of what? Afraid they would make a mistake; afraid to ask for help; afraid that the other children would laugh at them; afraid of reprimands from teacher and parents; and most of all, afraid of tests. Secondly, they felt pressure, both in the classroom from their teachers and companions, and from home, pressure to make a good grade, pressure to be as good in arithmetic as father or elder brother.

EVALUATION OF THE CLINIC

Pupils, parents, and teachers evaluated the clinic. One of the evaluative measures used by the teachers was a standardized test. It was recognized by the staff that this was questionable as a device for real evaluation since almost all the children had evidenced a fear of tests. But even with this handicap the results were gratifying. It should be kept in mind that the clinic lasted only two weeks for one and one-half hours each day and that the emphasis had been upon building basic concepts instead of upon computation. Of the 21 children who took the final test,[4] 15 gained over their test results in May. Six (all girls) either did not gain or lost. The average gain was 9 months, the highest gain was 2 years and 8 months. (See page 232.)

The children themselves evaluated the clinic at the end of the two weeks. All except two said at the beginning of the clinic that they disliked arithmetic; all but two liked it better at the close. The number of replies to "What did you like best about the clinic?" and "What did you learn at the clinic?" far exceeded their answers to "What did you dislike about it?" They liked the individual work; they were glad that they "found out what my trouble was" and that they had "a better understanding about arithmetic." They disliked it because it spoiled their vacation and because they did not like to show their weaknesses in arithmetic.

The real test of the clinic is what has taken place during the school year following it. The following questionnaire was sent to the children:

Eight months after the close of the arithmetic clinic, I would like to have your opinion on the following items:
1. What mathematics (or arithmetic) are you now taking?
2. Do you think the clinic helped you?
3. Do you like arithmetic any better than before?
4. Are you more successful in arithmetic or mathematics than before?
5. Are you afraid to take tests?
6. What suggestions have you which you think would improve next year's clinic?
7. Will you ask your parents to write how they felt about the clinic and what suggestions they have?

---

[4] Two forms of the Metropolitan Arithmetic Test on Fundamentals were used, one in May, and Form T at the Clinic.

The answers which were received to the questions (about a 50 per cent response) were gratifying. All thought the clinic helped them. Three do not like arithmetic any better than before. Two are still afraid of tests. Their suggestions for later clinics were: "have a longer period," "give more boys and girls a chance to go," "follow-through with a teacher that understands the problem." The parents made practically the same suggestions and were all grateful that their child had had the opportunity to attend.

The teachers of these pupils were sent the following questionnaire:

_____, who is in your school this year, attended the arithmetic clinic during the summer of 1952. I am interested in finding out what progress $\frac{he}{she}$ is making this year, and would appreciate the following information.

What mathematics is $\frac{he}{she}$ taking this year?

What has been $\frac{his}{her}$ success thus far?

Does $\frac{he}{she}$ seem to be afraid of mathematics?

If you have any test data or grades this year, please list below.

The teachers reported that four seemed to be afraid of mathematics, but only one failed to succeed. Of those who reported test data the average yearly gain was 1 year and 4 months. Of those eighth-graders who went into high school, 8 out of the 12 were able to succeed in algebra. (Ninth-graders are segregated into general mathematics and algebra, depending upon their mathematical ability.)

An evaluation would not be complete without including the teachers' judgment of what the clinic meant to them. Above all they liked the demonstrations by the director with the children. Seldom do persons in supervisory positions have opportunity to demonstrate with children whom they know and in situations which are normal. Yet teachers constantly ask supervisors to demonstrate and rate demonstrations as a valuable inservice aid. As a follow-up of the clinic, the author has worked in classrooms with students having arithmetic difficulties. This provided a natural reason for demonstrating diagnostic and remedial techniques without making the teacher appear inadequate to the children, a condition which can easily exist.

Teachers also enjoyed the informal congenial atmosphere of the clinic, the sharing of teaching devices, and the privilege of knowing and working with people from other schools. They requested for another year a laboratory in connection with the clinic in which they could make materials to be used in the clinic and in their own classrooms.

SUGGESTIONS TO CLASSROOM TEACHERS

The findings of the clinic staff have implications for all teachers. Can arithmetic trouble be prevented? Can we cure it if it already exists? First of all, the child must experience success. Only upon this foundation can he progress. We must discover where his trouble first started, and start from there. A test may indicate that he does not know how to add with carrying. But perhaps his real difficulty is that he does not understand the number system, perhaps his attention span is too short to add a column of figures, perhaps he knows the addition facts but does not know how to add higher decades, perhaps he is just afraid he will get the wrong answer, therefore does. Just as in the medical field a symptom may indicate a number of possible causes, which if treated in the wrong way might be fatal, so a wrong treatment arithmetically may result in a mathematics fatality.

The child must be given the power within himself to discover the correct arithmetic process, based not on memory but on meaning. If he has seen the need for the process in a social situation, if he has worked it out with actual objects at home or in the classroom, if he has seen or drawn pictures to illustrate the problem, has laid the problem on the table by means of semi-concrete objects such as markers and tallies—then and only then is he ready for the abstract computation. When future difficulties in abstractions arise, he has the preceding stages upon which to draw. He must be given the opportunity to do so by having facilities in the classroom for his use. It is better for the child to succeed in a little and be confident in his ability to progress, than for him to get the right answer to some problems but be afraid to try again because he might make a mistake.

Perhaps we have overemphasized mistakes by relating them

always to the child's grade. The child should realize that a mistake should be "used," not covered up. They want to cover it up only because of pressure from other people, pressure for good grades, and good test scores. Children need approval by parents, teachers, and peers. In the case of one child, a simple marking device was causing frustration because back of it was pressure from some source to make good test scores. (See page 229.) The classroom teacher can do much to remove pressure.

Roosevelt said, "The only thing the American people have to fear is fear." Perhaps mathematically the only thing our children have to fear is fear. We can remove that fear and prevent it in the future by relieving pressure and restoring the confidence of our children in themselves and their ability to succeed. We can demonstrate our sympathetic understanding by giving help and encouragement.

CONCLUSIONS

1. The arithmetic clinic was the author's most satisfactory experience with both teachers and students.

Perhaps a feeling of satisfaction should not be the main objective. However, if the two main objectives, to discover the cause and possible cure of the arithmetic ills of children and to train teachers in techniques of prevention and cure, were reached, a feeling of satisfaction is justified.

2. It pointed up some neglected techniques in remedial work in arithmetic.

No longer should we be guilty of the "shot-in-the-arm" procedure, the rule and drill technique. Real remedial work involves starting at the beginning, working with concrete objects and leading through pupil-discovery to abstractions.

3. It is a valuable instrument for public relations.

The expressed desire to have the clinic repeated, the frequent telephone calls inquiring about future clinics, the note of sympathy from adults for these youngsters because they too have had similar experiences, the expressions of appreciation from the parents, all emphasized the public relations angle. Here again this is not an aim in and of itself but it is indicative of its value to the children and their parents.

4. It is a superior instrument for inservice training for teachers.

In the last analysis remedial teaching is simply correct teaching, teaching which begins at the child's level and aims toward the highest level of accomplishment of which he is capable. Clinics should continue but clinical procedures should become a technique of the regular classroom and with a growing emphasis upon prevention.

CASE HISTORIES

I

K. was 13½ years of age, a seventh-grader and small for her age. She was emotionally disturbed and was much more concerned about being liked by her peers than about her arithmetic. She had had eye trouble which the mother, at the first interview, suggested might be the cause of her problem. Her nervousness was indicated by biting fingernails and pencil tapping. Her attention span was very short. The physician's opinion was that her eye condition might contribute to her nervousness but not seriously. K., herself, did not mention her eye difficulty.

In a class discussion concerning tests, K. remarked that "the teacher marks with a red pencil the problems we don't have time to finish." Her difficulty with arithmetic seemed to have started about two years before (perhaps with a "red-penciled" test). She constantly refused to work with concrete objects; the reason for this was undetermined. She was extremely upset over the test.

At the second interview, the mother volunteered the information that the father excelled in mathematics, that he insisted that K. bring her arithmetic work home for help, and that the helping session ended with loss of patience and shouting. The clinic teacher recommended that all of K.'s arithmetic work be done at school.

K. made little gain during the clinic, but in the questionnaire she reported favorably on all the questions. Her teachers report that her social adjustment is much improved, her arithmetic only moderately.

II

M. was 14 years of age and an eighth-grader. He was the champion speller in his school. His IQ was 114 and the Chicago Non-Verbal Test bore this out. His achievement scores on the Metropolitan test in May were: Reading, 11.0; Spelling, 11.3; Language, 8.8; and Arithmetic, 5.9.

In the initial interview with the mother she emphasized the fact that none of the family could ever do arithmetic. At the first session with his teacher his only reply to "What do you want help with?" was "I don't know." He was extremely nervous. After some group work he finally expressed a desire to do subtraction with borrowing; this was done using dollars, dimes and pennies to represent hundreds, tens, and ones. He soon voluntarily stopped using the money to work subtraction problems and wanted to do some division problems with the money. At the time of the final test he asked permission to use concrete objects. His score on this test was 6.2, a growth of three months.

M. was succeeding and gaining confidence but was still insecure as evidenced by his remark: "Algebra might not be too hard. I will have to wait until fall to see whether I have learned anything at the clinic."

M.'s success in high-school mathematics has not indicated that he gained much at the clinic. Frequent absence during the year has retarded his learning, but his teacher reports that he is becoming "more willing to participate in class activities."

III

J. was 12 years of age and in the seventh grade. She has a medically diagnosed brain injury and in addition has other problems which have upset her emotionally. Her attention span was short, particularly when working in a group. When she began to make mistakes in a process, it was necessary to change the type of the problem. J. had been given no aids to help make a process easier and to clarify her thinking. She welcomed the use of objects. She was given techniques to compensate for her short attention span.

According to authorities, the brain-injured child is usually highly active, distractible, erratic, and unable to concentrate. Ineffectiveness in arithmetic in these children is common. They can be helped to live with themselves and can frequently take their place in the world. Behavior problems seem to lessen as they are less dominated by adults.

J.'s growth in arithmetic was not great at the clinic but she is steadily improving and is now achieving at almost normal standards in arithmetic computation.

J.'s case is included in this report to emphasize the necessity for parents and teachers to be aware of an entire picture, whatever the elements of that picture may be. J.'s brain injury was discovered only comparatively recently; but in this short time through the co-operation of parents and school people she has shown great improvement.

IV

T. was 13 years of age and in the sixth grade. She was deaf and unable to read lips readily. A hearing aid helped to some extent.

Her IQ was listed as 84 but in the Chicago Non-Verbal Test she rated at the 66th percentile. Her arithmetic training had been purely memorization and computation by rule. It was therefore necessary to reorient her thinking in mathematics completely and build the fundamental basic concepts on the primary level.

Because of this change of approach she lost ground during the clinic, if test scores are an indication. However, during the school year, with some outside help from her clinic teacher, she has improved. She is up to seventh-grade level in arithmetic and achievement, a growth of three years, and is taking her place with the hearing children without any difficulty.

T.'s case is included to show that through the use of concrete materials an adequate mathematical vocabulary and ability to compute are easily developed.

V

L. is an attractive 12-year-old seventh-grader who came to the clinic because his mother wanted to send him. He felt that it spoiled "his whole day." He (and his mother) blamed his arithmetic trouble on a long absence with no help from the teacher when he returned. He had been called "dumb" in arithmetic by others and had tried to live up to that reputation. His reactions to arithmetic and his resistance to it were expressed as follows. "I just hate arithmetic. If I like it I can do well. Sometimes I can't make myself like it. I had to do well in my achievement test so I made myself like it."

During the two weeks at the clinic, with somewhat irregular effort he advanced from 7.0 to 9.8. By September he had dropped back to 8.2. He requested that he be put in the class of a teacher who would make him work. During the year he has overcome his many careless habits, has become a reliable citizen of the school and in the April 1953, test rated 11.1. His mother said, "he tells us it is fun to be able to understand what the teacher is saying and be able to do the same work the other students do."

L. lacked confidence, perhaps due to pressure from home and from his peers. He is now able to stand on his own feet and to withstand that pressure.

Developmental Mathematics in New York City

LAURA K. EADS

THE current elementary-school mathematics program in New York City may be characterized as experimental and developmental. This program has been developing on an experimental basis for a quarter century or more. During these years, leaders in education concerned with curriculum, research, child development, and arithmetic have had a marked influence on the program. Such leaders include nationwide experts, as well as educators within the city school system.

In the 1920's, experimentation in New York City dealt mainly with diagnostic and remedial procedures (20). In the early 1930's an experimental program of meaningful arithmetic was developed in the primary grades of a few schools (2, 3). The results of this experimentation, although admittedly effective in the schools participating, did not become widespread at the time since methods in arithmetic currently in use throughout the country, as well as available teaching and learning materials, were based on a drill-type program rather than on a program emphasizing meaning in arithmetic. Remedial arithmetic materials (4, 5) were developed and used experimentally throughout the city from the middle 1930's through the early 1940's. Arithmetic continued, however, to be an area of discussion and dissatisfaction in the city. As the number and percentage of children entering junior and senior high schools increased, the need for reevaluating the curriculum in arithmetic became progressively more urgent.

CURRICULUM RESEARCH

One of the earliest comprehensive curriculum research projects was a study of intellectually gifted children. This study was initiated in 1940 and involved a number of schools and various types of class organizations. During the years of the study, curriculum adaptations for gifted children were greatest in the areas of art, science, social studies, reading, and creative writing, and least in the area of arithmetic. When the gifted children were asked to suggest the curriculum changes they would like, there were children in every group who stated that they wished they could understand what they were doing in arithmetic. It was suggested that, perhaps, these children were expressing a need for a program of meaningful arithmetic, not only for gifted children but for children of all levels of ability.

During the school year 1944–45 an exploratory study of children's concepts in arithmetic was made in one elementary school. This study indicated a need for an official statement with respect to meaningful arithmetic. In 1945 such a statement (11) was adopted and in 1947 a more definitive statement (12) was prepared. These statements were a synthesis of research and thinking in child development and elementary mathematics. Their official acceptance made it possible to plan and to initiate an experimental research program in developmental mathematics in the elementary schools of New York City.

Since September 1947, a long-term experimental study of children's concepts and learning in arithmetic has been in progress. This study has involved the co-operative efforts of supervisors, teachers, children, and parents. Supervisors and resource persons in the city and throughout the country have helped in evaluating procedures and materials. During the first year of the study (1947–48), experimental classes in Grades I–IV were involved. The experimental program was gradually extended to include higher grades, and a city-wide curriculum program was implemented in lower grades. During the year 1953–54 children in

Grades VI–VII are being studied experimentally, while children in Grades I–VI are involved in the city-wide developmental mathematics program. Curriculum adaptations are made co-operatively sometimes "on-the-spot" in the classrooms. During the early days in the experimental classes it became evident that children were using mathematical terms without adequate meaning. When children were asked to "tell it another way," or to "explain what she (another child) said," or to "show it with pennies," they became confused, or gave meaningless or erroneous explanations.

As experimentation proceeded, it became necessary not only to rethink the content of the mathematics to be taught but to consider also principles upon which the teaching and learning of young children should be based. Principles which have been accepted as basic to the New York City program of developmental mathematics were developed by teachers and supervisors in the city (13). Among these are the following:

1. The mathematics is derived from children's experiences. A teacher who gives children opportunities to engage in worth-while experiences in school is helping children build a background for the development of mathematical concepts and understanding. Even more, perhaps, children are helped in their personal-social adjustments if they are given opportunities to live the things they learn in school.

2. Concrete materials are used to represent mathematical ideas and relationships. Such materials include the actual materials of children's experiences, as well as materials such as beads in rows of 10, discs, dimes and pennies, squared material, fraction material, and such things. Children use materials to discover mathematical relationships. They use them also to see mathematical principles and to derive mathematical generalizations.

3. Thinking, rather than imitative, repetitive learning is emphasized. Children are given time and opportunity to arrive at solutions in independent ways and to solve problems in a variety of ways, before standard and short-cut algorisms are presented and developed. Children are helped in the making of estimations. Children are encouraged to apply mathematical principles and generalizations to the learning of new concepts, facts, or processes. Drill on number facts is based on number relationships. For example, doubles and near-doubles may be developed in one drill period as: $6 + 6, 6 + 5, 5 + 6, 7 + 6, 6 + 7$. Other relationships may be emphasized at other times. Automatic response to number facts is interpreted as a final step in seeing relationships more and more rapidly.

4. The mathematical meaning of numbers and processes is emphasized. Children learn the structure of our number system. They use their understanding of this structure to develop processes with whole numbers and with fractions and decimals. They learn to see the relationship of one aspect of mathematics to another, as, for example: counting and addition, addition and multiplication, multiplication and division, divisions and fractions, and the like. Children build on earlier steps in the mathematical structure as more advanced steps are developed. Thus mathematics is developed sequentially more or less in accordance with the structure of our number system.

5. Concepts and topics in mathematics are developed for a long period of time after their initial introduction. This provides for the gradual growth of young children. It provides also for the wide differences to be found in any class. Less mature children, for example, may be given opportunity to deal primarily with experiences and with concrete materials while the more mature children in the class may be doing thinking without reference to material or may be developing skill in computation. This program provides for developing specific mathematical concepts on more and more mature levels, and for the maintenance of skills already developed.

Procedures for studying children's thinking, concepts, and achievement were varied. Among these are the following:

Children of various levels of ability were studied individually, in small groups, and in class groups. They were observed and questioned as they engaged in experiences, as they worked with concrete materials, and as they solved mathematical problems.

Teachers kept records of children's explanations as they thought out mathematical solutions. Teachers used these records for discussion in conference with other teachers and supervisors.

Teaching and test devices were devised, tried out, and discussed in conference.

Procedures for making various aspects of arithmetic more meaningful to children were discussed in conference, tried out, and evaluated.

Sequences for developing specific topics in arithmetic were developed, evaluated, and revised.

Teaching plans were developed and discussed in conference.

Teaching materials were tried out, evaluated, and adapted for use with children at various levels of ability.

Standardized tests were administered periodically, item analyses were made, individual children were asked to explain their responses, teachers and supervisors discussed results, and curriculum sequences and teaching procedures were adjusted.

Conferences with parents and resource persons were held, evaluations of materials and procedures were elicited, and curriculum adaptations were suggested.

Curriculum materials were prepared, tried out, discussed in conference, and revised.

Teachers were observed as they worked with children; problems were discussed in conference with these and other teachers and supervisors; and teacher training materials were prepared, tried out, and evaluated.

IMPLEMENTING THE PROGRAM

The developmental mathematics program is being implemented one year at a time. All Grade I classes in the city were involved during 1948–49; all Grade VI classes in 1953–54. Developmental Mathematics teachers have been assigned to the program to help in the orientation of classroom teachers of the particular grade being implemented each year, and to continue assisting teachers in earlier grades. Procedures for helping teachers include: in-school and after-school conferences, workshops, classroom demonstrations, exhibits, inservice courses, and district conferences organized by local assistant superintendents.

Conferences and seminars with New York City supervisors, and with instructors and professors who are responsible for teacher training in colleges in the metropolitan area have been held. The developmental mathematics program, including curriculum materials which are being developed experimentally, is being continuously evaluated by New York City teachers and supervisors, and by the college instructors and professors.

As the program progressed through the grades, it became apparent that if developmental mathematics was to be adequately implemented teachers and supervisors needed to learn:

1. Principles of mathematics, including the structure of the number system, and the application of these to methods of computing.

2. How to plan for classroom and school experiences, and how to develop the mathematics derived from such experiences sequentially.

3. How to devise materials and procedures which would help children develop mathematical understanding and skill, and how to use existing materials in line with the developmental mathematics program.

4. How to give children opportunities to think through mathematical relationships and to derive mathematical principles and generalizations, under classroom conditions.

5. How to provide for the optimum mathematical growth of children at various levels of ability.

6. How to appraise mathematical understanding.

APPRAISAL IN DEVELOPMENTAL MATHEMATICS

Because of the emphasis on understanding and thinking in the developmental mathematics program, it is necessary to use instruments which measure growth and ability in these aspects, as well as those which measure skill in computation and problem-solving. Inventories (7) geared to the philosophy of the elementary-mathematics program are, therefore, being prepared for use in the New York City schools.

PARTICIPATION OF SCHOOL STAFF IN DEVELOPING PROGRAM

The developmental mathematics program has enlisted the efforts and support of hundreds of teachers and supervisors in the experimental phases. The enthusiasm and contributions made by these people have made possible a widespread program of implementation, involving the participation of approximately 20,000 teachers and supervisors.

This program has the attention of the major professional groups of the city, particularly those concerned with mathematics and curriculum development. Among such groups are: Association of Assistants to Principal, Association of Teachers of Mathematics in New York City, Curriculum Committees in Districts and Schools, Elementary School Curriculum Planning Committee, High School Standing Committee in Mathematics, Junior High School Curriculum Planning Committee, Junior High School Mathematics Curriculum Committee, Chairmen's Association of New York City, and New York Society for the Experimental Study of Education.

On the administrative level, significant contributions have been made by: Associate Superintendents Beaumont and Huggard, Assistant Superintendent Arthur Hughson, and Directors Bristow (Bureau of Curriculum Research) and Wrightstone (Bureau of Educational Research).

Inservice Education for Teachers
of Mathematics
Institutes—Workshops—Conferences

KENNETH BROWN

"THERE must be a simple and pleasant way to study mathematics," mused Professor Rankin as he wearily removed his spectacles. For many years W. W. Rankin had taught teachers better methods of teaching mathematics. "Why can't mathematics be studied in an informal way? Why can't it be fun?" he thought.

His trend of thought was broken by the sound of the bell that signaled the change of classes and the beginning of the lunch hour. The teachers handed in their final examination papers in "The Teaching of Mathematics." "I enjoyed the course this summer," a teacher of many years experience said, but the expression of her face as she shyly slipped her examination paper underneath the pile indicated relief that the course was over.

As Professor Rankin ate his lunch he said to himself, "Why don't teachers and pupils enjoy mathematics just as I am enjoying this lunch? Why shouldn't mathematics be palatable? That's it! It should be made palatable, and I believe it can be."

As Professor Rankin planned for the next summer session, he said, "This summer will be different."

Next summer did bring the teachers that studied ways of teaching mathematics a different experience.

On their first day of the summer session they did not take notes on a formal lecture. No, it could hardly be called a class. The teachers discussed practical problems in secondary mathematics whose solution required a knowledge of geometry and algebra. E. T. Browne contributed some problems from business, Professors Barton and Dessel suggested applications of mathematics in science and industry.

"Those applications from industry are just what I need," commented Miss Heddy during the discussion period. "You know," said Mrs. Harold, "I planned to look in some industrial magazines for some practical problems but with housekeeping and all I just didn't have time."

During the day the teachers visited the mathematics laboratory. They lingered in the little nook that contained the latest textbooks and in front of the machines and models from industry that showed mathematics at work.

The first day's session did not close at 4 o'clock. At 6:30 the discussions were only partially interrupted by an informal dinner. Even during the meal of Southern-fried chicken some conversations were of pupils and their problems in understanding mathematics.

Before everyone had completed eating the dessert, Colonel Crist began an after dinner speech on "Mathematics of Artillery Fire." The U. S. Army had provided a display of artillery which included several large searchlights that were placed near the building. The silvery beams of light tracing geometric designs on the dark sky were a stimulating setting for the discussion which followed the lecture.

The first day closed with a social hour; more of a "get-acquainted party." Everyone seemed to have a good time. Mrs. Rankin lingered near the door and greeted the late arrivals with a smile that melted any remaining icicles of formality. Professor Rankin just mingled with the teachers. It seemed only a few minutes until Miss Howard said, "Why, it is 11 o'clock! If I am awake in the morning to see Miss Stokes make mathematical models, we should get some sleep." Everyone seemed to agree. Miss Heddy, who was the last one to leave, grasped Professor Rankin's hand and said, "It has been a wonderful day!" Then she hurried to overtake her friends. As Professor Rankin slowly closed the door, his wife said with an understanding smile, "Perhaps you have found a simple and pleasant way to study mathematics." Thus the mathematics institute was born.

The present mathematics institutes have the original objective of providing a situation where teachers can work on their own problems in teaching mathematics and enjoy it. Some of the objectives in recent announcements of mathematics institutes are: To provide an opportunity for elementary, high-school, and college teachers of mathematics to meet together for a discussion of mutual problems and a free exchange of ideas; to increase professional spirit and widen horizons; to give enthusiasm and inspiration by contacts with other teachers in the field; and to share ideas of methods and materials used in teaching mathematics.

Thus the realization of the far-reaching objectives seems to lie in what happens to the participants and not in reports or accumulation of information.

Such values can only be realized through the involvement of the teachers in group processes of problem-solving in mathematics education. The first day's activities in the present mathematics institute usually consist of a get-acquainted hour and informal discussions of the problems in mathematics education that seem vital to the participants. Small discussion or work groups are formed of teachers with mutual teaching problems. The small groups contribute to the entire institute through reports, exhibits, and roundtable discussions at general meetings. A specialist from industry usually makes a contribution each day by a lecture on the uses of mathematics in his industry. With this exception, the activities are planned and carried out by the teachers. These activities may include the construction of models, teaching guides, and resource units, preview of films, review of recent textbooks, methods of presenting certain topics in mathematics, and field trips to local industrial plants to see modern applications of mathematics in technology.

The evaluation of the institute does not emphasize the appraisal of the individual. The evaluation is of the groups and the entire institute. This includes the opinions of the participants, the reports of the work or discussion groups, and in many cases a final report which is made available to other teachers.

Perhaps a summary of the distinguishing features of a mathematics institute would include: (a) periods of social activities for recreation and fellowship; (b) organized small groups for studying problems of mutual interest; (c) lectures by specialists in business and industry presenting the applications of mathematics to their particular areas; (d) field trips to industrial plants that show applications of mathematics; (e) an emphasis on enrichment and applications of mathematics rather than the study of the manipulative processes in mathematics; (f) the encouragement of the participants to take an active part in the plans and work of the institute; (g) an exhibit of recent textbooks and films; (h) a mathematics laboratory where aids to teaching are exhibited and instruction in constructing models and aids is provided; (i) the provision of visiting consultants; (j) an absence of marks or collegiate credit; (k) evaluation of the institute by a critique or a report and the absence of an individual examination; and (l) a session of one to two weeks.

In addition to mathematics institutes, groups of teachers have continued their inservice education in workshops and conferences. The objectives of the workshop and conference are usually those of the institute. The procedures are, in some cases, similar to those described for the institute; however, there is usually a difference.

The workshop places less emphasis on the applications of mathematics in industry; college credit and marks are given; tuition is required; and the session is usually three to eight weeks.

The conference seldom provides field trips or a mathematics laboratory; the fee is small; and the session is less than one week. Although these differences usually exist, there are no sharp lines of demarcation between workshops, institutes, and conferences. All have been of great service to mathematics teachers. Evidence of their worth is indicated by the many letters and comments from the participants, the master's and doctoral studies that have emerged, the publications that have been prepared, and the effect upon courses of study. Perhaps even greater evidence of their value is the growth of this type of inservice education for teachers of mathematics. Attendance has included teachers from every state and several foreign countries; the number attending has varied from 50 to several hundred.

Issues of *The Mathematics Teacher* in the past two years have contained announcements of institutes, workshops, and conferences at the following institutions:

INSTITUTES

Colby College, Waterville, Maine. The Institute in New England is
    held at various institutions—Wellesley College (1949); Tufts College
    (1950); Connecticut College for Women (1951); The Phillips Exeter
    Academy (1952); and Colby College (1953). It is sponsored by The
    Association of Teachers of Mathematics in New England
Duke University, Durham, North Carolina

Louisiana State University, Baton Rouge
Rutgers University, New Brunswick, New Jersey
University of Houston, Houston, Texas
University of Michigan, Ann Arbor
University of Virginia, Charlottesville.

WORKSHOPS

Eastern Oregon College of Education, La Grande
Indiana University, Bloomington
Kent State University, Kent, Ohio
Northwestern University, Evanston, Illinois
Ohio State University, Columbus
Teachers College, Columbia University, New York City
University of Arkansas, Fayetteville
University of Colorado, Boulder.

CONFERENCES

Capital University, Columbus, Ohio. Sponsored by the Ohio Council of
    Teachers of Mathematics
Illinois State Normal University, Normal
St. Mary's Lake Camp, Battle Creek, Michigan. Sponsored by Michigan
    Council of Teachers of Mathematics
University of California at Los Angeles, Los Angeles
University of Wisconsin, Madison
Western Illinois State College, Macomb.

The following is typical of the daily program of a mathematics
institute:

AUGUST 7, MONDAY

7:45–10:00—Study Groups
  1. Problems in the junior high school.
     This group will consider methods and devices for making word
     problems more meaningful to the pupils.
  2. Skills in the senior high school.
     How can the skills in mathematics be maintained? How much time
     should be spent about mathematics rather than on mathematics?
     These and other questions of concern to the group will be discussed.
  3. Developing resource units in general mathematics.
     Resource material for such topics as money management, taxes,
     and applications of percentage will be developed. A specialist in
     this area will suggest sources of material and assist teachers in
     developing units as requested by the teachers.

4. Thinking in life situations.

In this group, the teachers of geometry will consider the applications of deductive proof and experimental proof. The theorems
that are used extensively in industry will be discussed.

10:00–10:30—Social Period

Tea, games, or relaxation.

10:30–11:45

Mathematics in Medicine—lecture by R. T. Jones, St. Luke's Hospital.
After Dr. Jones' presentation of applications of mathematics in
medicine, opportunity will be given for questions and discussion.

12:00–1:45—Luncheon

"One Thing That I Did To Motivate the Study of Mathematics."
Three members of the institute will speak five minutes on this
topic. There will be time for questions.

2:00–4:00 P.M.—Laboratory Groups

1. Aids in the study of general mathematics.

Models and instruments will be constructed that will aid in more
effective teaching. Their proper use will be discussed.

2. Experiments in algebra.

Experiments will be presented which use mathematical principles
in algebra. Teachers will take part in constructing the equipment
from inexpensive material.

3. Visual aids in the senior high school.

The construction of inexpensive aids for teaching solid geometry
will be emphasized.

4. Skills in mathematics.

Devices that motivate drill and emphasize the meaning of the
process will be constructed. Devices for remedial teaching will be
discussed.

4:00–5:00

1. Preview of films on the teaching of algebra.

2. Recent textbooks on general mathematics will be on the exhibit
table.

3. Mathematics laboratories will be open with a consultant for special
work.

4. Planning committee meeting.

7:00–9:00—Dinner

Lecture—"How We Can Evaluate Growth in Mathematical Concepts" by A. L. Smith. After the lecture the planning committee
of the institute will suggest procedures for compiling a report of
the institute for the help of other teachers.

Emerging Practices in Mathematics in Bethlehem, Pennsylvania

RUTH W. OVERFIELD

DURING the 1947–48 school year a consultant was appointed[5] to aid in a revision of the mathematics curriculum in the Bethlehem School District. The administration and faculty sensed a need to reexamine the present college preparatory courses and to write syllabi for these subjects. In order to make this revision, it was felt essential first to make a survey of the background and the needs of the students.

Since Bethlehem is located in an industrial center and an education center, most students must be trained either to meet the demands of our industries for skilled labor or to enter one of the many institutions of higher learning in this vicinity. Through a survey it was revealed that about 33 per cent of the students planned to continue their education beyond high school as compared with 11 per cent of the parents who had had college educations. This information raised the serious problem of the type of mathematics which should be provided for the other 67 per cent not continuing their school education.

The answer to our problem was a two-track program. This was in addition to the courses offered in the vocational department of the high school where students were being trained for various trades. The name which was given to the new track was High School Mathematics for Grades X, XI, and XII. Since September, 1948 to the present time studies have been made concerning this new program—studies of the contents of these courses, textbooks to be used, current material written on the subject, reports of progress in other schools, methods of teaching and evaluating the new courses, guidance of students into the proper track, the reports of the commissions, guidance pamphlets, and other such studies.

High School Mathematics 10, 11, and 12 courses were made available for three years before final courses of study were written. There were many misconceptions, disappointments, and dissatis-

---

[5] Howard F. Fehr, Teachers College, Columbia University.

factions in the initial stages of the program. At first the contents of high-school mathematics was a *diluted* course in plane geometry, and high-school Mathematics 11 was a *watered* intermediate algebra course. Some of the teachers were of the opinion that it was better to keep a student in the college preparatory class, even if he failed, than to place him in the new track, because in the end he would know more mathematics. If this were true, there was something wrong with our program. It was not that there was no need for this program since it was an established fact that there was a large group of students who did not elect the sequential courses and were maladjusted if they did.

The real difficulty was that the contents of the new courses were not meeting the needs of the students. The college preparatory classes were far superior in contents studied and methods of instruction used, and this situation was given as the main reason why students, who should have been in the new courses would get more from the traditional courses. The basic need for all students in mathematics regardless of which track he follows is *to develop the individual's mathematical competence.* It is with this general need of students in mind that the courses in high school mathematics have been developed—courses on the same high educational plane as algebra, geometry, trigonometry, and such subjects.

A few other factors considered in developing the high-school mathematics courses were as follows: teachers must be *sold* on the course first; standards do not have to be low in these classes; proper guidance should be an aid in selecting these courses; the teacher must have broad experience, be sympathetic, be a practical psychologist, and be intensely interested in the subject and be prepared to work long hours gathering and assembling material; the number of high-school mathematics classes should be divided equally among the teachers; courses should be mathematically sound in their contents.

A central theme for each year seemed desirable for purposes of motivation. These were the same as stressed by the state of Pennsylvania course of study (14) in mathematics:

Grade X—High School Mathematics 10—the worker
Grade XI—High School Mathematics 11—the citizen
Grade XII—High School Mathematics 12—the consumer

The general needs of students concerning their social, economic, psychological, and cultural life were the same for the new track as those for the college preparatory courses. The general objectives of the three-year program were to compare favorably with the list prepared by the Commission on Post-War Plans of the National Council of Teachers of Mathematics and published in the November 1947 issue of *The Mathematics Teacher*.

As E. R. Breslich (10) has stated, although mathematical needs vary with individuals, schools, and school systems there exists a body of mathematical concepts, principles, and skills important to all vocations, necessary for intelligent citizenship, useful to all persons, and helpful in solving quantitative problems encountered in everyday life. This is also true about the type of courses to be included in our program. Although our general courses will differ from those of other schools because of the local situation, there are some basic ideas which prevail in all programs. These ideas are embraced in the topics: (a) arithmetic, (b) geometry, (c) algebra, (d) statistics, (e) graphical representation, and (f) numerical trigonometry. It is around these topics that the high-school mathematics courses for Grades X, XI, and XII have been planned.

After the general objectives and six basic topics to be included in the three-year program were agreed upon, the contents for each year were selected as follows:

High School Mathematics 10—Basic Arithmetic
                        Basic Algebra
                        Basic Geometry
High School Mathematics 11—Basic Arithmetic
                        Basic Algebra
                        Basic Geometry
High School Mathematics 12—Consumer Mathematics

The tenth and eleventh years appear to be exactly the same in content but there is a difference. In the tenth year the algebra which is to be taught does not include work beyond the linear equation; but in the eleventh year, algebra is continued to the quadratic equation. Geometry in the tenth year is to cover plane figures and areas, but in the eleventh year solid figures and volumes are included. Basic arithmetic for senior high school will be remedial in nature and will be taught on an individual basis throughout all three years.

In order to understand the difference between the tenth and eleventh year courses, an outline of these two programs follows:

High School Mathematics 10

1. Remedial Arithmetic
   addition
   subtraction
   multiplication
   division
   per cent
2. Basic Algebra
   formulas
   literal numbers
   signed numbers
   exponents, radicals
   linear equation
3. Basic Geometry
   plane geometric figures
   areas and perimeters
   constructions
   ratio, proportion
   metric measure
   experimental geometry
   indirect measurement—rule of
      of Pythagoras

5. Optional Topics
   air navigation
   travel—maps
   money exchange
   time zones
   consumer mathematics
   applications to vocational
      trades

High School Mathematics 11

1. Review of
   whole numbers
   decimals
   fractions
2. Basic Algebra
   formulas
   literal numbers
   signed numbers
   exponents, radicals
   linear equation
   quadratic equation
3. Basic Geometry
   plane geometric figures
   solid geometric figures
   areas and perimeters
   volumes
   constructions
   ratio, proportion, variation
   scale drawings
   concept of proof and how to
      use it
   trigonometry—similar trian-
      gles and trigonometric
      functions
4. Statistics
   collection of data
   graphs
   average, mean,
      median, mode
5. Optional Topics
   magnetic compass
   reading a micrometer
   tolerance
   areas of irregular figures
   consumer mathematics

Those topics which are identical for each grade are to be approached through the themes which have been suggested in the Pennsylvania state plan. Problems in the tenth year would stress the worker and in the eleventh year the citizen. For example, the study of graphs in Grade X will include material on occupations, such as graphing salaries, numbers employed in various occupations, graphs needed in occupations such as the nurse, the weatherman, the storeman, and such persons. In the eleventh year graphs will be centered around the citizen, such as graphing the results of a community chest drive, graphs of social agencies, graphs of elections, and other community activities.

The High School Mathematics 12 consisted of consumer mathematics. The last year of high school was the logical place to study banking, savings, investments, budgets, mortgages, installment buying, and taxes. Many students who terminate their college preparatory mathematics in the eleventh year will find this course beneficial.

There are other topics which will be studied by some students in the two-track program but the six which have been listed are the ones which are essential for all the pupils. The methods of teaching these classes would vary with classes and individuals. Several points would be kept clearly in mind in instructing these students. One point is that the pupil must acquire an understanding of mathematical concepts and principles, not a tendency to work mechanically by rules. Meanings must grow out of repeated concrete experiences provided in the teaching.

Another point to be considered was that good teaching methods can be incorporated if the topics start with the interest of the pupil. This will make the subject meaningful. The understanding of the thing learned both increases the opportunity for recall and at the same time strengthens the significance of that which is being learned. The result will help the student to acquire attitudes favorable to learning.

Not only should the interests of the pupil be considered but also what the teacher wishes to teach. That which should be taught in high-school mathematics classes has been listed previously under six major topics, arithmetic, geometry, algebra, statistics, graphical representation, and numerical trigonometry. In addition to these, there will be other areas of study which interest various groups or individuals. Since this was true, the outlines of the courses of study for each grade level were purely outlines of the essential materials to be covered in each group with ample time provided to extend the teaching in any topic or include an additional topic as needed or desired. The activities and approaches to units of study will also vary with groups and therefore mere suggestions are found in outlines above so that the development could be flexible.

Remedial arithmetic is an essential topic for the senior high-school level. Students entering the high school have often acquired faulty habits very detrimental to future mathematical progress. Undoubtedly many of these habits could be prevented by the right kind of teaching in the earlier grades. There is nothing to do for the high-school teacher but to trace these disabilities to their sources, and to reteach or teach for the first time these fundamental processes. This mis-learning or no learning will be found in these 10 common errors: lack of number concept, errors in reading numbers, difficulties in the proper formation of numbers, errors in number combinations of the four fundamental processes, zero difficulties in all operations, errors in addition, errors in subtraction, errors in multiplication, errors in division, and difficulties in thought problems.

These errors are easier to correct than psychological disturbances, but it is also a slow and concrete process. Here is an outline of a technique which is suggested for the senior high school:

I. Locating the difficulty
   A. Use of diagnostic tests—both teacher-made and standardized tests
   B. Oral interviews—doing the examples aloud
   C. Use of mental mathematics—solving a problem by the student's own methods
II. Locating the cause of the difficulty
   A. Lack of fundamental concepts and skills
   B. Mis-learned facts and concepts—false knowledge
   C. Lack of readiness—low ability—slow learning
   D. Unfavorable attitude
   E. Unfavorable social and economic conditions
III. Reteaching and/or new teaching
   A. Starting from scratch

    B. Using primary concepts with concrete material
    C. Building concepts—using various situations
    D. Relating principles learned to some structure
    E. Practicing the principle.

This technique is used on an individual basis and the class period used largely as a laboratory or work period.

Another point considered in organizing the double-track program was the amount of credit these courses would receive. Each grade level of high-school mathematics will receive one full Carnegie unit toward graduation, since it is a full year course for five days a week with outside preparation required. Some institutions of higher learning will give entrance credits and some will not—it depends on the institution and the course to be pursued. It is the desire to have all places of higher learning give entrance credit for these courses if mathematics is not a basic requirement in the field of study to be taken (this would not include such courses as engineering, chemistry, and physics). A suggested amount of entrance credit is two units for a four-year sequence of high-school mathematics.

Another question to be settled was how a student should be guided into selecting the proper track in mathematics. Proper guidance for selecting the proper course is obtained through the guidance counselors, the pupil's mathematics teachers, and the student himself. The student is fully informed as to the difference in the courses in the two tracks. He should realize that if he is slow in mathematics, or does not need or desire the college preparatory courses, he should select high-school mathematics. By the twelfth year many do not desire a course beyond Algebra 2; they should be encouraged to elect High School Mathematics 12, which consists of consumer problems. Every student should have a class in mathematics on his schedule each year of school, and with the addition of this new type of mathematics, there will be a course offered each year which will meet his individual needs and desires.

As a result of having studied and developed the two-track program in mathematics at Bethlehem High School, some very definite conclusions have been observed. Every teacher in the department is *sold* on the program and thinks the double-track is good and worthwhile. *It has strengthened the college preparatory classes.* The number of high school mathematics classes has increased from a few the first year to two classes of High School Mathematics 10, three classes of High School Mathematics 11, and three classes of High School Mathematics 12 for the 1953–54 school year (there is an average class size of 30). The pupils have accepted the course, and the stigma which had been placed on the student in this course is erased. The contents of the course are sound mathematically, not oversocialized to the point where mathematics is incidental.

One of the major problems, which has not been satisfactorily solved, is the selection of the proper textbook. Since the idea of a 3-year sequential course in general mathematics is of fairly recent origin, there have been few schools prepared to include it in their program. Since a great demand for books was not present, there were not many books from which to make a selection. Of the books which are available, few meet the type of program which was developed at our school.

There should be teacher evaluation of this new program. This has to be done by periodic written reports on the good and bad points of the program and any suggested additional material. These reports are written at the conclusion of each unit. An example of the form to be used in Bethlehem is:

1. Name of the unit
2. Date started
3. Date completed
4. Favorable criticism of unit
5. Unfavorable criticism of unit

6. Methods or materials used which were found to be
   a. successful
   b. unsuccessful
7. Additional remarks.

When all the teachers who are teaching the same course have completed a written report on a unit, a discussion meeting follows and recommendations are made to improve it for the next year. In evaluating a unit, the teacher considers pupils' opinions as well as his own. It is through experimentation, study, and discussion that the best possible high-school mathematics program which meets our own situation, can be developed.

Professional Classes of the Seattle Public Schools

Elizabeth J. Roudebush

Since 1928 the Seattle Public Schools have offered professional courses as part of the Inservice Training Program. Each course is planned to meet a need for the teacher who participates. Some of the courses emphasize subject matter that teachers have not acquired. Other courses are devoted entirely to problems of classroom teaching. All areas of the curriculum are represented in the program of the professional classes at some time. The administration of the program is under the Director of Adult Education. Each director of a subject matter area works with the Director of Adult Education in planning the courses to be offered in his field.

A teacher who completes a professional course receives one or two professional credits. A course that meets for eight sessions of one and one-half hours or six sessions of two hours offers one professional credit. Classes from 7:00 to 9:00 p.m. as well as Saturday morning classes have been tried but the most popular class time is from 4:00 to 5:30 p.m. once a week. Occasionally a course meets for 12 sessions of two hours and offers two professional credits. The credits earned in professional courses may be used for advancement on the salary scale. The professional credit is considered equivalent to one credit from a college or university. The Seattle salary scale has three classifications above a bachelor's degree. The first step above the bachelor's degree is a master's degree or its equivalent. A teacher with such preparation receives an extra $100 per year. The second step is the master's degree or its equivalent plus 15 quarter hours and means another $100 per year to the teacher. The third step on the salary scale is the master's degree or its equivalent plus 30 quarter hours which gives the third $100 per year to the teacher. All teachers in Seattle receive an annual increment of $150 until the maximum salary is reached. Each classification has a different maximum.

A teacher enrolled in a professional class earns professional credit by meeting two requirements. The first requirement is attendance. In classes meeting six or eight times one absence is permissible, while two absences are permitted in classes meeting 12 times. The second requirement for professional credit is performance. Each instructor sets up definite goals of accomplishment for members of his class. The goals vary in different classes and might consist of papers, reports, units of work, projects, acquisition of proficiency in a particular skill or skills, or other evidences of growth. No grades are given in the professional classes. So far it has been possible to offer professional classes for a cost of about one dollar for one credit; however, when instructors from outside the teaching field give the courses the fee is often larger. This low cost is only possible because of state aid for adult education.

Each summer the Curriculum Department of the Seattle Public Schools conducts a workshop for teachers at all levels. The workshop is in session for a week and offers three professional credits. Speakers and consultants from various parts of the United States are brought in for the workshop. In 1952, William A. Brownell of University of California was a headliner. Dr. Brownell gave two addresses on general education philosophy. In addition Dr. Brownell worked as a consultant with a group of teachers that was particularly interested in the teaching of arithmetic. Individuals in the group raised questions for discussion. The suggestions and advice of Dr. Brownell were both practical and helpful.

Although the first group of professional classes in 1928 included a class for teaching arithmetic in the primary grades and another class for teaching arithmetic in the intermediate grades, it was not until 1946 that classes for teachers of secondary-school mathematics began to appear in the program. A class entitled "Use of Engineering and Navigation Instruments in Mathematics Instruction" was offered. The class was received enthusiastically. Although several instruments were discussed briefly, the class thoroughly enjoyed the project of "shooting the sun" with a sextant and the actual surveying problem worked out with transits. The last project was done at two Saturday sessions.

A shop teacher taught a class in "Shop Mathematics for Junior and Senior High School Algebra and Geometry Teachers." The course was given in a shop of one of the high schools. It is difficult to plan such a course to include the active participation of each teacher. Unless the teacher does actively use shop equipment, the course will not be popular. A course in "Algebra and Geometry Used in High School Physics" started with lectures by the instructor; however, the lectures were given too rapidly for the teachers to take notes. At the request of the teachers enrolled, the procedure and locale of the class were changed. The class then met in a physics laboratory and had the opportunity to see and examine the new equipment in use in a high-school physics laboratory. The physics instructor was very skillful in demonstrating basic mathematical principles and the entire class became most enthusiastic as soon as the laboratory equipment was used.

A course in "Approximate Measurement and Computation" proved to be very helpful and unusually popular with the teachers who enrolled. The class was conducted as a real problem course in which the teachers used figures obtained by actual measurement as the basis for computation. At the end of the course some teachers were heard to say, "The only criticism is that it didn't last long enough."

A former executive officer of the Department of Mathematics at the University of Washington is an outstanding student of geometry and he graciously consented to give a course to our teachers entitled "A Cultural Course in Geometry." The eight lectures included such topics as history of geometry, nature of geometric truth, geometric reasoning in everyday life, methods of geometric research, geometric constructions (possible and impossible), geometry of ornamental design, projective and non-Euclidean geometry and their relation to Euclidean metric geometry, and geometry of higher spaces. This mind-stretching course was an intellectual delight to the teachers enrolled in the class.

For the last three years we have offered classes in methods and materials used in teaching mathematics. A class entitled "Teaching of Arithmetic in the Primary Grades," another called "Teaching Arithmetic in the Intermediate Grades," and a third listed as "Teaching Arithmetic in Grades Seven and Eight" have been favorite courses that appear again and again on the list of professional classes. The most recent course we have made available, "Method and Materials for Teaching Algebra and Geometry" was warmly received by the teachers. All of the methods and materials courses show teachers how the proper use of visual material in the classroom improves the children's understanding of the principles of mathematics. Teachers find it helpful to see these materials and to note how easily any teacher can make inexpensive teaching aids. Teachers who took the course "Methods and Materials for Teaching Algebra and Geometry" have requested a laboratory course where some of these aids can be made by individuals in the class. Such a class can be given in any high-school laboratory that has the necessary space.

Over the years there has been a steady growth of teacher interest in our professional classes. Often the teachers themselves suggest the type of classes they believe would be helpful. During the year 1952–53 a total of 2000 teacher enrollments in professional courses were recorded. There were 26 classes offered the first semester and 22 classes the second semester. In many instances the curriculum directors and consultants are the instructors. Members of the faculty of the University of Washington and laymen from the community occasionally act as instructors. Classes that provide an opportunity for the class members to exchange ideas and discuss mutual problems seem to contribute the most to teacher growth.

The experience of participation in a professional class is of particular value to the new teacher in the corps. In addition to learning about methods and materials to use in teaching mathematics, he becomes acquainted with other teachers. He also learns that the more experienced teachers have similar problems to his and they exchange ideas. Teachers who have been in the corps for several years frequently find that working with other teachers in these professional classes is a refreshing experience that helps give new perspective to the vital task of guiding students along the path of mathematics.

Such classes as these seem to us to be of particular value at the present time when mathematics is becoming increasingly important in industry and research. The Seattle Public Schools feel that, in fairness to the pupils, the teachers must have the opportunity to keep abreast of current practices.

Expanding Horizons in Mathematics

NANETTE R. BLACKISTON, EUNICE BOWERS,
GROVER W. NORRIS, AND S. LEROY TAYLOR

THROUGH the years, the department of mathematics in the Baltimore public school system has s. onsored activities and developed programs designed to do thr:e things: encourage the professional growth of teachers, improve the level of instruction in mathematics, and promote curriculum changes which better adjust the offerings to the needs of high-school pupils. In other subject areas similar programs are being conducted.

A Professional Development Comn:ittee was organized a few years ago to co-ordinate the activities in the several areas of instruction and to suggest additional courses for the professional development of teachers. This committee, in turn, organized five subcommittees to study the inservice programs in the following areas: elementary division, secondary division, vocational division, business division, and adult division.

One of the methods used by the subcommittee at the secondary level was to ascertain the desires of teachers by requesting them to submit two lists: one of courses which they felt should be offered and one of courses in which they desired to participate. Of the 49 courses suggested the seven listed below fell directly in the area of mathematics:

1. A content course in mathematics
2. The teaching of geometry in the secondary schools
3. A review of subject matter in various fields
4. Field trips in mathematics
5. The use of mathematical instruments
6. Enrichment in mathematics
7. General mathematics in Grades IX and X.

Since the first three of these requested courses fell within the province of our local universities, it was decided that they—the universities—should be made aware of the teachers' wishes and given an account of the total number of teachers interested in each course.

If we were to meet the other requests these were pertinent questions: Should we go to the expense of inviting resource people? Are there members of our group capable of offering satisfactory courses? What inducements should be offered if such members were found? Who would be responsible for the planning of the course and its continuity?

The idea suggested by the first question was abandoned when a canvass of teachers revealed several with the special interests, abilities, and training to provide stimulating courses in the use of mathematical instruments and in the enrichment of mathematics. Two of these teachers showed a willingness to serve as instructors and, as a result, three courses were organized which were well received by the teachers. Edward H. Schmidt, an instructor at Patterson Park Junior-Senior High School, conducted a course in laboratory mathematics. The success of the course may be indicated by the fact that it was offered over a period of three semesters to care for all who wished to enroll. The instructional devices created and constructed by members of this group were later constructed in miniature by Mr. Schmidt and exhibited at the National Council of Teachers of Mathematics meeting in Pittsburgh and also at the annual meeting of the Maryland State Teachers Association.

Isadore Cohen, instructor of mathematics at Roland Park Junior High School, conducted courses in field mathematics one year and enrichment in mathematics the following year. In the course in field mathematics Mr. Cohen capitalized on his skill as a builder to acquaint the teachers with many novel applications of the more commonly used instruments such as the ruler, compass, tape, and 3-4-5 triangle. The less common instruments such as the transit, slide rule, plane table, sextant, and clinometer were also used. The course in enrichment the following year emphasized enrichment for all pupils at all levels rather than for the gifted pupils only.

These courses resulted in the increased use of laboratory work, a new approach to the various topics of instruction, and a wider use of the instruments which make mathematics more practical for the pupils.

There remained, however, an area as yet untouched—field trips in mathematics. What suggestions could be offered to teachers for conducting successful field trips? What places could be visited profitably? How should the necessary contacts be made? What preparations are necessary prior to the trip? What follow-up work should be done after the trip? The remainder of this article describes a course arranged to answer the above questions.

The June workshop of 1952, "Expanding Horizons in Mathematics," was planned and carried out by a committee consisting of: Nanette R. Blackiston, Eunice Bowers, Grover W. Norris, and S. Leroy Taylor. Long before the close of the school year certain parts of the activity had to be worked out so that deadlines could be met. Decisions about the course requirements, credit to be offered, time and length of meetings, and the general description of the course had to be made in time for the issue of the professional development catalogue which listed summer offerings. For a comprehensive overview and for insight into the general organization consider with us the Planning Activities, Workshop Trips, and Final Evaluation.

PLANNING ACTIVITIES

In preparation for the June workshop many places of business and industry were listed for possible visits. The planning committee discussed thoroughly which ones would offer the greatest number of opportunities for teachers of mathematics to observe the use that was made of mathematics. They finally agreed to select an Investment Banking House, the Custom House, the Airport, and the Bay Bridge which was then under construction.

Since the visits were to be planned for June and since schools would not be in session it was decided to arrange for one visit for each day and to schedule it in the morning.

A description of the workshop was prepared for the catalogue giving the purpose, general plans, time, requirements, and possible visits. Because there was a due date for applications, it was possible to know how many teachers were interested and what levels of teaching they represented before final arrangements and plans were completed.

The person on the planning committee responsible for each visit telephoned and asked permission for the visit on a particular day. At the same time he made an appointment for a personal interview to be held at the place to be visited with the appropriate person who would plan the details of the visit. This personal interview was originally intended to clarify the purpose of the visit, to explain the variety of teaching levels the teachers represented, and to insure that those who spoke to the group would indicate how all types of mathematics from elementary arithmetic through the calculus functioned. It would also give the person responsible for the trip a preview of what would be seen on the visit. Actually it became a co-operative planning enterprise with the hosts making many valuable suggestions that expanded the original plans. The Investment Banking House representative recommended contacting the secretary of the Bond Club of Baltimore who arranged for smaller groups to visit five Investment Banking Houses, instead of the larger group visiting one. He also suggested a general session before the visits with a speaker and a film to prepare the groups for a more worthwhile trip. In addition to this, he selected one person in each Banking House to receive the teachers and briefed that person on the objectives of the visit as well as the plan of the preliminary general session.

It was not possible for the group of 50 to be accommodated at the Custom House at one time and so the suggestion of visiting the Annex to see the modern tabulator divided the number into two groups and made the visit more promising.

The planning committee met a second time, having the names of participants and full information from each place to be visited. Since the fifth day was to be an evaluation and sharing session it seemed helpful to suggest some questions for discussion. A detailed schedule for the week was worked out and arrangements were made for transportation and lunches when these were necessary. The following schedule for the week with questions and check list were mimeographed and stapled together for distribution to all participants:

EXPANDING HORIZONS IN MATHEMATICS
JUNE, 1952; WORKSHOP J56

This workshop is organized primarily for teachers of mathematics who are interested in making mathematics functional. For the first four days visits have been planned. On the fifth day, Friday, an evaluation session will be held, at which time there will be group discussions followed by oral reports. In preparation for these discussions and for the reports the questions on the attached sheet are suggested as guides for each visit.

SCHEDULE FOR THE WEEK

Day	Time	Place
Monday, June 16	9:00–9:30	Room 1—2418 St. Paul Street (orientation)
	9:30–10:30	The Story of Investments—Harrison Garrett, Partner, Robert Garrett and Sons
	11:00–12:15	Calvert and Redwood Streets (visits to Investment Banking Houses). Visits arranged through the courtesy of William L. Reed, secretary of the Bond Club of Baltimore Group I. Baker, Watts and Company. Calvert and Redwood Streets. John Redwood, Jr. Group II. Alexander Brown and Sons. Calvert and Baltimore Streets. W. James Price Group III. John C. Legg and Company. 22 Light Street. Albert W. Thorpe Group IV. Stein Brothers and Boyce. 65 Calvert Street. Edward J. Armstrong Group V. Merrill, Lynch, Pierce, Fenner and Beane. Calvert and Fayette Streets. Albert G. Warfield
Tuesday, June 17. Group I	9:00–9:45	Custom House, Gay and Lombard Streets Processing of Income Tax Returns—Fulton D. Fields, Head Cashier, Division of Internal Revenue
	10:00–10:45	Hopkins Place Annex The Modern Tabulator—Francis X. Keelan, Chief of the Tabulating Section, Division of Internal Revenue
	9:45–10:30	Custom House, Gay and Lombard Streets (same as Group I)
Group II	10:45–11:30	Hopkins Place Annex (same as Group I) Visits arranged through the courtesy of Robert W. Lewis, Assistant to the Collector of Internal Revenue

Wednesday, June 18	9:45	Group will meet at 2418 St. Paul Street (tour of Friendship International Airport—Capt. Kunaneic, Head of Special Police). Visits arranged through the courtesy of Karl L. Clark, Manager of the Friendship International Airport.
	1:00	Lunch, Coffee Shop at Airport
Thursday, June 19	8:15	Group will meet at 2418 St. Paul Street (visit to Chesapeake Bay Bridge—Bruce A. Herman, Resident Engineer, Chesapeake Bay Bridge)
	12:30	Box Lunch, Sandy Point Park
Friday, June 20	9:00–10:45	Group Meetings in Room 1 at 2418 St. Paul Street (group assignments to be made at this session)
	11:00–12:00	Oral reports.

SUGGESTED QUESTIONS FOR DISCUSSION

1. How can this information be used with your classes in:
   a. curricular and
   b. extra-curricular activities
2. At what level, elementary or secondary, would it be most desirable to arrange class visits similar to these?
3. What suggestions would you give a teacher who is planning a class trip?
   a. elementary level
   b. secondary level
4. What suggestions would you offer concerning the follow-up of a class visit?
   a. elementary level
   b. secondary level
5. As a result of these visits, what new emphases may be placed in your own teaching? Cite examples.
6. Which of the 29 Functional Competencies have you observed on your visits? (See attached sheet.) Cite examples.
7. What visits would you suggest for another workshop?
8. How differently might a future workshop be conducted?

Groups for the first two days were arranged alphabetically on the basis of an equal number of people in each. A leader for each group was selected to meet the representative at the designated place. It seemed best in planning for the evaluation session not to have the groups assigned in advance, but to devise some plan whereby a random selection would be made. Numbers one, two, three, or four were to be drawn on the last day. The members of

CHECK LIST

29 FUNCTIONAL COMPETENCIES	BANKING HOUSES	CUSTOM HOUSE	AIR-PORT	BAY BRIDGE
1. Computation....................				
2. Per cents......................				
3. Ratio..........................				
4. Estimating.....................				
5. Rounding numbers..............				
6. Tables.........................				
7. Graphs........................				
8. Statistics......................				
9. The nature of a measurement.....				
10. Use of measuring devices........				
11. Square root....................				
12. Angles.........................				
13. Geometric concepts.............				
14. The 3-4-5 relation..............				
15. Constructions..................				
16. Drawings......................				
17. Vectors.......................				
18. Metric system.................				
19. Conversion....................				
20. Algebraic symbolism............				
21. Formulas......................				
22. Signed numbers................				
23. Using the axioms..............				
24. Practical formulas.............				
25. Similar triangles and proportion...				
26. Numerical trigonometry.........				
27. First steps in business arithmetic..				
28. Consumer problems.............				
29. "Proceeding from hypothesis to ... conclusion"....................				

the planning committee shared responsibilities of preparing for the week and eagerly awaited the day.

WORKSHOP TRIPS

It was Monday, June 16, the time 9 o'clock, the temperature rapidly approaching 90°. We started promptly and within a few minutes the roll had been taken and the schedule for the week distributed. Attention was called to the guiding questions to be considered on each visit and to the check list of functional competencies. There followed a brief word concerning certain special arrangements involving grouping, transportation, lunch at the airport, and the box luncheon at Sandy Point Park, which is adjacent to our new Chesapeake Bay Bridge.

Then when the speaker of the morning was introduced the complete program for the week had already been outlined. The "Story of Investments" as related by Harrison Garrett provided an effective orientation for our visits to the investment banking houses. We were told, appropriately, that a chart showing over-all production in the United States, 1875–1950, is quite a perfect spiral. To this growth three groups have made contributions:

1. The man with the idea and the scientific knowledge to put his idea to work
2. The man with the skill to use his hands and develop the new product
3. The man with the savings, large or small, and the faith to put his savings to work both for his own advantage and that of his neighbors.
   A further significant statement, among many, "In the history of the world it has ever been true that the dynamic prevails over the static."

There followed an informational film, *What Makes Us Tick*, which enabled us to take a technicolor trip to market and find out what stocks are, why there are stocks, and why there is a stock exchange. It was presented under the sponsorship of the New York Stock Exchange. Through the courtesy of the Bond Club of Baltimore we received two handbooks of factual information, *Investment Facts About Common Stocks*, and *Understanding the Modern Securities Market*.

A leader having been appointed for each group and the group identified, we then set out to visit the five investment banking houses downtown, including Alexander Brown and Sons, America's oldest name in the investment banking business. We were met by persons who served as guides and discussion leaders.

Our second visit was to the Custom House and the Annex Tuesday morning when we made quite an interesting study of the highly involved processing of tax returns including, to be sure, income tax statements.

One of the exciting experiences on this occasion was our introduction to that invisible mathematician, the amazing modern tabulator, where electronics plays an almost incredible role. It was mathematics, to be sure, the analytical approach provided by mathematics, that made possible the development and design of this complicated machinery.

Here again were capable guides who were ready and eager to answer our questions. But we were not too surprised when they earnestly stressed the importance of basic mathematics, of accuracy, and of checks. They gave us sample forms, including income tax blanks. We also had the privilege of making a comparative study of tax receipts over a period of years, a bit of research which would prove of special interest to pupils studying consumer mathematics, general mathematics, and business mathematics.

On the third morning came our trip to the Friendship International Airport where we studied the mathematics of the weather bureau, the cargo room, sales and reservations, and the airfield. Here again the emphasis was on arithmetic, facility with common fractions, decimal fractions, mental arithmetic.

One of the highlights of the day was our visit to the weather man in his laboratory. He described his weather maps, his rain gauges, his use of the distance formula, his use of signed numbers, and he stressed the necessity for accuracy. Observing activities in the cargo rooms and the sales and reservations divisions made us realize again that in addition to alertness and accuracy, speed, too, is significant.

As we inspected the great airliner and airfield itself comments like these were heard, "Aeronautics, another name for mathematical science," "Mathematics, partner of progress," "Without mathematics none of this is possible," "A miracle of technical advance." One could summarize by simply saying "fundamentally dependent upon mathematics."

The new Chesapeake Bay Bridge which was then just nearing completion was our destination on the fourth day. Upon our arrival a well-qualified associate of the resident engineer discussed with us the mathematics involved in the planning stages and in the actual construction. Launches were then provided and for guides we had enthusiastic recent college engineering graduates who delighted in pointing out numerous applications of geometry and trigonometry which were to be seen on every hand. Our bridge was, to be sure, but another evidence of the advanced state of the science of structural design, which is to say mathematical design.

There was considerable emphasis on the conversion of common to decimal fractions and on mental computation. For example, look at these decimal fractions:

Over-all Lengths

  7.727   miles—over-all length of project
  1.095   miles—west approach roadway
  2.268   miles—east approach roadway
  0.332   miles—filled causeway—east approach roadway
  4.35+ miles—shore line to shore line
  4.032   miles—bridge structure—abutment to abutment.

Maximum Span Lengths

1600.00 feet—suspension span
 779.86 feet—maximum through cantilever truss span
 599.89 feet—maximum deck cantilever truss span
 303.08 feet—maximum deck simple truss span
 200.00 feet—maximum deck girder span
  60.00 feet—beam span.

Roadway

  28.00 feet—curb to curb
   1.50 feet—emergency footwalks each side
198.50 feet—maximum roadway elevation above mean low water
   3.00%   —maximum grade.

Depth and Heights

   −88 feet—elevation of maximum water depth below mean low water
 −167 feet—elevation of maximum mud depth below mean low water (79 feet below bay bottom)
  −98 feet—elevation of bottom of deepest pier
 −203 feet—elevation of tip of deepest piles
 +354 feet—elevation of top of aerial beacon—highest point on bridge.

Horizontal and Vertical Clearances

1,500 feet horizontally and 186.50 feet vertically—main channel
  690 feet horizontally and 63 feet vertically—secondary eastern channel

Approximate Quantities—Shore To Shore

4,130 piles
328,153 linear feet piles
118,000 cubic yards cement concrete—using 210,000 barrels—
cement; 125,000 tons—gravel; 75,000 tons—sand.
60,000 tons steel consisting of 17,500 tons—piles; 30,000 tons—
structural steel; 6,000 tons—reinforcing steel; 3,000 tons—
permanent steel forms; 2,000 tons—miscellaneous steel for
handrailing and such; 1,500 tons—cable and suspenders
2,538,000 cubic yards—earth movable
151,400 tons—slope protection stone.

Estimated Traffic

1952–1,100,000 vehicles
1961–1,550,000 vehicles
(Bridge designed to carry 1500 vehicles per hour in one direction or
to carry a total annual traffic of 8,500,000 vehicles.)

Time of Crossing—Shore to Shore

5¼ minutes.

Estimated Labor Requirements

6,500,000 man-hours of labor at site.

Now about the evaluation session which was held on the fifth
day, how was it planned and what were the outcomes? As has been
stated previously, when the members assembled each selected
a card on which was written a number from one to four. Each
number represented one of the visits so that the grouping was
strictly by chance.

These groups met separately for a period of one hour and forty-
five minutes. They selected a chairman, a recorder, a reporter.
Each group considered the six guiding questions and the check
list of functional competencies as they related to the visit being
discussed. Following this the groups reassembled for the general
session and one member from each group presented his report.
The use of a tape recorder made possible a careful record of the
proceedings.

FINAL EVALUATION

The stimulating experience of the evaluation session with the
splendid reports given by the various groups leaders was one that
the planning committee felt should be shared with every teacher
of mathematics. To make this possible, a summary was prepared

for distribution at the September meeting of the secondary teachers. The highlights of the summary which centered around the six leading questions follow:

How can this information be used with your classes in curricular activities?

Baltimore Banking Houses
1. To understand and construct graphs
2. To read stock quotations
3. To use percentage
4. To round off numbers
5. To read and interpret tables
6. To study appropriate vocabulary
7. To understand the social significance of stocks and bonds.

Baltimore Custom House
1. To display sample tax forms
2. To fill out sample income tax forms.

Friendship International Airport
1. To stress fundamental operations
2. To emphasize facility with common and decimal fractions
3. To provide frequent opportunity for mental arithmetic
4. To apply the distance formula
5. To use directed numbers in temperature readings.

Chesapeake Bay Bridge
1. To provide practice in solving arithmetic problems involving conversion of common fractions to decimal fractions
2. To provide frequent opportunity for mental computation
3. To emphasize the checking of results to insure accuracy.

How can this information be used with your classes in extra-curricular activities?

Baltimore Banking Houses
1. To encourage talks by representatives of the various banking houses
2. To show films such as "What Makes Us Tick"
3. To arouse interest in a mathematics club.

Baltimore Custom House
1. To provide information for parents
2. To arouse interest in a mathematics club.

Friendship International Airport
1. To develop an appreciation of the various measuring instruments
2. To develop an understanding of weather maps
3. To make rain gauges
4. To make wet and dry thermometers
5. To use air maps for scale drawing
6. To make model airplanes
7. To arouse interest in a mathematics club.

Chesapeake Bay Bridge

1. To encourage talks by members of the Maryland State Roads Commission and various engineering firms
2. To show films about the bridge
3. To study an appropriate toll rate for amortization of the bond issue
4. To arouse interest in a mathematics club.

What suggestions would you give a teacher who is planning a class trip?

Take the trip yourself before taking the class
Motivate
1. Invite a speaker
2. Show an appropriate film
3. Provide significant literature
Make certain that safety provisions are clearly understood
Outline the purposes clearly so that all pupils will know what to look for
Provide guidesheets or suggestions for observation.

What suggestions would you offer concerning the follow-up of a class visit?

Discuss the visit in relation to the guidesheet
Suggest that essays be written
Have write-ups prepared for the school paper
Express the experiences through skits or plays
Arrange bulletin board displays
Stress the mathematical competencies observed.

Thus was concluded our most recent workshop, "Expanding Horizons in Mathematics." The topic was chosen advisedly. If we are to make of our teaching an art, if we are to make it a *vital transaction* between teacher and pupil, if we are to be enthusiasts in our profession we must constantly look beyond our daily experiences. We must learn more about the history of the subject that we teach, we must keep abreast of new emphases that are placed on certain aspects of that subject, and we must be aware of how it functions in the age in which we live.

Inservice training is one provision that is made for such growth. In this training, however, it is the teacher who takes the lead. He has a dual role; that of leader on the one hand and of participant on the other. It demands of those who lead and of those who participate, genuine interest in self-improvement, enthusiasm, resourcefulness, and sincerity of purpose. Can we, working together in the field of mathematics, meet these challenges? We can, through expanding horizons in mathematics.

PART FOUR
New Emphases in Subject Matter
Introduction

During the past half century we have been witnessing significant changes in the mathematical content of the school curriculum. Many arithmetic topics have been adjudged to be obsolete, and no longer appear in textbooks and courses of study. Emphasis upon factoring in elementary algebra has decreased. There has been a demand for (and some experience with) nongeometric subject matter for use in the teaching of demonstrative geometry. Some concepts of analytic geometry are appearing in courses in algebra and geometry. The need for a wider consideration of approximate computation is being recognized. Proponents of the concept of *general education* are urging wider acceptance of courses dealing with basic concepts, and with considerable emphasis upon the mathematics of the consumer. Descriptions of practices in these areas, and expositions of their place in mathematics education follow. J. R. C.

The New Emphasis in Teaching Geometry

Leroy H. Schnell

"No study is better adapted than Geometry to *discipline the minds of the young*. It is within their grasp; it interests, excites, tasks, and stores the mind; not only stores it with useful knowledge (as defined later, 'facts and principles for future use'), but furnishes it with valuable habits. . . . The memory is aided, fresh interest awakened, and the whole mind invigorated, by the *generalization of geometrical truths.*" The preceding quotation, taken from the introduction of a geometry textbook by Crosby, published in Boston in 1847, is a reasonable summary of the major purpose for teaching demonstrative geometry as viewed by the majority of teachers of the subject until early in the present century.

269

The same author illustrates the major emphasis in the conventional teaching of geometry with the admonition: "The *most rigorous exactness of demonstration* must be preserved. We want no tentative or experimental methods of proof. Empiricism is as bad in mathematics as in medicine. We want no practical results to be learned by rote, without proof. We must have proof, infallible proof, demonstration."

Undoubtedly Plato is responsible, at least in a large part, for the tenacious conviction held by generations of teachers, that a study of geometry, *ipso facto*, quickens the reasoning powers and improves a learner's ability to *think* clearly, independently, and logically in *any* type of problem situation. The often quoted inscription over the door of his school, "Let no man ignorant of geometry enter here," is sufficient evidence for this observation. Also, the rigid organization of Euclidean geometry tended to strengthen this conviction and to fix the teaching of geometry in an unvarying pattern. Euclid's *Elements* came to be viewed by most geometricians with deep reverence and was assumed by the initiated to be a revelation of the *eternal verities*—unchanging and unchangeable "truths" with which only the most irreverent would tamper. Undoubtedly many readers of this article have known sincere, zealous, but misguided teachers who emphasized to their students that the "truths" learned in geometry were irrefutable and were part of the divine plan of the universe. Teachers who held strongly to this belief failed to make their pupils aware of the assumptive nature of geometric reasoning and the fact that the entire structure is based on man-made assumptions which can be altered at will, thus changing the entire sequential arrangement as well as the conclusions of "irrefutable geometric *truths*."

Even though somewhat modified in sequence by Legendre in 1794, the very antiquity of Euclidean demonstrative geometry served as a safeguard against major or precipitous revisions. The conviction of pedagogues that the study of demonstrative geometry would store the mind with facts and principles for future use and that the reasoning techniques employed in this study would, in some mysterious manner, transfer to everyday reasoning situations was strengthened by the widely popular theory of mental faculties and formal discipline. Practice, form, repetition, and exercise were given prominent attention; pupil understanding was of secondary concern. It is reasonable to surmise that the teaching of geometry would not have undergone material change had not investigators, in the first two decades of the present century, demonstrated the fallibility of the theory of mental discipline by studies in the area of transfer of training. Particularly prominent in these early investigations were Thorndike, Woodworth, and Briggs.

An extensive study by Briggs in 1913 led to the conclusion that while rigid training in reasoning in one area tended to improve abilities in *that* area, improvement in reasoning in *other* areas was, at best, small and imperceptible in most instances. Briggs devised tests to measure improvement in the ability to draw tenable conclusions from given data, to reason syllogistically, to test definitions of all types after intensive, rigid training in formal grammar. The implications for transfer of learning from geometric reasoning situations to everyday, nongeometric problem-situations are obvious and were later affirmed by studies in the area of geometry.

It is impossible to assign major credit to any individual, group of individuals, or educational movements for the changes of emphasis in the teaching of geometry which have gained increasing momentum during the first half of the present century. This period is typified as one of great change in both elementary and secondary education and it is to the credit of *all* investigators, writers, and teachers of mathematics who contributed to improvement. In this article, only a few contributors can be mentioned. Those not mentioned are legion.

Beyond doubt, the basis for a new point of view with respect to Euclidean geometry, and to mathematical thought in general, is to be found in the contributions of mathematicians of the 17th, 18th, and 19th Centuries. The works of Descartes, Newton, Leibniz, Lobachevski, Bolyai, Riemann, and many others constituted a challenge to mathematicians and forced them to re-evaluate the validity of the Euclidean pattern of thought. In his presidential address delivered before The American Mathematics Society on December 29, 1902, Professor Moore observed that "had it not been for the brilliant success of Euclid in his effort to organize into a formally deductive system the geometric

treasures of his times, the advent of the reign of science in the
modern sense might not have been so long deferred." He urged
that in any reforms we not "repeat more gloriously the error of
those followers of Euclid who fixed his *Elements* as a textbook for
elementary instruction in geometry for over 2000 years." The
challenging effect of these statements, made by such an eminent
mathematician, on educators interested in instruction in geometry
is obvious. In the same address, Professor Moore urged a procedure
which has been applied by many teachers and which, it is hoped,
will be tried by increasing numbers. "When it comes to the beginning of the more formal deductive geometry why should not the
students be directed each for himself to set forth a body of
geometric fundamental principles, on which to proceed to erect
his geometric edifice? . . . The various students would have
different systems of axioms and the discussions thus arising
naturally would make clearer . . . precisely what are the functions
of the axioms in the theory of geometry."

A quarter of a century later, David Eugene Smith said that
"Early attempts at improving the courses (of secondary school
mathematics) were greatly hampered by the force of tradition."
However, in spite of this, he says that in the past 25 years "There
has been a more definite recognition . . . that the chief purpose of
demonstrative geometry is to show the application of logic to
the proof of mathematical statements. . . . The number of
demonstrated theorems, and especially of the corollaries, has
been greatly reduced. . . . The number of solved problems has
been proportionately reduced. . . . [and] The exercises have
greatly increased in number [and] decreased in difficulty" (37).
In 1930, Professor Upton emphasized that "I firmly believe that
the reason we teach demonstrative geometry . . . today is to
give pupils certain ideas about the nature of proof . . . [that is]
to show pupils how facts are proved . . . [and also] to familiarize
them with that rigorous kind of thinking which Professor Keyser
has so aptly called 'the if-then kind' " (55).

The foregoing quotations from the writings of Smith and Upton
point up the changes in emphasis in the teaching of geometry
with particular reference to the treatment of the subject matter
itself. Added to these trends, it must be observed that due to the

growth of the junior high-school movement, informal, intuitive geometry was introduced in the seventh and eighth grades. Furthermore, the tremendous growth in high-school enrollments, and the greater retention in secondary schools of children of widely varying abilities, made it urgent that the classical curriculum be supplanted with one that would more nearly meet the capacities of all children rather than only those of the more capable and select few. Even with a background of informal, intuitive geometry from junior high school, it became essential that even greater efforts than before be made to provide experiences in demonstrative geometry that would lead to maximum pupil-discovery and understanding as well as to give the study specific purpose by providing for meaningful applications to nongeometric as well as to geometric problem situations. Although many teachers continued to follow conventional procedures, an increasing number took the pupils "in on the secret" and encouraged them to work independently in discovering geometric facts inductively and in developing proofs of these self-discovered propositions on their own initiative rather than risk memorization by following too closely the textbook proofs.

During the second quarter of the present century, much attention has been given to the problem of transferring techniques of reasoning employed in geometry to everyday, nongeometric situations and to developing a critical attitude of mind on the part of pupils. The crux of this problem depends upon the answers to the questions: Can training in one area be transferred to another? And if transfer is admitted as possible, how can it be effected?

Vevia Blair says that psychologists "almost unanimously agree that transfer does exist" but that the amount of transfer "is largely dependent upon methods of teaching" (32).

According to Betz, "There are excellent reasons why school subjects 'as now organized' should lead to such a 'small degree' of transfer. We do not secure transfer *unless we train for transfer*" (6). Later Wheeler said that, "No transfer will occur unless the material is learned in connection with the field to which transfer is desired" (58).

Significant contributions were made by Harold Fawcett of

Ohio State University, and Gilbert Ulmer of the University of Kansas. On the basis of his investigation, Fawcett concluded, in part, that "mathematical method illustrated by a small number of theorems yields a control of the subject matter of geometry at least equal to that obtained from the usual formal course; by following (appropriate) procedures . . . it is possible to improve the reflective thinking of secondary-school pupils . . . [but] this improvement is general in character and transfers to a variety of situations." He also observes that the "usual formal course in demonstrative geometry does not improve the reflective thinking of the pupils" (17).

Professor Ulmer's investigation led to the conclusions that "it is possible for high-school geometry teachers, under normal classroom conditions, to teach in such a way as to cultivate reflective thinking, that this can be done without sacrificing an understanding of geometric relationships, and that pupils at all IQ levels are capable of profiting from such instruction. The results also indicate that even what is commonly regarded as superior geometry teaching has little effect upon pupils' behavior in the direction of reflective thinking unless definite provisions are made to study methods of thinking as an important end in itself" (53).

In 1942, Dr. Ulmer compiled *Some Suggestions for Teaching Geometry to Develop Clear Thinking* in monograph form. In it he gives many examples of everyday reasoning situations that employ geometric modes of thought. These examples are as useable today as they were a decade ago (54).

It is heartening to observe that now, in 1954, all widely used geometry textbooks give some attention to reasoning in non-geometric situations. This statement could not have been truthfully made 10 years ago. Obviously the treatment and the amount of attention given vary, depending on the approach of the various authors. However, here is evidence of an emerging practice in the teaching of geometry.

In summary, from an examination of the professional literature and of geometry textbooks of recent date, it appears that the following items indicate points of current emphasis in teaching geometry; at least strong trends in each are apparent.

1. In most instances, materials are presented in such manner that the *nature and the meaning of proof* are emphasized.

2. Formal demonstrative geometry is approached gradually, after adequate informal and inductive experiences are provided to lead the pupil to an understanding of the basic concepts.

3. Many authors give frequent opportunities for independent effort on the part of pupils on the obvious assumption that greater understanding will accrue if they discover, experimentally, relationships that in a conventionally taught course are presented bluntly as propositions to prove. In some textbooks, considerable effort is made to encourage pupils to develop their own proof of theorems rather than to study, exclusively, proofs presented by the author.

4. Considerable care is generally given to *developing* the basic assumptions from informal experiences and to making it clear to the student that the assumptions are merely agreements upon which reasoning is to be based. In the majority of textbooks, assumptions are used to defend simple *if-then* problems before using them as defenses in formal demonstrative proofs.

5. Specific attention is generally given to inductive versus deductive reasoning and the pupil led gradually to realize that demonstrative geometry employs deductive reasoning, thus eliminating some of the uncertainty of the inductive method in helping to determine whether or not certain relationships hold for all possible cases.

6. More attention is given to the *function* of the assumptions in a sequential, logical pattern of thought, than was true in the textbooks of 50 years ago.

7. There is a growing tendency to devote specific effort to helping pupils appreciate and understand the course of plane geometry as a complete and interrelated pattern of thought. In some books, pupils are asked to trace the "dependency" of the proof of various theorems back to the basic assumptions. Such experiences, properly guided, cannot help but lead the student to understand the meaning of an independent versus a dependent theorem as well as to emphasize the function of assumptions in a system of assumptive-sequential reasoning.

8. Ample opportunity is given for pupils to do independent

thinking in developing the proof of originals. The majority of textbooks give adequate *cumulative* groups of original exercises, frequently graded in terms of difficulty.

9. A number of authors give attention to developing some of the basic concepts of solid geometry. Although not closely correlated with the facts of demonstrative geometry, there is also a growing tendency to introduce some elementary analytic geometry.

10. There is an increasing tendency to provide organized drills to maintain the important mathematical skills previously learned.

11. Exercises are provided to transfer the modes of reasoning employed in demonstrative geometry to everyday reasoning situations.

In conclusion it must be agreed that demonstrative geometry as taught today represents significant changes when compared with the course taught half a century or more ago. While change does not necessarily mean progress and improvement, it cannot be denied that the changes and new emphases in the teaching of geometry are sound. We have a right to feel encouraged and to hope for even better things to come.

Nongeometric Exercises in Geometry

MYRON F. ROSSKOPF

About 500 B.C. the Pythagoreans set up their school curriculum, called the *quadrivium* and composed of geometry, arithmetic, astronomy, and music. From that day until the present, some knowledge of mathematics has been considered a requirement for an educated person. Mathematics was studied for several reasons; among them the following seemed important: (a) a study of mathematics supplements and illuminates the study of philosophy; (b) a knowledge of mathematics is needed in applications; (c) a study of mathematics sharpens and quickens the mind. It is the last of these reasons for studying mathematics that concerns us. From the time of the Pythagoreans until the latter part of the 19th Century there occurred little questioning of the *efficacy* of mathematics in training a student's mind, although there was questioning concerning the *method* of teaching used.

One of the first persons to attack the content and teaching of plane geometry was John Perry. In a series of papers, beginning with one in 1880, he deplored the memorization of Euclid, almost book by book, and recommended changes in teaching method and content that he believed led to a better knowledge of mathematics on the part of students. The Perry Movement in England was brought forcefully to the attention of his colleagues in 1901 by his presentation to the British Association of a suggestion for a new mathematics syllabus (38). Although the teaching of geometry in the United States was not as rigidly Euclid's as in England, still E. H. Moore's reference to Perry in his 1902 address to the American Mathematical Society had a profound effect (30). For the speech served to bring to the attention of a large and influential group the need for improving the teaching of geometry if students were to be trained well in logical thinking.

It is significant to note that the reports of committees and commissions that studied the mathematics curriculum agree that one important objective of the teaching of geometry is the development of logical thinking. The report of the conference on instruction in secondary-school mathematics of the Committee of Ten (35: 116) stated in its concluding paragraphs that ". . . whatever the training [in geometry] may accomplish for him geometrically, there is no student whom it will not brighten and strengthen intellectually as few other exercises can." Clearly the members of the conference were convinced that one of the important objectives in the teaching of geometry is the improvement of the quality of thinking of students. Implicit, too, is a belief in a psychology of learning that assumes the existence of mental faculties like judgment, memory, and will.

The researches of E. L. Thorndike (52) on transfer of training showed that the sort of logical thinking done in geometry does not transfer automatically to situations outside of geometry. His formulation of a psychology of learning and a theory concerning transfer of training had farreaching effects on both curriculums and methods of instruction in mathematics. Somewhat later Charles H. Judd (24) emphasized the importance of generalizations in learning. All of us who teach mathematics can appreciate this point of view, for we know today more concerning the role of generalization in learning mathematical concepts.

Reorganization of Mathematics in Secondary Education (32: 9) states that one of the disciplinary aims of mathematics is:

"The development of *ability to think clearly in terms of ... ideas and concepts*". In connection with this aim it is well to give a quotation from a statement of Charles H. Judd (32: 99), which he made in answer to an inquiry concerning transfer of training. His statement is important because it is an early expression of a concept of teaching mathematics (geometry) that appeared much later.

I do not think that any subject transfers automatically, and in every case. The real problem of transfer is a problem of so organizing training that it will carry over in the minds of students in other fields. There is a method of teaching a subject so that it will transfer, and there are other methods of teaching the subject so that the transfer will be very small. Mathematics as a subject cannot be described in my judgment as sure to transfer. All depends upon the way in which the subject is handled.

The *Third Report of the Committee on Geometry* (3) is important because the members of the committee who prepared the report studied the ideas of many teachers of mathematics in the United States and Europe and surveyed the opinions of teachers of geometry in this country by means of a questionnaire. The report brought together in one place an analysis of papers dealing with teaching methods and teaching programs in geometry; it summarized these publications and drew from them generalizations. The work of the committee was significant to those teachers who were revolting against a rigid organization of geometry; they found in this report their "feelings" epitomized and justification for proceeding with their experimentations. These teachers must have been encouraged by the following results of the committee's questionnaire (3: 334, 335):

Teachers agree that the main outcomes of demonstrative geometry pertain to logical thinking .... There is equally enthusiastic response to the proposal that instruction in demonstrative geometry call attention to logical claims of theorems, . . . and bring the pupil to appreciate the nature of a mathematical system, the need of undefined terms, the arbitrariness of assumptions, and the possibility of other arrangements of propositions than that given in his own text.

This concise historical sketch indicates that teachers of geometry have believed for a long time that an objective of their teaching is the development of logical thinking. The most recent reports simply reiterate this thesis. For example, the Joint Commission of the Mathematical Association of America and the National Council of Teachers of Mathematics in its report (33) discusses the means by which mathematics teaching can contribute to the objective of establishing and judging claims of proof. It is pointed out that it is necessary to teach more than the propositions and exercises of geometry if students are to make development in this objective; experiences must be provided which allow students to apply the inductive and deductive thinking of mathematics outside geometry. Another report that urges this practice be carried even further is *Mathematics in General Education*. In a discussion of "Proof" this report states (13: 202):

> Questions as to whether logical principles should be made explicit first in connection with mathematical work, and then later applied in the analysis of nonmathematical situations, or whether the opposite order should be followed, cannot be answered without further experimentation. . . . Perhaps the practice of beginning with familiar nonmathematical situations, making a transition to mathematical examples as a means of clarification, and then applying to additional nonmathematical problems may in most instances be superior to either of the above alternatives.

It is clear that the committee had in mind a class that would consider more than geometry.

This section ends with a quotation of item 29 from the Check List of the *Guidance Report of the Commission on Post-War Plans* (43: 319):

> *Proceeding from hypothesis to conclusion.* Can you analyze a statement in a newspaper and determine what is assumed, and whether the suggested conclusions really follow from the given facts or assumptions?

This is one of the competencies that study of mathematics is to develop. How can such competence be developed? An indication of possible answers to the question is contained in the section that follows.

EXPERIMENTATION IN THE TEACHING OF GEOMETRY

In all statements concerning the development of logical thinking there is implicit a belief that the amount of transfer is large enough to make teaching significant. Reports of the last 50 years have been careful to use language that is acceptable to psychologists, but every piece of evidence was seized by the writers of the reports to support the thesis that transfer does take place. Inextricably woven into experiments in the teaching of geometry is this question of transfer of training. It is a question that one cannot shut his eyes to. A recent statement concerning transfer of training in the Twenty-First Yearbook of the National Council of Teachers of Mathematics presents the situation today (46).

There are three important researches into the question of whether geometry can be taught so that the logical thinking developed through a study of geometry will transfer to life situations or nongeometric situations. All of these experiments were doctoral studies. The first of these is that by Harold P. Fawcett, published as the Thirteenth Yearbook of the National Council of Teachers of Mathematics (17). The second study was carried out by Gilbert Ulmer and reported in the *Journal of Experimental Education* (53). The third study is contained in the unpublished doctoral dissertation of Richard E. Gadske (20).

Since the two published studies of Fawcett and Ulmer had a wide distribution, their impact on teachers of mathematics was great. These two studies emphasized the following aspects of logical thinking (17, 53):

1. If-then or postulational thinking
2. Importance of defining key words and phrases
3. Reasoning by generalization
4. Reasoning by analogy
5. Detecting implicit assumptions
6. Inverses and converses
7. Indirect proof
8. Name calling.

Fawcett's study might be said to have had a methodology emphasis while Ulmer's study emphasized the problem of transfer. However, both studies used new instructional techniques and both studies discussed the results in terms of transfer.

CURRENT SITUATION

It is probably true that at the present time a majority of plane geometry classes are taught with little reference to nongeometric situations. However, it is also true that several recent syllabi or courses of study in plane geometry include among their recommendations indications of ways in which teachers can promote transfer of logical thinking. In addition, all recently published textbooks on plane geometry include nongeometric exercises. Since syllabi and textbooks affect greatly what goes on in a classroom, it must be concluded that some geometry classrooms contain students who are studying nongeometric material.

There are some leaders in mathematics education who believe that there is a movement to return to teaching geometry as a way of thinking about spatial relations. Implied is that geometry will be studied for its modes of attack on relationships in space, that from this study will be abstracted those methods that permeate many areas in mathematics. Such a study of geometry will be good for those students who study more mathematics, but it seems a regrettable movement so far as other geometry students are concerned. It seems as if every geometry student should come away from his year's work with not only a knowledge of geometrical relationships and logic as applied to mathematics but also a working acquaintance of the way in which these logical processes apply to his life outside of mathematics.

Slowly and through experimental classroom teaching mathematics teachers are finding that plane geometry is not the only area that can make a contribution to logical thinking. Algebra, too, properly taught, can help to develop in students many of the same logic concepts as geometry. At one time some geometry teachers considered a domain of subjects that included propaganda analysis, *if-then* thinking, principles of logic, reflective thinking, and political analysis, as well as geometry. It is realized today that every class in a school makes a contribution to logical thinking. For example, social studies classes are particularly appropriate in which to analyze propaganda and political movements; science classes can make a major contribution to the objective of reflective or scientific thinking. This does not mean that mathematics makes no contribution to development in these aspects of thinking nor that social studies and science make no contribution to development of students in the use of logic, but it does mean that each area is finding the aspect of thinking to which it can contribute in a significant way.

So far as plane geometry is concerned it seems that there are points in the organization of the course and particular topics into which nongeometric exercises fit very well. Moreover, it seems to those teachers who have experimented for a period of years with several approaches to plane geometry that the nongeometric exercise is the most natural doorway to a meaning of the logical principle the geometry demonstrates. So both those who believe in geometry as a study of spatial relationships and those who believe geometry is the best area in which to teach logical thinking are finding a place. There is a body of knowledge in geometry with which a student of the subject should be familiar; and, in order to motivate the study of geometry, to develop logical thinking, and to facilitate transfer, the nongeometric exercise is necessary.

One of the most effective points at which to use nongeometric situations in geometry is at the beginning of the course. At this point a teacher desires to emphasize for his students the reason for undefined terms, assumptions, and definitions. A teacher wishes to develop quickly an attitude in his students of being critical *about* thinking and statements. Familiar nongeometric exercises are particularly effective for this purpose. Nongeometric exercises are more effective than geometric exercises: for example, to make students realize the meaning of the principle of logic; if you accept the assumptions, then you must accept the conclusions that follow logically from these assumptions.

The introduction to synthetic proofs through a study of geometric proofs seems somewhat meaningless to most students. They learn by analogy, studying correct proofs, and trying to arrange the proof of an original in the same form. It speaks well for the intelligence and adaptability of the students that they gradually learn to give correct, logical proofs. Would it not be more meaningful to begin with a study of syllogisms, using exercises that were both nongeometric and geometric? When students become familiar with syllogisms, they are shown how syllogisms can be connected to form a proof that has more than one step. Gradually students are led to develop an understanding of the logical principles involved in proofs of both geometric and nongeometric exercises. The syllogism is very effective also in putting meaning into the analytic method of proof, helping to avoid analysis becoming a rote method of obtaining a proof.

Inverses, converses, and contrapositives are quite abstract for students of plane geometry if these concepts are developed only through geometric exercises. Some textbooks of plane geometry are making the nongeometric exercises an integral part of the development of these concepts. Much work has been done in recent years to improve the teaching of indirect proof, but much remains to be done to make the logical principles involved so meaningful to a student that he will understand how to use them to make an indirect proof. Here again, the nongeometric exercise seems essential. Recently published textbooks consider locus from the point of view of necessary and sufficient conditions. Students just do not realize the force of a statement that is both necessary and sufficient through the use of geometrical statements alone.

SUMMARY

From an abbreviated history of the appearance of the development of logical thinking as an objective of the teaching of mathematics it was indicated that this objective has persisted until the present. Experimentation in classrooms with different ways of organizing and teaching plane geometry led to the major studies of Fawcett, Ulmer, and Gadske that were cited in this paper (17, 53, 20).

Although textbooks, for the most part, have been unable to weave together the geometric and nongeometric materials, all textbooks include materials of both sorts. Efforts of textbooks most recently published have been more successful in making the nongeometric material an integral part of the course in plane geometry. There is a movement away from an extreme emphasis on nongeometric materials to a position that a meaningful approach to logical principles can be made through a process of study of nongeometric exercises in connection with geometric exercises. There are particular points in a course when such a classroom procedure is most effective; these have been indicated in the foregoing paragraphs. In conclusion it can be said that many plane geometry teachers are using in their classrooms a meaningful approach to a study of spatial relationships and principles of logic that are used throughout mathematics.

The Slope Concept via Experimental Data

W. B. White

A few preliminary comments seem necessary to fix the position of this particular article in the area of emerging practices in secondary education. However the bulk of the article will be material intended for direct classroom use.

Mathematics, because it is a logically organized subject, has an inherent difficulty, especially at the secondary-school level, in keeping up-to-date. Current events can be handled easily in a social studies class but current mathematics would be meaningless without extensive preparation. In spite of this it would seem that someone, perhaps even we teachers, should be making a more deliberate, more strenuous attempt to sift and simplify the mathematics of the last three or four centuries. Certainly in that time mathematicians have developed some areas of value sufficient to justify the inclusion of their basic concepts or simpler concepts in the high-school curriculum. Science and industry have not been so tardy in their acceptance of modern mathematics.

At the moment we find the simpler topics in analytic geometry and calculus—well over 300 years old—infiltrating at least the appendices of some geometry and advanced algebra texts—a short but important step in the right direction. The approaches are usually mathematically sound; but because the flavor of the college texts from which they were derived is retained, the degree of abstraction is often beyond the appreciation of secondary-school students. They prefer some meat on the skeleton of logical development. One method of achieving this is to associate the mathematical ideas with data from simple experiments.

Science experiments in the mathematics classroom have their problems. Any attempt at complete co-ordination of science and mathematics sacrifices the sequential organization of at least one of them. Neither classroom nor teacher may be equipped to handle much science. And many students do not have the scientific background which would be necessary to give meaning to many experiments.

In the selection of the two following experiments dealing with the concept of slope or rate of change an attempt has been made to minimize the objections of the preceding paragraph. They require little apparatus and only the simplest knowledge of science. The emphasis is on interpreting the data obtained rather than on the experiment itself. The first deals with the implications of a constant rate of change, the second with the implications of a variable rate. A second-year algebra course would be the most suitable place to present them, the first coming after the class has had some introduction to the notions of slope and intercept in relation to linear graphs, and the second after some work with curved line graphs or as a part of an introduction to differential calculus.

EXPERIMENT I

A study of the relationship between the length of a spring and the weight attached to it.

Apparatus Needed. A coil spring, a support for it, a set of weights, a meter stick.

Method of Presentation. A demonstration by the teacher or by one or more students; or, if sufficient apparatus is available, separate experiments by different groups. There is opportunity for as little or as much student planning as you believe desirable. The questions which follow are used as a written assignment or as a basis for discussion as the experiment progresses.

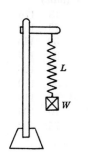
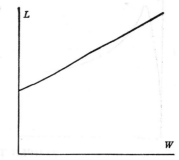

W (gm)	L (cm.)
0	8.5
20	9.6
50	11.2
100	14.1
130	15.6
200	19.5
220	?

SAMPLE TABLE AND GRAPH

Questions for the Student.

1. Make a table showing the relationship between the length, *L*, of the spring and the weight, *W*, attached to it.

2. Graph this relationship using the values of *L* as ordinates.

3. Determine the slope of the graph and its *L*-intercept. From these write the formula in which *L* is the dependent variable.

4. Use the formula to estimate lengths for weights not previously used. Check your results experimentally.

5. Can you tell from the graph: The amount the spring stretches for each additional gram added? The original length of the spring?

6. How can you get the amount of stretch per gram from the table? From the formula?

7. What does the *L*-intercept of the graph represent? What does the slope of the graph tell about the spring? Does the *W*-intercept have any meaning?

8. How would the graph appear if heavier weights were also used? Would the formula be accurate for these weights?

EXPERIMENT II

A study of the rates at which water heats and cools.

Apparatus needed. A pan of water, source of heat, thermometer with range of 60°F. to 220°F., watch.

Method of Presentation. The necessary data may be obtained in advance by a student or the teacher using a candy thermometer at home. With a bunsen burner or electric plate and a *small* amount of water, data could be obtained in class. Data in the questions below would have to be modified to correspond with that actually obtained; or the sample data given below could be used. The water is heated to boiling, boiled for a short period, and then permitted to cool, temperature readings being taken at frequent time intervals.

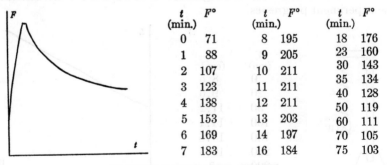

t (min.)	*F*°	*t* (min.)	*F*°	*t* (min.)	*F*°
0	71	8	195	18	176
1	88	9	205	23	160
2	107	10	211	30	143
3	123	11	211	35	134
4	138	12	211	40	128
5	153	13	203	50	119
6	169	14	197	60	111
7	183	16	184	70	105
				75	103

SAMPLE TABLE AND GRAPH

Questions for the Student.

Making and Reading the Graph:

1. After the necessary data have been tabulated note the range of values for each variable. Plot the graph carefully using temperatures as ordinates.

2. Find the temperature 5 minutes after the heat was turned off. (Not given in the table.)

3. After how many minutes heating was the temperature 200°? When was it 200° again?

Studying Rates of Heating and Cooling:

1. How many degrees did the temperature increase in the first five minutes? What average rate was this in degrees per minute?

2. What is the rate of heating during the next five minutes?

3. Compare the rates in the two previous questions. What feature of the graph indicates the result of this comparison? If the rate of increase of temperature were constant, how would the graph appear?

4. What is the nature of the graph between the 10th and 12th minute (while the water is boiling)?

5. In general the average rate of change in temperature is found by dividing the *change* in _____ by the corresponding change in _____. This ratio also gives the average _____ of the graph between the two points concerned, or the _____ of a chord joining the two points.

6. Apply the rule in question 5 to find the average rate at which the temperature changed from the 13th to the 75th minute. Note that a temperature drop is a negative change. What straight line segment would have the result for its slope?

Studying Instantaneous Rates of Change:

7. Repeat question 6 for the time intervals 13 to 30, 13 to 20, 13 to 15, and 13 to 14 minutes. In each case draw the chord having the resulting slope.

8. The chord whose slope indicates the average rate of temperature change between the 13th and 14th minute is almost a tangent to the curve. Draw a tangent at the point of the curve whose abscissa is 13. Determine the slope of this tangent. This slope is the instantaneous rate at which the temperature is changing 13 minutes after the beginning of the experiment.

9. What is the rate at which the temperature is changing after 40 minutes?

Other topics in the traditional courses can also be made more meaningful through the use of experimental data. The experiment with the spring can be modified or extended to examine the functional relationship between the amount of stretch (instead of the length) and the weight applied—an instance of direct variation. A pendulum and a watch are ample equipment to illustrate an inverse square relationship. Vectors can be studied by inserting spring scales in the strings by which a picture is suspended. The interpretation of data in general, i. e., the related subjects of probability and statistics are often bypassed by both the mathematics and commercial departments in the secondary school. These could serve as a basis for the study of inductive reasoning with at least as much justification as we have for using geometry to study deductive reasoning. To those who wonder how we would do all this in our already crowded hours I suggest that the mathematics curriculum, like a family, needs to move occasionally if only to get its attic cleaned.

Mathematics in General Education at San Francisco State College

JACK D. WILSON

TRENDS

The current widespread interest in general education is shared by many mathematics teachers, including teachers at the college level. In this article a college mathematics teacher traces 30 years of developments in "general mathematics," noting changes in opinions and practices and considering implications for today.

GENERAL education consists of those educative experiences which are designed to assist our youth to become worthy members of a democratic society. Recently there has arisen a great interest in general education at the college level. The question arises: Should mathematics be included?

The mathematician is quick to point out that many aspects of modern life are quantitative in nature. To leave out mathematics is to neglect a unique aspect of human living. The general educator, remembering his own experience with algebra and probably somewhat suspicious of the motives of the mathematician, has to be convinced. Perhaps his doubts are partially removed if the course is called "general mathematics" for it does seem possible that it can make a useful contribution to general education.

What is this general mathematics?

It is not a new expression. Many references have appeared in the literature during the past 30 years but until recently the term has been used mainly to describe certain courses offered at the secondary-school level (Grades VII–XII). Now with colleges beginning to map out and to put into effect certain requirements in general education, interested persons are asking whether general mathematics should be included as a compulsory course. If the answer is "Yes," a great challenge and a great opportunity are given to the mathematics department. However, the traditional offerings do not appear to meet the needs of the general education student. Unfortunately, large masses of college youth are so mathematically illiterate that they cannot profit from these courses. So with the opportunity comes also a perplexing problem, that of deciding what experiences to include in the new general mathematics offering.

The instructor who is to teach the new course may possibly seek a partial answer through a study of the history of general mathematics in the high school. Here, unfortunately, he will find a situation which is still not encouraging, even after 30 years of effort. He will notice, however, certain interesting trends in opinion and in practice over this period.

In the 20's general mathematics had already become an important issue in the literature, if not in the classroom, although there was confusion as to what should be included in the course. Meyers (29: 146) said that much that called itself by the name "general mathematics" was of small value. Hassler (29: 145) said that he did not believe in forced fusion of unrelated subject matter. Despite the uncertainty, several authorities gave definitions. Judd (25: 98) described general mathematics as "the fusion of algebra and geometry." Reeve (42: 148–49) suggested that the courses in algebra, in geometry, and in trigonometry be replaced by a definitely arranged and psychologically ordered course in mathematics. Hart (34: 212) went so far as to insist that algebra was no longer algebra but rather a desirable form of general mathematics when enriched by continuous attention to arithmetic, graphs, and geometric concepts. The National Committee on Mathematical Requirements, 1923, suggested that at the senior high-school level, as well as in the junior high school, teachers should be able to present their material more effectively in combined courses unified by one or more of such central ideas as functionality and graphic representation.

As defined in the 20's, general mathematics did have certain merits. It used better psychology of learning and had a much more real and natural organization than did the traditional courses. It did not force the teacher to confine himself to a single field of mathematics. Nevertheless, one may ask: "Did it meet the real needs of the student body as a whole?"

Apparently not. The position of mathematics in our high schools became even more insecure during the 30's. A Midwestern superintendent of schools (42: 7) summed up the opinion of many when he said that "we do not need to worry any longer about teaching mathematics in the secondary school."

It would be unfair, of course, to blame the crisis in mathematics on the failure of general mathematics because most schools still retained the traditional sequence. Nevertheless, the general course was not meeting with success. Boyce (8: 106) said that in most instances it had turned out to be little more than a repackaging of the old product done up in small bundles. Betz (5: 343) asked how a few snapshots of this or that topic could provide an adequate vehicle for continuous growth. Schorling (47: 16) suggested that the country had been oversold on the idea of general mathematics.

A growing body of mathematics educators felt that general mathematics as already defined had failed because it did not fill a real need in the pupil's life. Douglass (16: 362) believed that there had been a totally inadequate treatment of the mathematics needed by the general population for home and family life, for health, for safety, and for government. Boyce (8: 107) suggested that mathematics be employed to clarify the controversial issues of the social studies. These opinions were typical of a trend that gathered further strength during the 40's.

Today mathematics for general education is frequently defined as those ideas and techniques that are essential for the solution of the quantitative problems which will probably be encountered in life. Freeman says:

Only that mathematics is important for general education which the individual will use (19: 249).

Kinney (26: 6) points out that the one thing lacking in our economic system is an educated, enlightened, socially responsible consumer who knows what goods and services he wants and how to get them. Breslich asks for a college program which will qualify teachers for the difficult job of teaching mathematics for use. He says:

> The student preparing to teach should, therefore, at some time make a thorough study of the uses of mathematics in the affairs of everyday life, not only of that which is used but also of the mathematics which could be used advantageously and which should be used (10: 203).

Textbooks devoted almost exclusively to consumer mathematics are now being published. Apparently mathematics for general education now means mathematics for use, including social mathematics and consumer mathematics.

This history of general mathematics in the high school does not supply the answer to the college instructor teaching mathematics in a general education program but perhaps it does give an indication of the experiences which will be received with favor and the difficulties involved in providing such.

A compulsory general mathematics course required of nearly all students (as at San Francisco State College) is of necessity under close scrutiny both by administration and by students. Its purpose must be in harmony with the philosophy of general education at the college. Its contents must provide experiences clearly recognized by students as contributing to a more effective personal and social life. Such a course is difficult to organize, more difficult to teach. Nevertheless, the task must be undertaken because personal and social problems can be dealt with effectively only at a quantitative level. In this respect mathematics can make a unique contribution, but in the college, as in the high school, success may hinge on the meaning attached to the phrase "mathematics for use."

IMPLEMENTATION AT A STATE COLLEGE

The foregoing historical introduction is important in the light of developments at San Francisco State College because it helps to explain and to justify the form that the general education mathematics course has taken at this institution.

The course outline was written by Arthur J. Hall. He made
the decision that the objectives could be best attained by organizing the course around subject matter of recognized social significance, subject matter of real interest to young adults. But, in
implementing this plan, he took great care to select broad areas
which could clearly serve as a vehicle for teaching in systematic
fashion the basic mathematics needed in life. Dr. Hall has prepared outlines for five broad areas of instruction. All instructors
are required to follow these general outlines but each instructor
is free to use his own methods and materials within this general
framework.

The writer will undertake, in the remainder of this paper, to
describe some of the specific methods and materials that he has
developed for the teaching of one of these broad areas, the unit
on statistics. A more detailed report, giving the history, philosophy, objectives, content and an evaluation of the course as a
whole, will probably be made by Dr. Hall in the not too distant
future.

STATISTICS: CONTENT AND METHOD

Preliminary Statement. What kind of statistics? The answer,
the kind endorsed by the American Mathematical Society when
it stated (23):

> The committee thinks for one thing that the study of statistics
> should be made a part of a liberal education. Statistics do, indeed, turn
> up everywhere in the American way of life. Batting averages, betting
> odds, and stock market quotations are statistics. Safety authorities
> predict the casualties of a holiday week end by studying statistics.
> The popularity of radio programs, the chance of a political candidate,
> and the probable weather for a week from Wednesday are figured by
> statistics. The average American is surrounded by figures almost from
> the cradle to the grave. It has become a minor mathematical problem
> to determine the cheapest way to travel. The wage earner's pay is a
> result of mathematics, especially subtraction.

Now even at the high-school level, implementation of the above
recommendations is not easy. In the college further difficulties
are experienced, for college students will not tolerate a sort of
"dime store" mathematics. The problem essentially reduces to

the selection of material which is socially useful and interesting to young adults but which can be organized in such a way as to present the basic mathematics for intelligent consumership in a systematic fashion—consumership in the broad sense, of course, including the consumption of mathematical ideas appearing in magazines and newspapers.

In the unit on statistics this is attempted under the headings, Problem-Solving and Collection of Data, Presentation of Data, Organization of Data—Averages, and Interpretation of Data.

Problem-Solving and Collection of Data. This first unit gives a pleasant introduction to the course; consequently computational mathematics is minimized. A major objective is to develop awareness of the concept "representative sample." Analyses of public-opinion polls, such as the *Literary Digest* and the Gallup Polls, quickly gains the interest of the class, besides acting somewhat as a sedative for those who are plagued by the highly popular "mental block" towards mathematics.

Some simple arithmetic does enter this unit with questions like the following:

A factory has 2000 workers as below:

	Age in Years				
	20–29	30–39	40–49	50–59	60 and over
Men.............	200	240	312	285	120
Women..........	250	350	158	85	0

A sample of 300 is to be selected for an interview. How many should be included in each age-sex group to make the sample representative with respect to age and sex?

Frequently the students carry out sampling studies on topics of their own choosing, some of which have proved of real interest to the administration of the college.

Presentation of Data. The mathematical objectives are: (a) understanding of tables, graphs, and index numbers; (b) review of percentage, common fractions, and decimals. The social vehicle for developing these concepts is the "California Trend." Current materials from newspapers, magazines, and pamphlets are utilized, but most valuable are the publications of the *Bank of America*, booklets which give the California Trend in words, in pictures, and in graphs.

The social setting is indicated as follows (1: 2). We present the case of California not as a boast, but as information bearing on the national scene:

When one state accounts for one-fifth of the nation's population increase during a decade, with related gains in buying power, business, and agricultural activity, the facts become matters of importance to those who think, plan, and operate on a national basis. When pace-setting growth places in California approximately one-fourteenth of the nation's population and jobs, more than one-twelfth of its income and trade, better than one-tenth of all new building, and nearly one-tenth of all motor vehicles, that is something with which men everywhere are concerned.

The pattern of California's growth is like its mountains; ascending in saw-tooth fashion, steep ascents, shallow dips. The dips are the state's occasional response to cyclical influences. The upthrusts are the product of a series of major developments which leave permanent impress: discovery of gold, transcontinental railroad building, oil discovery, irrigated agriculture, entertainment as big business, and the current industrialization of the state. All this creates a desirable atmosphere in which to live and do things.

Tables and graphs are utilized to develop the general theme of the unit. Presentation of the latter takes three forms: sketches on the board, dittoed sheets handed out to students, and constructions on heavy paper prepared in advance for use in class. The writer usually draws on the blackboard one or two bar graphs, one or two line graphs, and one circle graph, all carefully selected to illustrate the California Trend.

Examples of graphs which have been used are given on these pages. The bar graph showing motor vehicle registration was selected because it is related to two critical problems in San Francisco—parking and municipal street railway service. The line graph showing population gain since 1900 was chosen because it is the key which explains many of the currently pressing problems existing in the state. The graph showing trend in employment by industry groups between 1940 and 1951 (see page 301), was selected because it is sufficiently complex to furnish the basis for a series of short questions related to industrial development within the state. This last graph is one of several which were dittoed and handed out to the individual students.

Following the description of the California Trend, the purposes and uses of the different graphs are summarized. The essential features in the construction of each are pointed out and a few

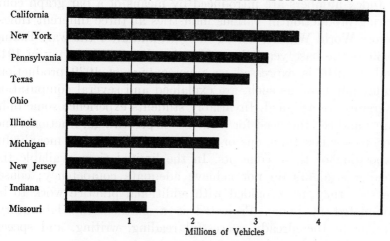

LEADING STATES IN MOTOR VEHICLE REGISTRATION

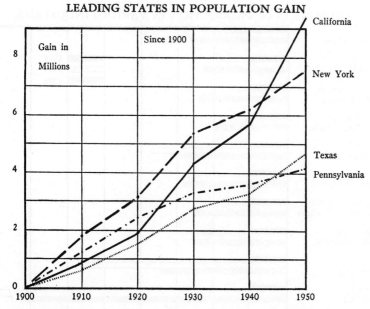

LEADING STATES IN POPULATION GAIN

exercises related to the construction and reading of graphs are assigned. One such is a series of line graphs, all on the same axis, showing monthly maximum temperatures for a 12-month period for representative areas of the state, this to illustrate the diversity of climate patterns and the effect on population and industrial development.

Index numbers are introduced by means of a bar graph comparing production in various industries at three different times; before World War II, during the war, and after the war. Taking 1939 as the base year, the production for each industry in 1943 and in 1946 is expressed as a percentage of 1939 production. Index numbers, as such, are explained and several computation exercises are assigned. Invariably students experience some difficulty and see the need for a review of percentage, fractions, and decimals. Class time, one or two hours, is devoted to meaningful exposition of these concepts. In the limited time available the weaker students do not achieve adequate competency; consequently they are provided with additional practice work to be completed at home. Projected is a mathematics laboratory, similar to the already successful reading, writing, and speech

COMPARISON OF PRODUCTION IN VARIOUS INDUSTRIES

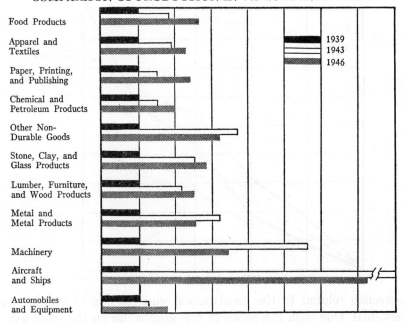

laboratories, into which students in need of diagnostic and remedial instruction may be directed.

Then one final social application: the cost of living of Californians as reflected in the U. S. cost of living index. The presentation is at a popular level: how the old index was constructed (1935–39); how it controls directly the paychecks of 3-million workers and indirectly those of 20 million more; how it has been criticized by management and labor alike; and finally the story of the new index as worked out in 1951–52. The unit is completed with numerical exercises in index numbers and other percentages.

COST OF LIVING IN CALIFORNIA

Organization of Data, Averages. The mathematical objectives are: (a) understanding of the various kinds of averages; (b) ability to compute averages; (c) understanding of frequency distributions, histograms and frequency polygons; and (d) increased competency in arithmetic.

The presentation, while systematic, is designed to show the importance of averages in daily life. The following illustrations indicate the method:

1. A cartoon, showing 11 little men who constitute the labor force in a small factory, is drawn on the blackboard. Below each man is written his wage.

THESE MEN ARE DEMANDING AN INCREASE IN WAGES

$2000 $2500 $3000 $3000 $3000 $3100 $3200 $3300 $3400 $3500 $10,000

Suppose you are the owner and do not wish to grant their request. You want to prove that their average wage is already quite high. What would you give as the average? . . . Suppose you are the union representative. You want the average to appear low. Now what would you say it is? The ensuing discussion brings out the definitions of the mean, the median, and the mode.

2. Following a class test, the scores are listed on the board in the same order as in the class-roll book. Students notice the difficulty in picturing the over-all class performance from these unordered scores and readily see the need for some informative method of grouping scores such as the frequency table, the histogram, and the frequency polygon. An opportunity is available to acquaint the students with the normal distribution and some of its properties. Computation of averages from grouped data furnishes practice in arithmetic.

3. Illustrations from newspapers are utilized to indicate the need for the intelligent consumer to understand averages. The following story, headlined by the *San Francisco News*, February 26, 1951, is an example:

THE AVERAGE AMERICAN IS A WOMAN

Washington, Feb. 26. The Census Bureau reported today that the American woman, who has gradually undermined male supremacy in many fields, now has taken over for the first time as the "average" American. . . . According to the bureau, the "average" American is a native-born woman who is 30 years of age, married, and living in her own city home with 2.4 other persons.

Hollywood, Feb. 24. Jane Russell, to everybody's surprise, qualified today as what the Census Bureau says is the "average" American.

Miss Russell, decidedly above average in some respects, is 30, married, and a woman. This fits the Census Bureau's description of the average American on the basis of its 1950 count.

Like any other woman, Miss Russell was distressed to hear that there are more females than males for the first time in history, 100 to 98.1.

"I hope this predominance of females is only temporary," she said. "I wish the average American were a man—in fact, I wish the average American were just like my husband." He is football star Bob Waterfield.

Interpretation of Data. The amount and kind of interpretation is limited by the mathematical equipment of the students. The objective is to develop critical awareness that statistics, although capable of revealing much useful information, may frequently conceal what is vital.

Topics include stretching the vertical scale, cutting the bottom off a graph, interpolation, extrapolation, overgeneralization, definitions, hidden assumptions, and hidden implications.

The problem is to develop these concepts somewhat systematically in a significant social situation. "Teacher and Classroom Shortage" was selected since many of the students are planning to become teachers.

Current conditions are described using graphs clipped from newspapers and magazines. To illustrate the situation in the lower grades in San Francisco, the writer drew on the board a line graph, showing trends in kindergarten enrollment, exactly as the graph had appeared in the *San Francisco Chronicle*. Besides imparting useful information, this indicates the manner in which cutting off the base can exaggerate 1950–51 increase in enrollment and consequently deceive the careless reader. Similarly, the effect of stretching the vertical scale is explained.

What is the reason for the current shortage of teachers and of classrooms? Did not educators foresee this trend? Students are

CHILDREN IN SAN FRANCISCO KINDERGARTENS

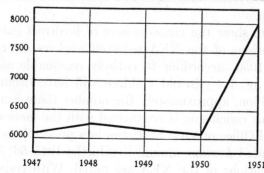

likely to answer that present conditions are due to virtual cessa-
tion of building activities and teacher education programs during
the war. The following graph was selected to show that this is not

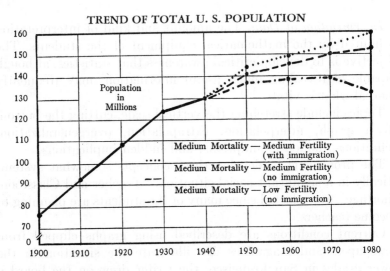

TREND OF TOTAL U. S. POPULATION

the only reason and to point out that prediction of future trends
through extrapolation is particularly hazardous and difficult.
Taken from the NEA bulletin, *Schools and the 1940 Census*, it
shows what thoughtful investigators in 1940 believed our population would be in the years 1950, 1960, 1970, and 1980 under
various possible conditions of mortality, fertility, and immigra-
tion. (Note that the population in 1953 has already equaled the
highest estimate for 1980.) These extrapolations—the instructor
points out—were made, not as a theoretical exercise, but as the
basis for action—the building of new schools and the education of
new teachers.

In order to show the consequences of incorrect extrapolation,
some conclusions of the NEA research workers are read to the
class. "By 1950, according to entirely reasonable assumptions,
the number of five-year-old children will have declined to less
than 1.9 million, approximately the number there were in 1903"
(36: 40). This conclusion is contrasted with the facts released by
the National Office of Vital Statistics in a press release, March 6,
1952: estimated average annual live births 1945–50, 3.5 million.
Recommendations of the NEA are noted. With respect to new

schools (36: 41), "Overexpansion in any type of building activity will need to be avoided. Continued expansion . . . would likely prevent the development of a modern instructional program. With respect to new teachers (37: 228), "With a declining child population and consequent decreases in school enrollments, the demand for large numbers of new teachers will decrease." These class activities develop an awareness of the hazards involved in extrapolation and of the consequences which may follow when action must be taken on the basis of such extrapolation.

The above illustrations indicate some of the concepts developed in this unit. Besides assignment of numerical problems in extrapolation and interpolation, specially prepared exercises in interpretation of data are an important source of student activity. These consist of tables and graphs, each accompanied by a series of statements which the students judge as true, probably true, not sufficient data to pass judgment, probably false, or false,

EMPLOYMENT IN CALIFORNIA BY INDUSTRY GROUPS

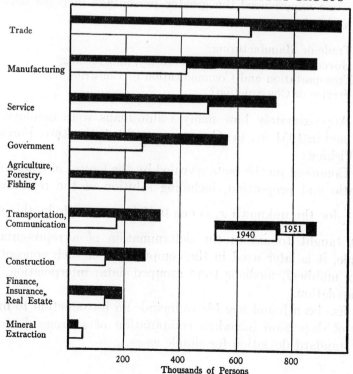

using only the information appearing on the graph or in the table.

Use the graph on page 301 to answer the following questions:

1. In 1951 employment in Trade was about: (a) double, (b) one-half, (c) one and two-thirds, (d) three-fifths, (e) three times what it was in 1940.

2. In 1951 employment in Manufacturing was: (a) double, (b) one-half, (c) three times, (d) four times, (e) three-halves what it was in 1940.

3. In 1951 employment in Finance, Insurance, and Real Estate was about: (a) 200 per cent, (b) 300 per cent, (c) 100 per cent, (d) 150 per cent, (e) 66 per cent of what it was in 1940.

4. Which areas experienced at least 100 per cent increase in employment between 1940 and 1951?

5. In which industry group did employment decrease between 1940 and 1951?

6. For each of the following pairs of industry groups, determine which one experienced the greater percentage increase between 1940 and 1951.

a. Trade or Manufacturing?
b. Government or Agriculture, Forestry, and Fishing?
c. Transportation and Communication or Construction?
d. Service or Construction?

7. Approximately how many Californians were employed in 1940 and in 1951 in: (a) Government; (b) Agriculture, Forestry, and Fishing?

8. Comment on the facts revealed by the figures in Question 7.

Ratio and proportion, including solution of the relationship $\frac{x}{a} = \frac{b}{c}$ for the unknown x, is one unifying principle in this unit. First taught to aid in the determination of a representative sample, it is later used in the computation of such concepts as index numbers, medians from grouped data, interpolation, and extrapolation.

It has been found feasible to include an introduction to measures of dispersion including computation of average deviation and standard deviation for simple cases.

SUMMARY

This paper has outlined the history of general mathematics in the high schools and has indicated the possible implications for a course in general education mathematics at the college. It has outlined the methods and materials employed by the writer in one specific area, the field of statistics. It has not implied that the content or the methods are good for other groups differing from ours in mathematical background or vocational interests.

Student reaction has been favorable, even enthusiastic. Still, the hope is that the senior high schools will soon develop and require all students to complete a good course in basic consumer mathematics. At such time mathematics in general education at this college may well be elevated to a much more sophisticated *mathematical* level.

Einstein vs. Heisenberg—Shall We Discuss Current Mathematics?

Edna E. Kramer

"Peace Offer from China!"

"Shift in Soviet Policy!"

"New Einstein Theory Unifies Basic Concepts of the Universe!"

These are the newspaper headlines at the time this article is being written (April 1953). In English, history, civics, and economics classes throughout the United States, the first two items are being analyzed in great detail. By contrast, probably not one high-school mathematics class in 1000 is holding any prolonged discussion of the third news release, even though Einstein's offering may have a more lasting, if less immediate or direct effect on civilization than a diplomatic gesture by any person or group.

If mathematics is to integrate with related science or compete with instruction in the humanities, then it would seem that, (a) current developments should be part of the regular course of study, (b) recent discoveries that are advanced in nature should be popularized by extracting those elementary features which can be associated with functionality, variation, graph, or other fundamental concepts, (c) we must reexamine the postulates of mathematical pedagogy so as to enlarge the present set of principles in the light of recent scientific progress, since suggestion (b) will not lead to adequate treatment in many cases.

As an example of how the first two of these suggestions can be carried out in a specific instance, let us give a condensed version of how our own classes discussed the news of Einstein's complete unification of his theory.

"I cannot believe that God plays dice with the cosmos," says the creator of relativity. What does this figurative statement mean? Just that Einstein has always sought *exact* formulas in his explanations of scientific phenomena. In our elementary mathematics, formulas like $I = PRT$, $F = 9/5C + 32$, tell precisely how simple interest is computed, how centigrade readings may be converted to Fahrenheit. On the other hand, insurance companies make no exact statements as to the fate of any individual man but refer to a fictitious "average" man. In the preparation of mortality tables, actuaries have found, say, that about 1.1 per cent of 45-year-old men will die before reaching their 46th birthday, or that the "probability" of death is about 0.011. In analogous fashion, the quantum physicists have been using statistical inference— "playing dice," so to speak, in predicting the behavior of subatomic entities.

Actuaries and nuclear scientists will doubtless continue to use probability theory and statistics with great success. We must grant, nevertheless, that any formula, however grim, that would give exact information on the mortality of the *individual* man would be superior to a statistical estimate involving a whole set of people. Hence Einstein, as mathematician, physicist, philosopher, has sought over many years a formulation more exact than the statistical methods of the quantum theory. One of the foundation stones of that theory is the Heisenberg Uncertainty Principle, which asserts the impossibility of predicting the behavior of individual atomic entities. As a corollary, this uncertainty in the atom extends to the entire cosmos, a situation which has seemed intolerable to the greatest "universe builder" in history.

We come now to the third of the proposals forming the theme

of this article. We shall not presume to formulate the many new principles which up-to-date pedagogy should add to the conventional list. Our illustration would suggest that more emphasis on probability and statistics should be one of them, and this thread will reappear in our subsequent discussion. It is the major tool in *inductive inference*, a concept which is bound to link a large number of 20th Century scientific discoveries to the everyday, elementary work of the junior or senior high-school mathematics class.

Over and over again in our teaching we emphasize the *deductive* nature of mathematics. We do use inductive procedures occasionally in experimental intuitive geometry, in the heuristic anticipation of some fact or formula, or such thing. We make sure to indicate the dangers of hasty generalization, and our students are made to realize that even a million, a billion repetitions of an experiment resulting in the identical outcome would not justify the conclusion that the result will always be the same. We quote or else paraphrase for our pupils Bertrand Russell's, "In the final form of a perfected science it would seem that everything ought to be deductive—that is, deducible from a few fundamental propositions, called postulates."

The attitude of the pure mathematician permits these axioms to be quite arbitrary and all he demands of them is *consistency*. If, however, we are interested in *applied* science, then the postulates should be derived from observations by use of some type of inductive reasoning. In this way, deductive branches of mathematics may rest on foundations which are inductive. Again, when the logical consequences of the postulates have been worked out, the physicist, astronomer, geneticist, and the engineer must devise new experiments to check once again the agreement of his theoretical results with facts observed in the external world. Thus we see that deduction is sandwiched between an empirical start and an experimental ending. Is it any wonder that Russell's collaborator, Whitehead, remarked that "the theory of induction is the despair of philosophy—and yet *all*, absolutely *all* our activities are based upon it."

Are we then to ask our 12-to-18-year-olds to master a concept which defies the philosophers? No, indeed! We shall be able to get along with two much simpler notions. The first of these is *statistical induction* (sometimes called *ampliative* induction). We define a statistical induction as a *generalization* made from a limited number of observations. If we wish to be more elegant in the definition given to advanced students, we may say: A statistical induction is the *assumption* that an event which has occurred in n trials, where $n \geq 1$, will occur in trials $n + 1, n + 2, n + 3$, and such, forever.

As one example of such an induction we may cite the assumption that rain or snow usually follows the appearance of heavy clouds. Here n may be thought of as a large number, since the generalization results from meteorological observations over a long period.

Why can't we have a perfect induction instead of a statistical one? The answer is that if an *absolute* induction is to be based on observations, it will be admissible only after we have observed *all* of a set of things. It would then merely be a summary, arising merely in trivial situations, e.g., after measuring the heights of all students in a class, we might form the absolute induction: The pupils in this class range in height from 4 ft. 8 in. to 6 ft. 1 in. Suppose however, that

U.S. scientists complete an H-bomb of a certain type for an experimental tryout on an atoll. As a result of this *single* trial, they make various pronouncements on the approximate size of the area which will be destroyed, radioactive effects to be expected of any H-bomb of the same type, size, etc. used under the same conditions.

This is obviously a statistical induction where $n = 1$, the case of a generalization after one observation. The U.S. might not be able to try out many H-bombs because human life might thereby be endangered, or else the financial expense might be too great.

The mathematics teacher may not like such inductions, but we emphasize again: (a) that they are *assumptions* and, (b) they are a practical necessity. In addition, if $n = 1$ or some small number, the experimenter does his best to control conditions so as to make them typical.

Jerzy Neymann handles the matter of inductive inference gracefully by placing the stress not on the induction itself, but on the use we make of it. We name him as authority for our second basic concept, that of *inductive behavior*, which he describes as the *adjustment of our behavior to limited amounts of observation*. In our meteorological illustration, the inductive behavior could be the act of taking cover when heavy clouds appear. We see that it would not matter whether our statistical induction were correct or not. The worst risk in our inductive behavior would be a waste of time if precipitation did not occur. Possible inductive behavior in the H-bomb generalization would be for the U.S. to adopt the bomb as a suitable war weapon. Here we see how great a risk might be involved in inductive behavior after one experiment.

Thus far we have made no numerical measurements of such risks. To do so we inevitably fall back on the simple models furnished by games of chance. Let us consider an example:

A coin-tossing machine, perfectly adjusted, performs a dozen tosses of a coin which the observer has not been allowed to examine. Each time the coin turns up heads. What conclusion might he draw? Interpret this judgment as an "induction." Give a numerical estimate of the chance that this induction is wrong. If he had come to the same conclusion after the appearance of 6 heads, what would the chance of error have been? If he refuses to draw any conclusion until after 20 trials, and all 20 have been heads, what is the chance of being wrong?

Answer: Since the machine is perfectly adjusted, the conclusion might be that the coin has two heads or else is loaded for extreme bias. "Common sense" without any knowledge of probability would dictate such a judgment. Either judgment is a statistical induction because we are concluding either that *all* subsequent tosses will yield heads or else a very large percentage of heads.

If the coin were fairly homogeneous and symmetrical, with two different faces, then on the average, in about one out of every 4000 coin-tossing experiments like the one performed, 12 heads would appear in succession. Thus there is the chance that we have hit just this "one in 4000" freak situation. In the case of an "ideal" coin, the classic theory of probability would give 1/4096 as the chance that our induction is wrong.

In the case of the induction after 6 heads, the chance for error, by common sense, should be greater, in the case of 20 tosses less. The ideal, classic figures are $1/64$ and $2^{1/20}$ (approximately one in a million).

There can be many variants of this exercise. The probability of a faulty induction can be figured in other situations involving dice, cards, and such things. Such exercises should not be confined to advanced algebra classes, but are simple enough for the ninth year. Any permutations or combinations involved can be visualized if small numbers are used, and the teacher can merely furnish the figures when they are large.

When the *transistor* makes the news these days, we may not be able to discuss the scientific principles it applies, but we can hold a discussion of the general question of the manufacturing processes associated with production of parts of electronic apparatus, and therefore consider questions like the following:

In a certain manufacturing process there are lots containing 100 articles. The inspection scheme used calls for examination of a random sample of 10 from each lot. The entire lot will be accepted if the number of defective articles in the sample is 3 or less. Otherwise, the lot will be rejected. From experience, it has been found that the maximum number of defectives the consumer can tolerate in any lot is 7. If there are actually 9 defectives in a lot, what is the chance that it will pass inspection? This is called the *consumer's risk*. Figure the consumer's risk if there are 15 defectives in a lot. If the producer has standardized quality at an average level of 5 defectives per lot, what is his risk, that is, what is the probability of unjust rejection of a lot?

To prepare for general sampling inspection issues, we resort once more to the idealized model of a game of chance:

Jack offers Bill the following game. Jack will fill a bag with 10 marbles, some white and the rest blue, in a proportion which Jack will select himself and vary as the game continues. The game will consist of drawing one or two marbles from the bag. They are returned to the bag, which is then mixed thoroughly. Bill is to bet on the color of the next draw. Consider the following rules which Bill may adopt for his inductive behavior.

1. Before the betting, Bill draws just *one* marble. He replaces it and mixes thoroughly. He bets "W" or "B" for the next draw according as his sample was "W" or "B" respectively.

2. Bill draws one marble, replaces it, mixes thoroughly, draws another. If the result of the two drawings was "WW," he bets "W" for the next draw, otherwise "B."

> a. Let x be the proportion of white marbles and y the probability that Bill will bet "W." Let $x = 0$, $\frac{1}{5}$, $\frac{2}{5}$, $\frac{3}{5}$, $\frac{4}{5}$, 1. Find the corresponding values of y for Rule 1. Plot the table of values as a graph. Repeat for Rule 2. What is the equation for y in terms of x in each case?

(Each formula and graph is called an *operating characteristic* function and curve respectively.)

b. If Jack knows Bill is going to use Rule 1, how many white marbles should be put in the bag so that he, Jack, will have the best chance of winning the game? (Answer: 5.)

c. If Bill uses Rule 2, what number of white marbles in the sack will give Jack the greatest chance of winning? (Answer: 6.)

d. Show that by substituting different items in place of marbles, different attributes instead of "W" and "B", e.g., articles in a lot, defective and acceptable respectively, this abstract problem may illustrate many different practical situations.

e. Plot on one set of axes the two OC curves for betting "W" or betting "B" in Rule 1. Note that corresponding probabilities are complementary, always totaling one. The two curves together are termed the *performance characteristic* of Rule 1.

f. Plot the performance characteristic of Rule 2.

g. Make up a game similar to this one, but involving 3 possible courses of action. Plot the performance characteristic which will now contain 3 curves.

Bill's behavior in the preceding example illustrates *statistical decision functions*, a recent development in mathematics analogous to elementary functional relationships. We arrive at a powerful summarizing general concept in the *Definition*: If R is any rule of inductive behavior relating to some random experiment with different possible outcomes $E_1, E_2, \cdots E_n, \cdots$ and $a_1, a_2, \cdots a_n, \cdots$ are the corresponding actions prescribed by R, then the statistical decision function $a(E)$ establishes a correspondence between outcomes E and actions a. The independent and dependent variables in this functional relationship are E and a respectively.

In our illustration, Rule 1 is applied to two possible outcomes and prescribes two different corresponding actions, while Rule 2 involves four outcomes but only two possible courses of action. Both rules yield *2-valued* decision functions, while part "g" above will lead to a *3-valued* function.

Working with Approximate Data

CARL SHUSTER

It is an unfortunate fact that we live in a world of approximate data. No one in the whole history of civilization has ever made an exactly accurate measurement of any kind, and it is quite safe to assume that no one ever will. In addition to measurement there are many other sources of approximate data. The table on the properties of saturated steam in the *Handbook of Physics and Chemistry* contains 3591 approximate numbers. There are hundreds of similar tables in this and the many other handbooks. Trigonometric functions, logarithms, square and higher roots, division, and the use of conversion factors produce other approximate numbers.

Approximate data and processes producing approximate numbers are used in many phases of the work in mathematics and science now taught in the elementary and secondary schools. It is not at all difficult to teach the simple rules for computing with approximate data in the seventh, eighth, and ninth grades. In fact, it is far easier to teach all the student needs to know about the topic in these grades than it is to change the computational habits of graduate students who have always used "exact" computation.

It would be possible and perhaps desirable to teach certain phases of computation with approximate data as early as the fifth and sixth grades. As soon as the pupil begins to measure and to use decimal fractions he should learn to distinguish between exact and approximate numbers. If the topic is not introduced at this time, textbook writers and teachers should be very careful to avoid rules and techniques that will have to be radically changed in future work.

The concepts and rules necessary for the correct use of approximate data do not necessarily mix-up or confuse the pupil. This occurs only where the teacher is confused and inept. A famous textbook author recently told the writer, "I would like to put computation with approximate data in my seventh and eighth grade texts. I know the pupils could understand it, but I am afraid of the teachers."

Actually only two very simple concepts are necessary. The first suffices for addition and subtraction of approximate data.

All approximate quantities that are to be added or subtracted should be measured or rounded to the same unit of measurement. (Note that the second concept used for multiplication, division, roots, and powers is given on page 318.)

The *Unit of Measurement* is the smallest unit used in a measurement. In the measurement $18\frac{3}{16}$ inches the unit of measurement is $\frac{1}{16}$ inch. That is, the measuring instrument must have been graduated in $\frac{1}{16}$ inch. In the measurement 4.06 inches the unit of measurement is 0.01 inch.

The unit of measurement in each of the following measurements is given in the parentheses.

1. 436 feet (1 foot)
2. 8.63 feet (0.01 foot)
3. 4° 6′ 3″ (1″)
4. 16 lbs. 3 oz. (1 oz.)
5. $9\frac{7}{16}$ in. ($\frac{1}{16}$ in.)
6. $11\frac{9}{128}$″ ($\frac{1}{128}$″)
7. 1242 ft. 7 in. (1 in.)
8. 2.000 in. (0.001 in.)
9. 6.347 m. (0.001 m.)
10. 3786 mi. (1 mi.)

The *precision* of a measurement is determined by the *unit of measurement*. The smaller the unit of measurement the greater the precision will be. The measurement 6.382 feet is more precise than the measurement 5.86 feet or the measurement 412.7 feet because the first has the smaller unit of measurement (0.001 feet).

SIGNIFICANT DIGITS

It is assumed that a careful measurer will not make an error of more than one-half of the *unit of measurement* in any measurement that he makes. Where this is true all the digits of the measurement are said to be *significant*.

If a distance has been measured so accurately that it is known to be nearer to 476.4 feet than it is to 476.3 feet or 476.5 feet, or if the distance is between 476.35 feet and 476.45 feet, then the error in the measurement will not be more than one-half the unit of measurement (0.1 ft.) and the measurement 476.4 feet will have four significant digits. That is each digit will have significance or will have a definite meaning.

For every digit of a measurement to be significant every digit except the last must be exactly correct and the error in the last digit must not be greater than one-half the unit of measurement.

The teacher should be very careful to see that the pupils thoroughly understand the terms, *unit of measurement, precision* and *significant digits*. A fourth concept *accuracy* will be given later.

If a farmer or surveyor wished to find the perimeter of an irregular field, he would first decide how *precise* he wished his

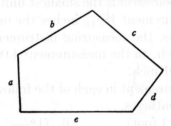

measurements to be. He would select the *unit of measurement* that best fit his needs and then would measure each side to the same precision.

Depending on the unit selected he might get the following results:

	I	II	III
a	214 ft.	213.8 ft.	213.78 ft.
b	328 ft.	328.2 ft.	328.23 ft.
c	352 ft.	351.7 ft.	351.67 ft.
d	196 ft.	196.3 ft.	196.34 ft.
e	427 ft.	427.4 ft.	427.39 ft.
	1517 ft.	1517.4 ft.	1517.41 ft.

However no rational person would measure the sides of the field as shown in IV, and yet examples of this type are found in many of our modern texts. Examples of this type are called "ragged decimals."

IV

a	214. ft.
b	328.235 ft.
c	351.67 ft.
d	196.3 ft.
e	427. ft.
	? ft.

Addition examples like IV and subtraction examples like V and VI below should be eliminated from all texts and tests.

V	VI
4. in.	12.6135 mi.
2.1634 in.	8. mi.

The only answers that could be accepted for V and VI are 2 inches and 5 miles.

Authors of textbooks at the present time are almost forced to include a few examples having ragged decimals because they do appear on obsolete "standard tests" prepared by persons with little knowledge of mathematics, and they are demanded by teachers entirely out of step with modern uses and trends.

In texts containing ragged decimals the pupil is sometimes instructed to "fill the empty places with zeros and then add or subtract." Actually there is no more justification for making the 4. in V 4.0000 in. than there would in making it 4.1111 in., 4.3634 in., 3.9999 in., or thousands of other measurements any one of which might have been the correct measurement if a smaller or more precise unit of measurement had been used. *It is never permissible to annex zeros in addition or subtraction.* Examples like IV, V, and VI do not occur in real life, and they should not appear in up-to-date books. Reeve says, "Not only is an example like 12.7 − 4.0396 a nonessential, but it is an evidence of educational ignorance" (50).

Writing about similar examples found on so-called standard tests (9.4 − 4.00083 and 9.2 − 3.00061), Upton says, "How is a teacher to keep her balance when presumably authoritative tests give problems like the above?" (56). Brueckner and Grossnickle say in connection with similar examples, "The teacher who gives examples of this type is defeating one of the purposes of teaching decimals. Neither business nor science uses such procedures." And, again, "Ragged decimals never occur in social usage" (11).

It should be noted that if the zeros in an example like VI are not significant, the example violates the rule that all measurements to be added or subtracted should be measured, or rounded, to the same unit. This is another case of "ragged decimals." In Example VII the measurements are decimal whole numbers.

VII
46 ft.
210 ft.
3,400 ft.
163,000 ft.

Examples IV, V, VI and VII *violate the fundamental rule that all measurements to be added or subtracted should be measured to the same unit.* Certainly no experienced person would think of using four different units in one set of measurements. No one uses a yardstick for part of a set of measurements and a micrometer for the balance.

Computation never increases the accuracy of the data. Cullimore says, "The frequent habit of carrying results to a greater number of significant figures than the data warrants comes perilously near to lying with figures" (14). The teacher who annexes zeros in examples like IV, V, and VI and thus makes people believe that rough data are very accurate data is no longer "perilously near," he has arrived.

A measurement like 4 inches (V) is a very rough measurement, whereas 4.0000 inches is a very precise (small unit) and accurate (five significant digits) measurement. In no sense are 4 inches and 4.0000 inches equivalent. If the 4.0000 inches has been measured correctly to the nearest 0.0001 inch the zeros are significant and no practical measurer would omit them.

In a set of measurements like those shown in "a," each measurement should be given to the same unit; in this case the tenth of a foot is the unit of measurement, and each measurement is made to the nearest tenth of a foot.

a.	42.6 ft.	b.	26.24 ft.	c.	9$\frac{8}{16}$ in.
	80.0 ft.		30.00 ft.		4$\frac{3}{16}$ in.
	76.3 ft.		16.36 ft.		5$\frac{1}{16}$ ft.
	8.0 ft.		41.30 ft.		3$\frac{9}{16}$ in.
	206.9 ft.		113.90 ft.		21$\frac{12}{16}$ in.

In set "a," the zeros are significant and must be written as shown. In set "b," since the unit of measurement is 0.01 foot, the zeros are significant and cannot be omitted. In set "c," the unit of measurement, $\frac{1}{16}$ inch, is clearly indicated. The $\frac{8}{16}$ inch should not be reduced to $\frac{1}{2}$ inch. The $\frac{9}{16}$ is necessary to show the same unit has been used for each measurement. The $3\frac{3}{16}$ in "c" is just as necessary to show that this measurement is accurate to the nearest $\frac{1}{16}$ inch as is the 8.0 feet in "a" to show that this measurement is accurate to the nearest 0.1 foot. There is a vast difference between exact, abstract fractions, and the concrete fractions obtained by measuring. The fractions obtained by measuring are never exact and must be treated as all approximate data are treated. The last digit of each measurement in "a" and "b" is a nearest digit and may be slightly too large or slightly too small. That is, the 42.6 ft. in "a" may have actually been 42.613 or 42.596 ft. had the unit of measurement been 0.001 ft. Because of this the last digit of the answers may not always be correct but in practical work the usage is to retain the full answer as was done in "a," "b," and "c." If all the data in addition and subtraction are correctly given (no ragged decimals) there is not the slightest difficulty in adding or subtracting approximate numbers provided the pupil can add and subtract ordinary numbers.

Rounding Numbers. All elementary texts teach pupils *how* to round numbers, but they usually *do not teach* them the really important concepts and practices: *when* to round numbers or *why* the answers to certain problems must be rounded, and *how to determine the number of digits to retain* when rounding data or answers. Some situations in which it is desirable or necessary to round numbers follow: (a) In constructing graphs, it is usual to round data to two, three, or, in very large graphs, four significant digits. (b) Data obtained from handbooks may be more accurate than are needed to work a problem. Thus, the value of π to six digits is 3.14159. To find the circumference of a circle 8.6 feet in diameter, π should be rounded to 3.14, or to one digit more than the measurement it is used with. All conversion factors and similar data are rounded in this manner. (c) Data to be learned are usually rounded. Thus the speed of light is usually rounded from 186,284 miles per second to 186,000 miles per second; the diameter of the earth at the equator is usually rounded from 7926.8 miles to 8000 miles; the acceleration due to gravity at sea level (latitude 45°) is usually rounded from 32.172 feet per second to 32 or 32.2 feet per second; and the length of the light year is usually rounded from 5,875,156,800,000 to 6×10^{12}. (d) Computation usually introduces digits that are not significant. Such spurious digits must be rounded off. (e) If an answer accurate to only n digits is desired, it is customary to round all data to $(n + 1)$ digits before computing. (Some authorities round to $(n + 2)$ digits.) Later in this article rules are given to determine the number of digits to be retained in rounded answers.

The following rules may be used for rounding numbers:

1. If a number, correct to a certain number of significant digits, is to be rounded to a smaller number of significant digits, digits that are dropped should be replaced by zeros, with the exception that when the digits that are dropped are located to the right of the decimal point, they should not be replaced by zeros. Thus the polar radius of the earth, 3949 miles, rounded to two digits is 3900 miles; but 1° of latitude at the poles, 69.41 miles, rounded to two digits is 69 miles.

2. If the first of the digits that are to be dropped is 5, 6, 7, 8, or 9, the last digit retained should be increased by 1. The mean distance from the earth to the moon, 238,854 miles, rounded to three significant digits is 239,000 miles; and 1° of latitude at the equator, 68.71 miles, rounded to two significant digits is 69 miles.

Some texts say that when the digit 5 is dropped, the preceding digit should be increased by 1 if it is odd but left unchanged if it is even. Since there are as many even as odd digits, when a large number of addends are summed, the errors will tend to compensate if this rule is used.

Accuracy. It is necessary to know the meaning of accuracy before working problems involving multiplication, division, roots, and powers. The ordinary criterion for accuracy is the number of significant digits. The measurements 4,832 feet, 48.32 feet, and 0.4832 feet are all equally accurate, since they have the same number of significant digits. A measurement having three significant digits, or three-digit accuracy, is more accurate than a measurement having two significant digits, or two-digit accuracy. An approximate number having four significant digits, or four-digit accuracy, is more accurate than one having three significant digits, or three-digit accuracy. An approximate number having $(n + 1)$ significant digits is more accurate than one having only (n) significant digits.

If two measurements have the same number of significant digits, the one that begins with the larger digit is the more accurate. Thus the measurement 99.9 feet is more accurate than 342. feet, 4.37 feet, 0.135 feet, 63.8 feet, or 10.0 feet. The measurement 99.9

feet is very near to four-digit accuracy (99.9 + 0.1 = 100.0), whereas the measurement 10.0 feet has just got into three-digit class (9.9 + 0.1). If there is an error of 0.05 feet in each of these two measurements, the error in the first is 0.05 in 99.9 or 1 in 1998, whereas the error in the second is 0.05 in 10.0 or 1 in only 200. It is easily seen that the error in the second measurement is far more serious than the error in the first. The ratio of the error in the measurement to the measurement itself is called the relative error. Where a rigorous criterion for accuracy is needed, the relative error should be used.

A measurement or the answer to a problem must have the decimal point correctly located, but the location of the decimal point does not indicate the accuracy of a measurement. Changing the three-digit measurement 35.6 millimeters to 0.0000356 kilometer does not change the accuracy of the measurement. Since 35.6 millimeters and 0.0000356 kilometer each have three significant digits, they are of the same degree of accuracy. This illustration also shows that the zeros in 0.0000356 kilometer are not significant.

The words *precise, accurate,* and *correct* should not be confused. Precision and accuracy are relative. The measurements 0.00064 inch and 2.43126 inch are equally precise (an equally small unit has been used), but the second measurement is far more accurate (it has more significant digits). If an answer is correct, no mistakes in computation have been made and finally it has been correctly rounded. A measurement or answer may be 100 per cent correct but can never be 100 per cent accurate or precise.

Zeros that are the result of correct measurement are significant. If the measurement 300 feet is correct to the nearest foot, or lies between 299.5 feet and 300.5 feet, the measurement has three significant digits and the two zeros are both significant. Zeros should not be written after a decimal point in a mixed decimal unless they are significant. One can be sure that the measurement 26.00 feet has four significant digits and that the measurement 3.0000 inches has five significant digits.

Zeros used to give the correct place value in a rounded number are not significant. If 186,284 is rounded to 186,000, the three zeros are not significant. Zeros are also used before significant digits in a decimal fraction to give correct place value. Zeros used in this way are never significant. The zeros in the measurement 0.0000356 kilometer as pointed out are not significant.

Many elementary texts state that "zero is only a place holder." This is unfortunate. Significant zeros are numbers like any other numbers. Zeros that are not significant are place holders but it should be noted that any digit may be a place holder. In the measurement 8006 feet the zeros are significant and are place holders. In the measurement 8446 feet the fours are significant but are also place holders. The unique function of zero is its use as a place holder when it is not significant. It is the only digit so used. It should be noted zeros should never be annexed in adding and subtracting approximate data but they may be annexed in division if necessary to secure the number of digits necessary for the best answer. In this case the zeros do not affect the digits of the answer.

Multiplication, division, roots, and powers. Only one fundamental concept is necessary for operations on approximate numbers involving the above processes. It is:

In computation involving multiplication, division, roots, and powers the answer can never have more significant digits than there are in the least accurate factor.

It may be necessary to use zeros that are not significant to locate correctly the decimal point. It should be noted that there may be one less significant digit in the answer than is found in the least accurate data. If two low-order N significant digits numbers are multiplied the answer may contain only $N - 1$ significant digits. This will be the case in multiplication when the product of the first digits of each factor is less than 10 as in A. In B the first three digits in the answer are significant.

	A.	21.4		B.	8.63
		1.36			73.4
		1284			3452
		642			2589
		214			6041
		29.104			633.442
		29. Best answer			633. Best answer

In A and B the last significant digits are "nearest" digits and not exact digits. These and any product involving them are printed in heavy type. Obviously it would be foolish to retain two uncertain digits in the answer. Pupils may be led to see the logical nature of the rules for computation with approximate data by performing a number of operations similar to A and B. They may use a red or blue pencil for writing the last or uncertain digits.

The exception to the rule shown in A may be omitted in the early grades. The important thing to remember is that *computation can not increase* the accuracy of the original data. A chain is no stronger than its weakest link and the answer to a "chain" of operations involving multiplication, division, roots, and powers is never more accurate than the least accurate factor involved.

The teacher may wonder why it is necessary to have two concepts. One concept for addition and subtraction (see page 311) and a second concept for the other processes. It can be seen from A and B below that the errors tend to stay in the last digit of the answer in addition and subtraction.

	A.	B.	C.
	6.33	63.7	5.38
	2.71	21.4	4.26
	4.15	———	———
	———	42.3	3228
	13.19		1076
			2152
			———
			22.9188

However in C the errors tend to contaminate the last several digits of the answer.

Using the concepts I and II and the concepts (a) unit of measurement, (b) significant digits, (c) accuracy, and (d) precision, the teacher is able to replace the incorrect rules and directions found in many texts with correct final rules and directions. These are:

1. *All measurements or other data to be added or subtracted should be measured or rounded to the same unit of measurement.* This rule eliminates the highly artificial "ragged decimals" and the seriously incorrect rule "annex zeros to fill empty places."

2. *Round answers in multiplication to the same number of digits as*

there are in the least accurate approximate factor. Most texts leave the poor pupil without any rule for rounding answers in multiplication.

3. *Round answers in division to the same number of significant digits as there are in the least accurate factor.* This gives the pupil the correct criterion for rounding answers in division and replaces the very faulty direction usually given—Round the answer to the nearest tenth, hundredth, or thousandth, etc.

A pupil taught to round answers to the nearest hundreth will certainly not get the correct answer to either "a" or "b" below.

    a. $0.216 \,\overline{)\,8351}$ b. $836.1 \,\overline{)\,0.1432}$

Following the rule the pupil will get 38662.03 for "a" and 0.00 for "b," results that are clearly ridiculous, however the pupils using Rule 3 above will get the correct answers: "a" 38,700 and "b" 0.0001713. Slightly better results may be secured in division by carrying the quotient out to one digit more than allowed by Rule 3 and then rounding back. The same is true with roots.

4. The answer to an example in square root, or any higher root, should contain the same number of significant digits as there are in the approximate number whose root is sought. The square root of 81 square feet is 9.0 feet and the square root of 81.000 square feet is 9.0000 feet. The square root of 56.42 square feet is 7.511 feet.

One of the great advantages of using decimal fractions is that the number of significant digits is instantly evident. Any seventh-grade pupil should be able to find the perimeter and the area of "A" but it is safe to say that less than 5 per cent of the teachers in the elementary and high schools of the country could get the correct area in B. It is harder to find the number of significant digits in B than to find the correct answer to A.

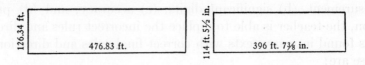

To find the number of significant digits when decimal measures are not used, express the measurement in terms of the unit of measurement (smallest unit used).

Thus 12.° measured to the nearest degree has two significant digits but 12° 0′ 0″ measured to the nearest second or 43,200″ has five significant digits. The measurement 9″ has only one significant digit but 9 $\%_{28}$″ or $^{1152}\%_{28}$ inches has four. The measurement $^{32}\%_{64}$ has two significant digits but $\frac{1}{2}$″ has only one. Because of this, concrete fractions should never be reduced. By reducing $^{32}\%_{64}$″ to $\frac{1}{2}$″ both the accuracy and precision are reduced. The measurement 9′ has one significant digit but 9′ 0″ or 108 inches has three and 9′ $\%_{16}$″ or $^{1728}\%_{16}$″ has four. The last measurement 9′ $\%_{16}$″ clearly indicates that it is correct to the nearest $\frac{1}{16}$″. The $\%_{16}$″ is as necessary as the 0 in 4.0 ft.

When such approximate numbers, π (3.14159265...), $\frac{1}{\pi}$ (0.3183098), $\sqrt{2}$ (1.73), trigonometric functions, physical constants, and the like are used with other approximate data they retain one more digit in the constant than there is in the approximate factor it is used with. Thus if the diameter of a circle is 2.8 feet the value π = 3.14 should be used. If the diameter is 28.43 feet the value π = 3.1416 should be used. When using conversion factors, 1 kilogram = 2.2046223 lb., 1 liter = 1.0566818 liquid quarts and 1 kilometer = 0.62136995 miles etc., the "one more" technique should always be used. To change 9.6 kilometers to miles use 1 kilometer = 0.621 miles.

If "one more" digit is used in the more accurate factor the error in this factor will not "contaminate" the digits retained in the answer.

When working a problem involving several approximate factors, slightly better results may be obtained by keeping one more digit in partial products (or quotients) than will be retained in the final answer.

1. Exact Numbers.

The rules for computing with approximate data should be applied only to the approximate factors. The 4, 3, 1, 2, 6, and 4 in the following formulas are exact numbers:

$$V = \tfrac{4}{3}\pi r^3; \qquad A = \tfrac{1}{2}ab; \qquad V = h/6(B + 4m + T).$$

Pupils must be trained to differentiate between exact and approximate numbers.

(a) When numbers are obtained by counting they are considered exact. This is especially true when the elements counted are practically identical, such as six nickels, eight 1-inch steel balls, 12 standard eggs of the same grade. When the elements counted are not identical, the "measurements" may be widely approximate for some purposes. If a new development contains 86 houses all built from the same set of plans and costing $7600 each, the 86 may be considered an exact number. However, if there are in a town 86 houses ranging in value from a mansion costing $95,000 down to a shack costing $800, the 86 is exact only in a "census" sense.

Large numbers obtained by counting should be carefully checked to see that counting produced no error. If we read that a certain city has 2,276,385 inhabitants, we may be sure, for a number of good reasons, that little confidence can be placed in the last two or three digits.

(b) Small whole numbers in various formulas are almost always exact.

(c) Hypothetical measurements may be considered exact. If the sides of a square were exactly 2 inches, the perimeter would be exactly 8 inches, the area would be exactly 4 square inches, and the diagonal $2\sqrt{2}$ inch. The $\sqrt{2}$ in this case could be carried out to any desired number of significant digits. It might be well to note, however, that no one could construct such a square or measure its sides exactly if it did exist. Abstract fractions may be reduced if desired. Thus $^{64}\!/_{128}$ and $\frac{1}{2}$ are equivalent but the concrete fractions $^{64}\!/_{128}$ in. and $\frac{1}{2}$ in. are not.

2. Approximate Numbers.

(a) All measurements of all kinds are approximate.

(b) Ratios of measured results are approximate.

(c) Many numbers, or ratios, such as $\frac{2}{3}$, π, ϵ, $\sqrt{3}$, $\tan x$, and so on, cannot be expressed exactly by an ordinary mixed decimal or decimal fraction. When the first n digits of such a number are taken as a satisfactory approximation, the number thus obtained is approximate.

(d) All rounded numbers are approximate. The answer to any problem in which approximate data are used is approximate and must be correctly rounded.

(e) Practically all the numbers taken from various handbook tables are approximate. There are hundreds of such tables, some of which contain thousands of approximate numbers.

(f) It is fairly safe to assume that practically all mixed decimals and decimal fractions are approximate.

It is relatively easy to obtain measurements accurate to at least 3 digits. Thus 42.0°, 16.8°, 12.4 lb., 18⅝″, 4′ 9½″, 32.6 feet, 18′ 0″, and 24.8 miles have three significant digits. However, many textbooks give "sloppy data" such as 4 feet, 6 miles, 8°, 9 lb.; only "sloppy" one digit answers can be given to such problems. This is one of the chief sources of dissatisfaction with the rules for computing with approximate data. It gives the average person somewhat of a jolt to be told that the area of a rectangle 6′ x 4′ is 20 square feet. The measurements 6 feet (5.5′ to 6.5′) and 4 feet (3.5 to 4.5) however are sloppy measurements. If more precise measurements 6.0′ x 4.0′ are given the answer will be 24. square feet or if the still more precise measurements 6.00′ x 4.00′ are given the answer will be 24.0 square feet. Since 0.01 feet is practically equivalent to ⅛ inches it is very easy to secure this precision. Textbooks for use in Grades VII through XII should not give sloppy one and two digit data and then expect four and five digit answers. It is reasonable to expect at least three digit data in these grades.

Approximate Data—Terminology and Computation

William A. Gager

In the past, on all levels of instruction from the grades through the universities, it has been the practice to think of all numbers as exact numbers. However, the truth of the matter is that there are innumerable numbers that cannot possibly represent exactly the conditions or the magnitudes to which they refer. Such numbers are appropriately called approximate numbers. It is an unfortunate misconception to think that approximate numbers can be considered as exact numbers in computations.

EXACT NUMBERS

Anytime one takes a count of the number of objects in a group, the total count is said to be an exact number. This means that the number used to express the count is perfect or it means that the count is 100 per cent exact.

When a county official reports that he has sold 24,576 automobile licenses one assumes that he has sold exactly 24,576 licenses. If a farmer says that he has 37 cows and 89 hens he means exactly these numbers. If you have counted and found that you have $1.83 in your pocketbook, you know that you have exactly $1.83 in your pocketbook. It may be said then that:

Exact numbers are those numbers that have been obtained by counting units. Computation with exact numbers, correctly performed, always produces exact results. Suppose that 37,642 people pay $3 each for a football ticket. In this example the unit is $1 and the total count of dollars is $112,926. Or suppose that each ticket cost $3.60. Then the unit would be $0.01 and the total count (amount) would be $135,511.20. These amounts are exact numbers.

APPROXIMATE NUMBERS

The ingenuity of man has never been able to build a perfectly precise measuring instrument. It follows then that there can be no such thing as an exact measurement of length, area, volume, temperature, time, weight, angles, and so on. Because all measurements are approximate it seems most expedient to designate all numbers which represent measurements as approximate numbers.

All entries in tables of logarithms, trigonometric tables, and a large number of similar tables, are approximate numbers. These are approximate numbers either because they represent measurements or because they represent numbers that have been rounded off. A vast array of numbers such as pi (π) and epsilon (ϵ) are also approximate numbers.

It is interesting to note that π, the number of times the circumference of a circle contains its diameter, has now been worked out to more than 2000 digits but still cannot be classed as an exact number. It becomes quite evident, then, that π expressed as 3.1416 (only 5 of the 2000 known digits) is an approximate number.

Bear in mind that the word *approximate* and the word *careless* have nothing whatsoever in common in mathematics. Within certain known limits, which may be a certain precision or a certain degree of accuracy, approximate numbers are very carefully obtained. Computations with approximate numbers are also very carefully done. There is nothing careless about the way the computational procedures are executed. In this connection it always helps to know that it is the data that are approximate, never the computations.

NUMBERS BOTH EXACT AND APPROXIMATE

There are situations that make it difficult to decide whether exact numbers or approximate numbers should be used. Suppose a person stopped at the grocery store for 3 quarts of milk. Is this 3 an exact or an approximate number? If one thinks in terms of "how many" quarts of milk (a count), then the 3 is an exact number. On the other hand if one thinks in terms of "how much" milk is obtained (measurement), then the 3 is an approximate number. As far as one would ever know, in this latter interpretation, there would be either a little less or a little more than exactly 3 quarts of milk.

UNIT OF MEASUREMENT

The unit of measurement is the smallest unit used in making a measurement. The size of the unit of measurement to be used must be decided upon before the measure of any object can be expressed.

If a measuring stick marked in feet only were used to measure the length of a hoe handle, the foot would be the unit of measurement. If a half-pint measuring cup were used to measure the syrup in a bucket, a half-pint would be the measuring unit. If a plot of land were measured by a 100-foot tape graduated to the nearest 0.01 foot, then 0.01 foot would be the unit of measurement.

The size of the unit of measurement determines the precision of the measurement. A unit of measurement of 1 foot is more precise than a unit of measurement of 10 feet. A unit of measurement of 10 feet is more precise than a unit of measurement of 100 feet.

When the unit of measurement is not specifically stated for a given measurement, always assume the least precise unit implied by this measurement. For example, if you should read that a jet-pilot leveled off at 24,000 feet, and do not know anything about how a jet-pilot takes his measurements, you should assume that this measurement is precise to the nearest 1000 feet. This is the least precise implied unit of measurement.

The use of decimal fractions to express measurements is rapidly replacing common fractions. The advantage of the decimal form is in the ease with which one can select the implied unit of measurement and thus determine its precision. Assuming the length of a table was found to be 4.8 feet, it is easy to observe that the unit of measurement used was 0.1 foot. The unit of measurement could not have been 1 foot because then the measurement would have been recorded as 5 feet. Neither could the unit of measurement have been 0.01 foot because then the measurement would have been one of the following: 4.76, 4.77, 4.78, 4.79, 4.81, 4.82, 4.83, 4.84 feet. The unit of measurement of 0.1 foot as implied by 4.8 feet means that the true length of the table is somewhere between 4.75 and 4.85 feet.

The acceptable procedure to follow in taking a measurement is this:

1. Drop any length that is less than half the unit of measurement.

2. Add a unit of measurement when the length is one-half or more than one-half, the unit of measurement.

This procedure makes clear the fact that the 4.8 feet previously stated as the length of a table is not necessarily the true length of the table. All anyone can know about the true length of that table is that it falls somewhere between 4.75 feet and 4.85 feet. Because the length was more than 4.75 feet (that is more than half the unit of measurement of 0.1 foot) it was recorded as 4.8 feet. Likewise, because the length was less than 4.85 feet it was recorded as 4.8 feet.

From an analysis like that in the preceding paragraph, the merits of the method used by the carpenters and the engineers to express measurements become more meaningful. They would express the length of the table as 4.8 ± 0.05 feet. From this expression they can see at a glance that:

1. The unit of measurement is 0.1 foot.
2. The minimum point is 4.8 − 0.05 or 4.75 feet.
3. The maximum limit is 4.8 + 0.05 or 4.85 feet.

Table 1 shows the units of measurement implied and the minimum and maximum limits for certain measurements.

TABLE 1

Measurement	Implied Unit of Measurement	Limits
25,000,000 mi.	1,000,000 mi.	25,000,000 ± 500,000 mi.
8,756 gal.	1 gal.	8,756 ± 0.5 gal.
43.8 lb.	0.1 lb.	43.8 ± 0.05 lb.
23.57 gr.	0.01 gr.	23.57 ± 0.005 gr.
1.0470 oz.	0.0001 oz.	1.0470 ± 0.00005 oz.
7⅞ in.	⅛ in.	7 ± ¹⁄₁₆ in.
37°4′25″	1 sec.	133,465 ± 0.5 sec.

In Table 1, in the sixth item under Measurement, you will notice the entry 7⅞ inches. The unit of measurement implied is ⅛ inch and the limits are $7 \pm \frac{1}{16}$ inches. In this case it would be entirely wrong to write 7⅞ inches as 7 inches. Seven inches implies that the unit of measurement used was 1 inch. This, of course, is false. The unit of measurement used to get 7⅞ inches was ⅛ inch, a far more precise unit than 1 inch. *When a measurement is expressed by a certain common fraction that fraction must not be reduced.*

As exact numbers it is true that 16⁴⁄₈ and 16½ have exactly the same value and the same meaning. But as a representation of a measurement 16⁴⁄₈ inches does not have the same meaning as 16½ inches. As a measurement 16⁴⁄₈ inches means that the measurement has been taken to the nearest ⅛ inch, while 16½ inches means that the unit of measurement was ½ inch, a much less precise unit. Thus measurements expressed as common fractions should be left in their original form. They should never be reduced.

POSSIBLE OR APPARENT ERROR

A measurement of 35 gallons implies that the liquid was measured to the nearest gallon, and that the true measurement was somewhere from 34.5 to 35.5 gallons. By using 35 gallons the largest possible error from the lower limit would be 35 − 34.5 or 0.5 gallon. The largest possible error from the upper limit would be 35.5 − 35 or 0.5 gallon. The error of 0.5 gallon is half the unit of measurement of 1 gallon. In general, *the largest possible error is not more than one-half the unit of measurement in either direction.*

When, in measuring distance the unit of measurement is taken as 1000 miles, the largest possible error is 500 miles. If in measuring time the unit of measurement is 1 hour, the largest possible error is ½ hour. If in measuring time the unit of measurement is 1 second, the largest possible error is ½ second. (See also Table 2.)

PRECISION OF MEASUREMENT

It has already been stated that *the precision of a measurement is determined by the size of the unit of measurement.* That is, a unit of measurement of 0.01 foot is more precise than one of 0.1 foot, and a unit of measurement of 0.001 foot is more precise than one of 0.01 foot.

As is indicated by Table 2, the precision of a measurement is evaluated in terms of the largest possible error. If the largest possible error is 5 feet the precision of measurement is also 5 feet, and if the largest possible error is 0.0005 feet the precision of measurement is 0.0005 feet.

TABLE 2

Measurement	Implied Unit of Measurement	Largest Possible Error	Precision of Measurement
ft.	*ft.*	*ft.*	*ft.*
312,540	10.	5.	5.
31,254	1.	0.5	0.5
3,125.4	.1	0.05	0.05
312.54	.01	0.005	0.005
31.254	.001	0.0005	0.0005

These facts may be observed from Table 2:

1. The size of the unit of measurement is indicated by the position of the decimal point.

2. The size of the unit of measurement determines both the size of the largest possible error and the precision.

3. The precision of a number depends upon the location of the decimal point.

4. The smaller the unit of measurement the more precise is the measurement.

ADDING AND SUBTRACTING APPROXIMATE DATA

Precision is the key word in the addition and subtraction of approximate data which represent measurements. If the measurements have the same precision, all one needs to do is to find the sum or the difference of the measurements and see that the result shows the same precision as the measurements which were added or subtracted. Since precision is based upon possible error, which in turn depends upon the unit of measurement, the following is a fundamental rule to be used in measuring to assure the same precision for all measurements to be added or subtracted: *Use the same unit of measurement for all measurements in the set.* (See example.)

$$243.1 \text{ ft.}$$
$$34.5 \text{ ft.}$$
$$0.8 \text{ ft.}$$
$$1.0 \text{ ft.}$$
_____
$$279.4 \text{ ft.}$$

What complicates the addition and subtraction of approximate data is the fact that different individuals in different localities use different units of measurement. One may record a measurement of an object to the nearest 0.1 inch, while another records the measurement of a like object to the nearest 0.001 inch. Then, too, there exists the totally inexcusable practice by some authors of textbooks and standard tests of presenting measurements to be added that imply different units of measurement. This practise is objectionable because such data are unreal and unreasonable. It is also objectionable because most individuals (young and old) have never been trained to add correctly data having different degrees of precision.

If data having different degrees of precision are to be added or subtracted, perform the computation in the usual manner, then round the result to the same precision as that possessed by the least precise measurement used.

In the addition example you will notice that 23 was measured to the nearest foot. It is the least precise of the four measurements. The sum resulting from the addition should therefore be

$$
\begin{array}{ll}
37.14 \ \text{ft.} & \\
478.5 \ \ \ \text{ft.} & \\
\ \ \ 2.143 \ \text{ft.} & 345.87 \ \text{in.} \\
23 \ \ \ \ \ \ \text{ft.} & \ 24.2 \ \ \text{in.} \\
\hline
540.783 \ \text{ft.} & 321.67 \ \text{in.} \\
\text{or } 541 \ \text{ft.} & \text{or } 321.7 \ \text{ in.}
\end{array}
$$

rounded to the nearest foot. Since the error in 23 may be as large as 0.5 foot, it is not necessary to be concerned about the tenths, hundredths, or thousandths shown by the other measurements.

The subtraction example shows 24.2 to be the least precise measurement. Therefore the result of the subtraction, 321.67, must be rounded to the nearest tenth, that is 321.7 inches.

SIGNIFICANT DIGITS AND ACCURACY

The accuracy of a measurement is always determined by the number of significant digits in the approximate number which represents the measurement. Therefore one must know which of the digits in a number are significant, and which digits are not significant, before he can determine the accuracy of the number.

The digits needed to express the number of times the unit of measurement is applied are significant digits. Take 23.1 miles as an example. For this measurement the implied unit of measurement is 0.1 mile. There are 231 units of measurement in 23.1 miles. It takes the 2, the 3, and the 1 to express 231. Therefore all three of the digits are significant.

In a measurement such as 0.004 grain the implied unit of measurement is 0.001 of a grain. Because there are only 4 units of measurement in 0.004 grain, 4 is the only significant digit in this measurement.

Table 1 shows an angle measurement of $37° \ 4' \ 25''$. The implied unit of measurement is 1 second and there are $37(60)(60) + 4(60) + 25$ or 133,465 units of measurement in the given angle. All six of the digits in 133,465 are significant because it requires the use of all six of them to express the total units of measurement present.

Table 1 also records the measurement 7 0/8 inches. It has previously been pointed out that the unit of measurement implied is ⅛ inch. It may not be quite so easy to determine the significant digits for measurement expressed in common fraction form. However the same principle applies here as elsewhere. Find the number of units of measurement involved. Each digit that makes up this number is a significant digit. As an improper fraction 7 0/8 inches is 56/8 inches. This shows that there are 56 units of measurement, ⅛ inch in size, in the given measurement. Thus 7 0/8 inches contains two significant digits. By similar procedure 9 lb. 3 oz. has 147 units of measurement of 1 ounce each and contains three significant digits.

Table 3 shows the significant digits for several other measurements.

TABLE 3

Measurement	Implied Unit of Measurement	Total of Units	Significant Digits	
			Actual	By Count
105.06 gr.	0.01 gr.	10,506	1, 0, 5, 0, 6	5
2570 bu.	10 bu.	257	2, 5, 7	3
0.0050 mm.	0.0001 mm.	50	5, 0	2
46.0 gal.	0.1 gal.	460	4, 6, 0	3
1.008 cc.	0.001 cc.	1,008	1, 0, 0, 8	4
3,467.21 ft.	0.01 ft.	346,721	3, 4, 6, 7, 2, 1	6

If each digit in an approximate number except the last one is correct and if the error in the last digit is not greater than half the unit of measurement, then all the digits in the number are significant.

The position of the decimal point, in a number representing measurement, is of prime importance in the determination of the precision of the number. In contrast, the position of the decimal point in a number has nothing whatsoever to do with the determination of the accuracy of the number. You will find that each of the following four measurements has the same four-digit accuracy but that these numbers all differ in the position of the decimal point and thus in their precision.

1. 562,400 yards with a unit of measurement of 100 yards
2. 5624 yards with a unit of measurement of 1 yard

3. 5.624 yards with a unit of measurement of 0.001 yard

4. 0.5624 yards with a unit of measurement of 0.0001 yard.

The necessary condition that approximate numbers have the same digit accuracy is that they have the same number of significant digits. An approximate number which contains $K + 1$ significant digits is more accurate than the number that contains K significant digits.

RELATIVE ERROR, PER CENT ERROR, DEGREE OF ACCURACY

If the length of a boat is given as 10′ 0″, the implied unit of measurement is 1 inch. Then the possible error is 0.5 inch, and the relative error is $0.5/120$ or $1/240$. In other words the *relative error is the ratio of the possible error of a measurement to the actual measurement. Per cent error is relative error expressed in per cent form.* That is, $100 \times 1/240$ gives 0.42 per cent as the per cent error.

Degree of accuracy means 100 per cent minus the per cent error. Thus the degree of accuracy in measuring the 20-foot boat would be $100 - 0.42$ or about 99.58 per cent.

The purpose of degree of accuracy is to show differences such as are indicated in the following cases. Using a 10-foot unit of measurement to measure 40 feet gives a result to one-digit accuracy. But using a 1-foot unit of measurement to measure 9 feet also gives a result to one-digit accuracy. Both results are accurate to one digit but there is nothing to indicate which one of the two measurements is the more accurate. To find the more accurate measurement it is necessary to compute the degree of accuracy of $5/40$ and $0.5/9$. This shows that the degree of accuracy of the 40-foot measurement is 87.5 per cent and the degree of accuracy of the 9-foot measurement is 94.4 per cent. That is, the 9-foot measurement is more accurate. In these examples (also in Table 4) you may notice that *when two approximate numbers possess the same digit accuracy, but the digits are not identical,* the number having the larger *left-hand digit is the more accurate.*

Table 4 gives some additional data to include relative error, per cent error, and degree of accuracy.

It is interesting to note from Table 4 that any approximate number that possesses one-digit accuracy has a degree of accuracy

TABLE 4

Measurement	Implied Unit	Precision	Significant Digits	Relative Error	Per cent Error	Degree of Accuracy (Per cent)
1 mi.	1 mi.	0.5 mi.	1	0.5/1	50	50
90 lb.	10 lb.	5 lb.	1	5/90	5.5	94.5
0.10 gr.	0.01 gr.	0.005 gr.	2	0.005/0.10	5	95.0
990 gal.	10 gal.	5 gal.	2	5/990	0.55	99.5−
10.0 qt.	0.1 qt.	0.05 qt.	3	0.05/10.0	0.5	99.5
999 kg.	1 kg.	0.5 kg.	3	0.5/999	0.05	99.9+
1,000 tons	1 ton	0.5 ton	4	0.5/1,000	0.005	99.95
999.9 bu.	0.1 bu.	0.05 bu.	4	0.05/999.9	0.0005	99.99+

of 50 per cent or more. Numbers with two-digit accuracy have a degree of accuracy of 95 per cent or more. Numbers with three-digit accuracy have a degree of accuracy of 99.5 per cent or more.

ROUNDING NUMBERS

Rounding a number is the process of dropping digits from the right end of the number. Zeros are used to replace the digits dropped only when it is necessary to do so to keep the decimal point in its proper place. Numbers may be rounded by one of these rules:

1. When the digit to be dropped is less than 5 the digit on its left should remain unchanged.

2. When the digit to be dropped is 5 or more the digit on its left should be increased by 1.

3. When a group of digits are to be dropped from a number, and the left-hand digit of those to be dropped is less than 5, the digit on its left should remain unchanged. If the left-hand digit of those to be dropped is 5 or more the digit to its left should be increased by 1.

Rounding an approximate number reduces both its precision and its accuracy. Table 5 shows how the precision and accuracy of numbers are changed by the rounding-off process.

The rounded number always indicates a unit of measurement that is larger than the unit of measurement for the original number. This makes the rounded number less precise than the original one. Also the rounded number has fewer significant digits than its

TABLE 5

Measurements		Implied Unit	Signifi-cant Digits	Precision	Degree of Accuracy (Per cent)
Original	Rounded				
27.573 m.		0.001 m.	5	0.0005 m.	99.99
	27.6 m.	0.1 m.	3	0.05 m.	99.8
36 m.		1 m.	2	0.5 m.	98.6
	40 m.	10 m.	1	5 m.	87.5
19,694 m.		1 m.	5	0.5 m.	99.99
	20,000 m.	10,000 m.	1	5000 m.	75.

original. Thus the accuracy of the rounded number is less than the accuracy of the original one.

MULTIPLICATION OF APPROXIMATE NUMBERS

To multiply two or more approximate numbers, and to express the product properly, requires the application of this very simple rule: *The product of two approximate numbers must show no greater accuracy than is expressed by the least accurate factor used.*

This principle is applied to the computation necessary to find the area of a plot of ground 30.6 feet long and 20.2 feet wide. The right-hand digits in 30.6 and 20.2 are not correct. They are marked with a slanting line to indicate that they are in error. Likewise each combination that the right-hand digits affect in carrying out the multiplication has a slanting line through it. This procedure makes it quite evident that the 8 in 618 is some-what in error. Since the 8 is in error there would be no justification in retaining any of the digits to the right of 8. Thus the best answer for the area of the rectangle is 618 square feet.

$$30.6$$
$$20.2$$
$$\overline{61.2}$$
$$6120$$
$$\overline{618.12}$$

618 square feet is the best answer.

The best answer for the area of a rectangle 32 feet long and 24 feet wide is 768 rounded to 770 square feet, where the two sevens are significant but the zero is not significant. It is often necessary to use zeros that are not significant to establish place value properly.

If more than two factors are to be multiplied, find the product of the first two and round the result to have one more digit than is to be retained in the final product. Multiply this rounded product by the next factor, and round as before until all the factors have been used. Then round the final product to contain the same number of significant digits contained in the least accurate factor used.

There is no difficulty in multiplying an approximate number by an exact number. An exact number is always exact. Thus the accuracy of the product depends upon the accuracy of the approximate number used.

DIVISION OF APPROXIMATE NUMBERS

As in multiplication, *the quotient of two approximate numbers must show no greater accuracy than is expressed by the least accurate number used in obtaining the quotient.* In division the quotient should be carried out one more digit than is desired and then rounded off one digit. (See example.)

$$
\begin{array}{r}
6.4 \\
6.3\!\!\!/\,0 \\
8.\!\!\!/\,0\,)\overline{\,5\!\!\!/\,6.8\!\!\!/\,7\!\!\!/\,1\,} \\
53\ 4 \\
\hline
3\ 4\!\!\!/\,7 \\
2\ 6\!\!\!/\,7 \\
\hline
8\!\!\!/\,0\!\!\!/\,1 \\
8\!\!\!/\,0\!\!\!/\,1 \\
\hline
\end{array}
$$

The quotient 6.4 is the best answer.

SQUARE ROOTS OF APPROXIMATE NUMBERS

To extract the square root of an approximate number with K significant digits, obtain the root to K + 1 significant digits and round the answer one place. The best answer for the example shown is 9.6. This may be checked by squaring 9.6 and obtaining 92.16, which should be rounded to two significant digits, giving 92.

$$\frac{9.59}{\sqrt{92}}$$

COMPUTATIONS WITH ANGULAR MEASUREMENTS

In the study of the triangle in trigonometry, it is necessary to associate certain approximate numbers which represent angles with certain approximate numbers which represent lengths.

The ratios in tables of natural trigonometric functions are approximate numbers in the form of unending decimals. In a three-place table, that is a table with three digits, the last digit in the ratio will, in most cases, not represent the true ratio. Likewise in a four-place table, a five-place table, a six-place table, or a ten-place table, the last digit in each ratio will usually be in error. Thus the result of computations in which trigonometric ratios are used can never be more accurate than the ratios in the particular table from which they were taken.

When measured numbers are being multiplied, divided, squared, or having their square roots extracted, the result must show no more significant digits than are present in the least accurate measurement used in the computation. This principle applies to angles in exactly the same way that it applies to lengths.

In solving for the side opposite 48° in a right triangle, when the hypotenuse is 9 feet, that is in solving for x in the equation $x/9 = \sin 48°$, one obtains a length of 6.687 feet. But there is no justification in keeping all four of these digits. The unit of measurement for 48° is 1°. Then 48° contains 48 units of measurement and justifies two significant digits. The length, 9 feet, has only one significant digit. This means that the result of the computation cannot have more than one significant digit. The best answer then is not 6.687 feet but 7 feet.

To find the side adjacent to the angle of 48° 13′ in a right triangle, when the hypotenuse is 274.6 feet, use the equation $x/274.6 = \cos 48° 13′$. Using a five-place table of trigonometric ratios, $x = 182.971472$ feet. In studying the given data it is found that 274.6 has four significant digits and that 48° 13′

amounts to 60 × 48 + 13 or 2893 minutes, which also possesses 4 significant digits. The result, therefore, should retain only 4 significant digits. That is, the best answer is 183.0 feet for the adjacent side of the right triangle.

GRADE PLACEMENT OF PROCEDURES

Numbers are used everyday by everybody either as exact numbers or as approximate numbers that represent measurement or as numbers that have been rounded. When using approximate data the only way to obtain answers that make sense, and to obtain them efficiently, is to apply the principles for computing with approximate data.

The study of computing with approximate data should start not later than the seventh grade. The least that should be done in this grade is to make clear the difference in meaning between exact and approximate numbers, and to apply the principle of rounding numbers.

Each grade should always make full use of what the preceding grade has taught concerning approximate data. It should also teach some new concepts. Grade VIII should assume the responsibility of teaching largest possible error and precision. It should also teach and give practice in the addition and subtraction of approximate data.

Grade IX has the responsibility of giving a meaningful and quick method of identifying significant digits, the use of significant digits in determining accuracy, and in stating the accuracy of the results of multiplying and dividing approximate data.

On the senior high-school level much attention should be given in Grade X to making proper use of the approximate data principles. Here, also, deeper insight into the meaning of the concepts of precision and accuracy should be made. The square roots of approximate numbers, the association of angles with lengths, and the meaning of relative error should be studied.

Relative error should be given further emphasis in Grade XI in connection with per cent error, and degree of accuracy. Relative error should never be contrasted with largest possible error. The effect on its accuracy and precision of rounding a number should also be considered in this grade.

The basic procedures of computations with approximate data that are not already thoroughly understood should be restudied in Grade XII. The important thing throughout this grade is to see that the rules of computing with approximate data are properly applied to all computations involving measurements or numbers that have been rounded.

PART FIVE
The Evaluation of Mathematical Learning
Introduction

IT IS relatively easy for teachers of mathematics to evaluate the ability to recall information and to perform certain skills. It is not so easy, however, to assess the growth of concepts and the development of understanding. It is still more difficult to gather evidence of the improvement in the ability to apply what is learned to situations beyond those in which the learning took place. Finally, it is a real challenge to be able to judge whether students are gaining certain attitudes and appreciations.

Information, skills, understanding, ability to apply, attitudes, and appreciations are all desirable outcomes of instruction. Since, however, considerable attention has been given to the evaluation of the first two of these for many years, this chapter will contain, almost entirely, samples and illustrations of the appraisal of the last four.

The relationship between teaching and evaluation is reflected in the following well-known operational analysis of the evaluation process:

1. Objectives are stated in terms of the desired behavior.
2. Situations are selected for observing the behaviors.
3. Methods are devised for recording the behaviors.
4. The records are interpreted in terms of the desired behaviors.

The methods of gathering the evidence for the purpose of evaluation vary in formality and in the kinds of media used. In his daily work the teacher judges whether learning is taking place by the responses to his oral questions, by the queries coming from the students, by their facial expressions and exclamations, such as, "I see" or "I don't get it," and by what is written on paper or on the blackboard. From class work and homework, periodic paper-and-pencil tests, newspaper and magazine clippings brought to class, and from projects and reports, the teacher makes other judgments of varying reliability. From personal interviews, small group conferences, his own log or anecdotal record, the comments of other teachers, and the reactions of parents, the teacher gains more insight into the progress of learning. In the process he learns much, too, about the effectiveness of his own teaching.

To incorporate this kind of evaluation into day-by-day teaching can be a large contract. First of all, the objectives are very numerous. To evaluate each of these separately can be very frustrating. H. C. Trimble spells out this problem forcibly:

Making the tests becomes a fulltime job, inadequately done in spite of the best efforts. Giving the tests, once they are made, calls for an unreasonable amount of time that belongs to instruction. It is all very well to say that evaluation and instruction are two inseparable parts of the same job. In practice it is easy to let evaluation become the tail that wags the dog. When this happens it makes little sense from an instruction-centered point of view. . . . Is there any compromise that is theoretically sound and yet applicable in day-by-day practice? I believe so. I believe we must at least *think* objectives in terms of behaviors. Beyond that we should strive to *state* our objectives in terms of observable behaviors that reflect progress toward our objectives. It is when we take the next step that we must look for a practical compromise between our enthusiasm for evaluation and our duties as classroom teachers. . . . At any point of time we should act in terms of the best we know compromised by the best we can achieve. . . .

We can ask questions such as: "Where did I fail to reach John?" Through item analysis we can raise and get partial answers to questions like "Where did I fail to reach this class?" "Why did eight students miss item 17?" "What desirable behaviors do these students still lack?" "Did they fail in this way, or was it in this quite different way?" "Do I need more items of this kind next term?" "Can I somehow get a more valid measure of this behavior as separate from that one?" "Can I delete my emphasis on this point and use my time better on this other matter?" Changes in the program of instruction for the next term will result from asking such questions. Tests and observational techniques will be improved. Both evaluation and instruction as such will improve.

It is desirable to have valid and reliable measures of each separate objective. It is also impossible. But evaluation instruments can be improved with experience. We can approach but probably not reach the ideal of a balanced measuring device, one that gives a weighted average of our pupils' achievements relative to our objectives.[1]

In 1914 Nunn wrote, "Mathematical truths always have two sides or aspects. With the one they face and have contact with the world of outer realities lying in time and space. With the other

---

[1] Letter from H. C. Trimble.

they face and have relations with one another." ... "One [aspect] never has existed and probably never will exist apart from the other. The view that they represent wholly distinct forms of intellectual activity is partial, unhistorical, and unphilosophical. A more serious charge against it is that it has produced an infinite amount of harm in the teaching of mathematics" (20). Nunn's first "aspect" is the subject of Section 2; his second is the principal concern of Section 1. Children can hardly come to understand mathematics without references to objects, actions, and experiences outside of the mathematical world of symbols and logic. On the other hand, children can hardly learn to apply mathematics, or be "functionally competent" in mathematics, if they do not possess certain mathematical meanings and understandings. If these statements are accepted, then it would seem to follow that the evaluation of the two aspects cannot be entirely separated.

Harding's paper in Section 2 implies that learning to understand and to apply should go together. For evaluating arithmetic learning in the elementary school he illustrates this view by a variety of procedures different from the paper-and-pencil test items.

Donovan Johnson in Section 2 shows the use of test items in evaluating the ability to apply geometric concepts and theorems to aspects of the world about us.

For many years teachers of mathematics have hoped that their students would exhibit in nonmathematical situations the reasoning standards demonstrated in mathematics. The National Council of Teachers of Mathematics even devoted one of its year-books, *The Nature of Proof* by Harold P. Fawcett (7), to a consideration of ways of making the hope a reality. The experiments of Ulmer (29), Gadske (8), and Lewis (15), among others, together with Fawcett's work, provided strong evidence of the feasibility of using plane demonstrative geometry as a backdrop for encouraging the improvement of reasoning in situations outside the field of mathematics. The published investigations of these men, the periodical literature, and the reports of the Eight-Year Study (21) and the National Society for the Study of Education (19) have indicated rather fully the procedures used to evaluate growth in the use of reasoning standards in a variety of situations. Myron Rosskopf (22) has summarized various paper-and-pencil tests used for judging the improvement of critical thinking.

Section 3 will consist of Bjarne R. Ullsvik's (28) illustrations of test items designed to measure certain specified aspects of reasoning and Harry Lewis' procedures (15) in going beyond paper-and-pencil tests in gathering evidence of maturation in applying criteria of thinking.

Evaluating attitudes and appreciations is probably the most difficult of all types of evaluation. These behaviors are usually less tangible than skills and exhibition of understanding. The nature and intensity of these two are inferred from evidence that requires keen and wise insight as well as unusual sensitivity to the human personality.

In the first part of Section 4, J. Wayne Wrightstone, Director, Bureau of Educational Research, Board of Education of New York City, reports a survey made of the techniques used by representative teachers and supervisors of New York City in evaluating attitudes and appreciations of mathematics students. In the second part, Howard F. Fehr, Head, Department of Mathematics, Teachers College, Columbia University, analyzes the nature of mathematical appreciation, provides criteria for detecting appreciation, and gives illustrations of evaluation of appreciation.

Over the years there has been great dissatisfaction with per cents and letter grades as a means for reporting to parents the progress and achievement of their children. At the same time, with the formulating of more and different kinds of educational objectives the task of the teacher in communicating to parents has become more complex and more burdensome. The use of checklists, letters home, conferences with parents, and self-evaluation by the students themselves has become more common in some schools and school systems.

Section 5 will consist of the contributions of Alice M. Hach, Slauson Junior High School, Ann Arbor, Michigan, and of Donovan Johnson, University High School, University of Minnesota. These contributions will be samples of some of the forms, accompanied by description of their use when it seems necessary.

The organization of the five sections is:

1. Evaluation of Mathematical Meanings and Understandings
2. Evaluation of the Ability to Apply Mathematics
3. Evaluation of the Application of Mathematical Reasoning Standards to Nonmathematical Situations
4. Evaluation of Attitudes and Appreciations
5. Reporting to Parents

Sections 1, 2, and 5 will consist principally of illustrations and test items. These are not comprehensive but limited to those received by the Committee from contributors.[2] Sections 3 and 4, consist of materials received through invitation.

J.J.K.

1

Evaluation of Mathematical Meanings and Understandings

Illustrations and Test Items

DONOVAN JOHNSON
H. C. TRIMBLE

A DISTINCTION has been made between the meaning of a statement and an understanding of it. Van Engen (30) claims that a student knows the *meaning* of "an inscribed angle is measured by one-half its intercepted arc" if he can consistently determine the size of the angle from the number of degrees in the intercepted arc. Of course, it is implied that the meaning of the *concepts*, "inscribed angle" and "intercepted arc," must also be known. As Brownell (5) observed, a student can hardly possess the meaning of a statement or generalization or proposition or theorem unless he knows the meaning of the concepts involved in the statement. On the other hand, knowing the meaning of concepts in isolation does not guarantee awareness of the meaning of a generalization which places these concepts in certain relationships.

---

[2] These sections were designed and compiled by John Kinsella.

Our student possesses an understanding of the inscribed angle theorem if he can give a logical explanation of *why* the relationship between the angle and the arc turns out to be what it is. Such an explanation might involve showing that the inscribed angle is only half as large as the central angle having the same arc by means of an argument involving the use of theorems about the isosceles triangle and the exterior angle of a triangle. Hendrix supports this notion of understanding by noting that the ability to frame a sequence of "if . . . then" statements of the implication type is one way to judge the quality of understanding (13).

Two warnings seem necessary at this point. First, there is more than one logical explanation for the appearance of some relationships. It is common knowledge that there are many logical proofs of the Pythagorean theorem. Hence, the test of understanding for such relationships is not just one, and only one, explanation. Second, there are degrees of understanding depending on the mental and mathematical maturity of the student. The college student who sees negative numbers as a special case of complex numbers has a much deeper understanding of the multiplication of (-3) (-5) than the student of elementary algebra at the ninth-grade level. Hence, the test of understanding will vary according to the background and ability of the student. Finally, it should be observed that meanings, as well as understandings, are not constant in number or depth. For example, in arithmetic we speak of at least three meanings of a fraction. It would be absurd to introduce all of these meanings to a child in one presentation.

Probably the ideal way to test meanings and understandings would be by means of individual interviews. However, under conditions of group instruction involving large classes this is hardly practical. Hence, the interview becomes a supplementary technique. With all of its limitations and failings, the pencil-and-paper test has to be relied upon heavily in any program for evaluating the possession of meanings and understandings. Hence, this section will consist principally of sample test items.

Most of these test items will be of the short form type. Whether a response is a guess or the result of memorization or the product of eliminating alternate responses or evidence of genuine understanding is uncertain in most cases. In testing for understanding it would seem desirable to supplement true-false test items with questions beginning with "why." The multiple-choice items should have enough novelty to them so that easy recognition of the correct response is not possible without some cerebration. The choices should demand discrimination so that the correct response is not spotted by the absurdity of the alternatives. The completion items should be more of an open-end type than those which require only the recall of a printed or spoken sentence. For testing some understandings it is likely that essay questions will yield more evidence than the short form type. The matching type of test item would seem to be suited to testing the ability to discern relationships, an important element in understanding.

Considerable work in evaluating understanding in arithmetic has been done by Brownell (4), Sueltz (26), Glennon (10), and Spitzer (25). Attention to evaluating some of the understandings and meanings of secondary-school mathematics was given by Hartung and Fawcett. The fact that the National Society for the Study of Education entitled Part I of its Forty-Fifth Yearbook, *The Measurement of Understanding*, gives an indication of the importance attached to the subject by a group of educators (19).

It seems important to emphasize once more that paper-and-pencil instruments can provide only partial and uncertain evidence of understanding. Having students say aloud what they are thinking as they attempt to do exercises and work problems is a very illuminating procedure. The kinds of questions they ask as well as the nature of their responses to oral questions of the teacher give important clues to the degree and extent of their understanding.

ARITHMETIC[3]

Place Value

1. In which of these numbers is the tens digit the largest?
   a. 49   b. 63   c. 256   d. 1947   e. 1.64   (HCT)

2. In the number 52.32 the number "2" written to the left of the "3" represents a quantity how many times as large as the "2" written to the right of the "3"?
   a. 6   b. 10   c. 100   d. 200   (HCT)

---

[3] The initials of Donovan Johnson, University of Minnesota, and H. C. Trimble, State Teachers College, Cedar Falls, Iowa, will indicate the sources of the contributions.

3. In the number 842, the 8 has a value that is:
a. twice the value of the 4; b. four times the value of the 2
c. twenty times the value of the 4; d. forty times the value
of the 2; e. two hundred times the value of the 4. (DJ)
4. The number .4 is one-tenth of which of these?
a. 40   b. .40   c. 4   d. $\frac{4}{10}$ (HCT)
5. Mark as true or false: The number of tens in 6853 is 685. (DJ)

Processes with Whole Numbers

1. How much is carried when adding 285 and 143?
a. 0   b. 1   c. 10   d. 100 (DJ)
2. Add the following exercises. Then place *t* next to those in which you need to "carry" a 10 and *h* next to those in which you need to "carry" a 100.

a. 733   b. 6472   c. 256   d. 15365
   +184   +815   +137   +1213
                                            (HCT)

3. How much is borrowed when subtracting 182 from 243?
a. 0   b. 1   c. 10   d. 100 (DJ)
4. In the problem 54 x 23, what is the best explanation for writing the 8 under the 6?
a. We write the product under the multiplier.
b. We write the product in the 10's place because the multiplier is a 10.
c. We move over one place when multiplying by the second figure.
d. We are using a short cut that works. (DJ)
5. The multiplication of 24 by $3\frac{1}{2}$ is the same as 24 multiplied by 3.5. Why do we not move over the 72 in the second example as is done in the first example?

24	24
3.5	$3\frac{1}{2}$
120	12
72	72
84.0	84

    a. The multiplier 3 has a different place value in each example.

    b. The multiplier .5 and ½ are not equivalent.

    c. The fraction ½ does not have place value.

    d. The multiplier 3 and ½ have the same place value.   (DJ)

6. Suppose you are explaining division by using bundles of sticks. You have single sticks, bundles of 10, and bundles of 100. Work out the four division exercises. Then write x or y or z next to the exercise which matches one of these three statements:

    x. There are enough 100's so that 100's bundles can be used in the answer.

          a. $3\overline{)75}$

          b. $6\overline{)1266}$

    y. It would be necessary to break a group of 10's into ones.

          c. $6\overline{)486}$

    z. There would be some odd sticks left over at the end.   (HCT)

          d. $4\overline{)165}$

Fractions

1. When we change ⅝ to ¾ we are reducing a fraction to lower terms. When we change ⅔ to ⁸⁄₁₂ we are raising the fraction to higher terms. What do the changes mean in terms of the *meaning* of the fraction?

    a. It is often more convenient to work with a fraction that is reduced to lower terms or raised to higher terms. So we divide—or multiply—both terms by the same number.

    b. It does not change the value of a fraction to divide—or multiply—both numerator and denominator by the same number.

    c. Changing the denominator means changing the size of the unit. If the unit is twice as large there will be half as many units.

    d. Changing ⅝ to ¾ should be called changing to higher terms since fourths are larger than eighths.   (DJ)

2. Each of the following groups of fractions, read from left to right, illustrates one of the principles listed below them. To the right of each group of fractions write the letter of the principle which is illustrated.

    a. $\frac{5}{100}, \frac{5}{16}, \frac{5}{10}, \frac{5}{8}, \frac{5}{4}$

    b. $\frac{2}{3}, \frac{3}{4}, \frac{4}{5}, \frac{5}{6}, \frac{7}{8}$

    c. $\frac{5}{8}, \frac{6}{8}, \frac{7}{8}, \frac{8}{8}, \frac{9}{8}$

    d. $\frac{5}{6}, \frac{4}{5}, \frac{3}{4}, \frac{2}{3}, \frac{1}{2}$

    x. If the number of parts increases but the size of the parts does not change, the size of the fraction increases.

    y. If the number of parts does not change but the size of the parts increases, the size of the fraction decreases.

    z. If the numerator and the denominator decrease by the same amount the fraction becomes smaller.

    w. If the numerator and the denominator increase by the same amount the fraction becomes larger.　(DJ)

   3. If we add $\frac{1}{2}$ and $\frac{1}{3}$ we must change to a common denominator. What is the reason we change to a common denominator? $\frac{1}{2} + \frac{1}{3} = \frac{3}{6} + \frac{2}{6} = \frac{5}{6}$

    a. Quantities to be added must be measured in the same units.

    b. Common denominators sometimes make it possible to reduce the answer.

    c. It is a short cut that gives the right answer.

    d. It makes it possible to add numerators without adding denominators.　(DJ)

   4. How much is borrowed—or exchanged—when subtracting $3\frac{7}{8}$ from $15\frac{1}{2}$?

    a. 10　　b. 1　　c. $\frac{1}{2}$　　d. $\frac{1}{8}$　(DJ)

   5. In thinking of $\frac{2}{3}$ as meaning 2 divided by 3, without using decimals, the quotient is _____, the dividend is _____, the divisor is _____, and the remainder is _____.

ALGEBRA

   1. The algebraic expressions below can be represented by at least one of the geometric drawings in the accompanying figure. On the line following each algebraic expression write the letter of the corresponding geometric figure.

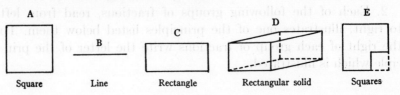

A   D   E

B   C

Square　　　　Line　　　　Rectangle　　　Rectangular solid　　　Squares

a. r ___; b. xy ___; c. $9t^2$ ___, d; $x^2 - y^2$ ___; e. $2x + 3y$ ___; f. $2twx$ ___.   (DJ)

2. If you wish to make a graph to show how the population of a city grew from 150 persons in 1890 to 40,000 persons in 1940, which of the following rules would *not* apply to this problem?

  a. Make the time axis horizontal and the population axis vertical.

  b. Use the same units of measurement on the two axes.

  c. Label the graph to show its subject and the time and place to which it applies.

  d. Indicate the units of measurement on both the horizontal and the vertical axes.   (HCT)

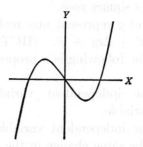

3. The above figure is the graph of one of the functions given below. Which function is it?

  (a) $x + 5x^2$ (b) $6x - x^3$ (c) $x^3 - 27x$ (d) $x^4 + x$
  (e) $6x - x^4$ (HCT)

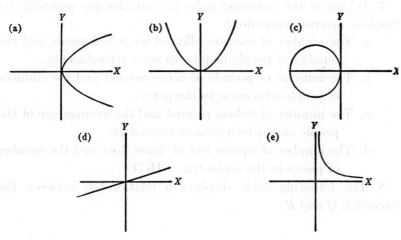

4. Given that $f(x) = f(-x)$ and that one of the preceding diagrams represents the graph of $y = f(x)$. Which graph represents $y = f(x)$?   (HCT)

5. In one of the following situations the variable x is *not* a function of the variable y. Which one is it?

    a. For any number assigned to the variable y, double this number for the value of x.

    b. Sixteen exercises (x = the number of the exercise) are given at the end of a certain chapter in an arithmetic text. Sixteen answers (y = the answer) corresponding to these exercises are given in the back of the book.

    c. In a table of squares and square roots, x = the number and y = its square root.

    d. $x = y$. x and y represent any real number.

    e. $(x + y)^2 = x^2 + 2xy + y^2$.   (HCT)

6. Which one of the following is a property of any linear function, $Y = f(x)$?

    a. Doubling the independent variable doubles the dependent variable.

    b. Increasing the independent variable by one unit always produces the same change in the dependent variable.

    c. The terms "linear function" and "direct variation" are synonomous.

    d. The graph will not pass through the origin.

    e. Correct answer not given.   (HCT)

7. Which of the following pairs of variables are probably related by inverse proportion?

    a. The number of minutes allowed for refreshments and the number of people helping to serve refreshments.

    b. The number of pounds of coffee needed and the number of people who came to the party.

    c. The number of tickets printed and the average age of the people on the refreshment committee.

    d. The number of square feet of dance floor and the number of pieces in the orchestra.   (HCT)

8. The following table displays a relationship between the variables, Q and R.

Q	3.0	4.5	6.0	7.5	9.0
R	60	40	30	24	20

You want to say in words how Q is related to R. Which of the following statements fits the given facts?

a. Q varies inversely as R.   b. Q varies inversely as R^2.
c. R varies inversely as Q^2.   d. R varies directly with Q.   (HCT)

9. Which of the following situations would illustrate one variable varying jointly as the product of two other variables?
    a. The area of a circle.
    b. The volume of a cube.
    c. The distance a freely falling body will fall in t seconds.
    d. Total cost of n lbs. of meat at $p\phi$ per lb.
    e. Correct answer not given.   (HCT)
10. Which of the following statements is *false*?
    a. Some people use formulas in their everyday work.
    b. Functional relationships are sometimes stated in words.
    c. Entries in a table of square roots are mostly approximate numbers.
    d. A fact like $7 + 5 = 12$ is true in itself and has nothing to do with the assumptions and definitions we choose to make.
    e. Tables often save people time by reducing the number of calculations they have to perform.   (HCT)

GEOMETRY[4]

The matching items which follow illustrate testing for the meaning of a concept by giving a specific example, imbedded in a context involving several concepts. There are two directions in this process. One is to name an object and then to ask which concept it represents; the other is to name the concept and then to ask for an object which illustrates it.

I. Knowledge of facts

    A. *Matching:* On the answer sheet, mark out the *one* letter

---

[4] All of the test items in this section were contributed by Donovan A. Johnson of the University of Minnesota High School.

which best matches each numbered item. Any letter may be used once, several times or not at all.

What geometric terms are illustrated by these lines?

1. Line ZP
2. Line ZW
3. Line XW
4. Line SW
5. Line XZ

Geometric terms for items No. 1–5

A. chord
B. diameter
C. secant
D. tangent
E. radius

What geometric figures are formed by these lines?

6. Lines ZP, ZW and WP
7. Lines ZP and PW
8. Lines ZP, PS and SZ
9. Straight line ZW and Curved line ZW
10. Lines SR and SW

Geometric terms for items No. 6–10

A. segment
B. sector
C. polygon
D. central angle
E. inscribed angle

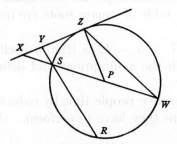

Drawing for items No. 1–10. Center of circle at P

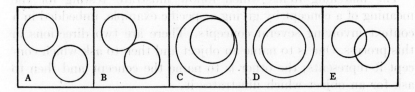

11. What figure above is an example of concentric circles?
12. What figure is an example of internally tangent circles?
13. In what figure can only one common tangent be drawn?
14. In what figure can only one common chord be drawn?
15. In what figure can four common tangents be drawn?

(Completion items seem fairly well adapted to testing whether concepts are partial or distorted in meaning. Of course, they have other uses as the following items will show.)

B. *Completion Items:* Mark on the answer sheet the letter which best completes each numbered statement.

1. *A major arc of a circle is always* (a) half the circumference, (b) the arc of an inscribed angle, (c) greater than a semicircle, (d) equal to the circumference, (e) greater than its subtended central angle.

2. *An inscribed polygon is a polygon whose sides are always* (a) tangent to the circle, (b) chords of the circle, (c) equidistant from the center of the circle, (d) inscribed by equal arcs, (e) equal to the radius of the inscribing circle.

3. *A tangent to a circle is never* (a) perpendicular to a radius drawn to the point of tangency, (b) equal to a second tangent from the same point, (c) a line which touches a circle at only one point, (d) the shortest distance from an external point to a circle, (e) tangent to another circle.

4. *Two parallel lines one inch apart intersect a circle whose radius is one inch:* (a) this is never possible, (b) the intercepted arcs are always one inch in length, (c) the chords of the intercepted arcs will always be one inch long, (d) the intercepted arcs between the parallel lines are always equal, (e) the segments of the parallel lines inside the circle are equal.

5. *If equal chords are drawn, one in each of two unequal circles, the chord of the larger circle* (a) intercepts the greater minor arc, (b) intercepts the same minor arc as the chord of the smaller circle, (c) intercepts the smaller minor arc, (d) is the same distance from the center of its circle as the chord of the smaller circle is from its center, (e) no one of these is true.

6. *If one circle is larger than another, the length of an arc of one degree in the larger compared to an arc of one degree in the smaller is* (a) greater, (b) smaller, (c) the same, (d) not comparable, (e) no one of these correct.

(Understanding a geometric proof involves at least an awareness of the design and sequence of the argument, an insight into the crucial steps of the proof, and judgment as to what is relevant or not pertinent to the proof. The following items of the multiple choice type are planned to test some of these aspects of proof.)

C. *Proofs.* Cross out the letter on the answer sheet which corresponds to the item that is correct for each proof below. *If no correct statement is given, cross out the letter "E" on the answer sheet.*

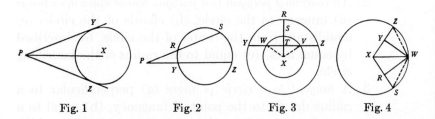

Fig. 1   Fig. 2   Fig. 3   Fig. 4

1. In proving the theorem, "Two tangents to a circle from an external point are equal," two triangles are proved congruent by showing that they have respectively equal (a) three sides, (b) two sides and the included angle, (c) two angles and the included side, (d) the hypotenuse and one side.

2. In proving the theorem, "An angle formed by two secants meeting outside a circle is equal in degrees to one-half the difference of the intercepted arcs," which of the following steps is appropriate in the most direct proof? (a) Parallel lines intercept equal arcs. (b) An inscribed angle is measured by its intercepted arc. (c) A central angle is measured by its intercepted arc. (d) An exterior angle of a triangle equals the sum of the two nonadjacent interior angles.

3. Given two unequal circles having the same center X, and the chord YZ of the greater circle intersecting the smaller circle at W and V. Prove $YW = VZ$. Which statement of the following proof is wrong or useless? (a) XT is perpendicular to WV. (b) YT is equal to TZ. (c) Arc YR equals arc RZ. (d) Triangle XWT is congruent to triangle XVT.

4. If perpendiculars are drawn to two radii from the midpoint of the arc intercepted by the radii, the perpendiculars are equal. Which statement in the following proof is wrong or useless? (a) Angle ZXW equals angle SXW, (b) SW equals XW, (c) Triangle XZW is congruent to triangle XWS, (d) Two right triangles are congruent if the hypotenuse and acute angle of one equals the hypotenuse and acute angle of the other.

2

Evaluation of Ability to Apply Mathematics

Emerging Practices in Evaluation of Elementary School Mathematics

LOWRY W. HARDING

THE standardized test of achievement in arithmetic is necessarily one of the essential elements in a program of evaluation. It is important because of its national norms, which provide data for comparisons, as well as for its comprehensive and balanced coverage of topics and skills. The home-made or teacher-made test of mathematical achievement is likewise a basic tool in evaluating children's progress. Its chief use is in reflecting the current emphasis in classroom instruction. It is especially helpful in providing coverage of topics which individual teachers regard as of special importance, or with which pupils have had unusual difficulty. These two types of "tests in writing" have long carried the burden of whatever evaluating has been done in arithmetic. They continue to be useful, and are not likely to be eliminated by changes in evaluative procedures.

Criticisms of paper-and-pencil instruments of appraisal have increased in recent years. Much of the attack upon standardized tests has been thoughtless and irresponsible. However, responsible criticisms have been directed toward the problems of poor administration of such tests and misinterpretation of results. Many teacher-made tests are poorly organized, represent skewed sampling of items, and lack reliability. They also suffer from poor administration and misapplication of scores. The major continuing limitation of paper-and-pencil instruments of evaluation goes beyond the criticisms usually voiced. It is the artificiality of the testing situation, the schoolbook character of the performance tested, the inevitable emphasis upon memorization or specified recall. The most valuable achievement in mathematics learning is thorough understanding as demonstrated in adaptation and application at the point of need for use. This is therefore the most appropriate behavior to evaluate. Since paper-and-pencil tests, even the best of them, can only simulate real-life conditions, many thoughtful, forward-looking teachers are going beyond them.

Among the evaluative practices emerging from classrooms of such teachers are methods of guided discussion, listening, observation, conferences with children, and co-operation with parents. Comprehensive coverage is aided by use of a concept inventory. Information is collected on children's use of mathematics in any form and in all activities, in and out of school, rather than limited to a single mathematics period. Data are preserved by means of anecdotal and observational records, a daily log or evaluation record, and the concept inventory. These several types of information are used, with standardized test scores, to develop accurate case histories to provide a comprehensive basis for evaluation of the individual pupil and of the class group. The chief emphasis, in these emerging practices, is upon functional competency in mathematics. Typical samples illustrating each of the procedures mentioned, and representing various age levels and activities, are presented below.[5]

GUIDED DISCUSSION

It was time for the morning story hour in the kindergarten program. Clarise was asked to get the book from the teacher's

---

[5] Miss Isabel Miller, Department of Education, Ohio State University, contributed several of the illustrations which follow.

desk and bring it to the circle. She returned with two books. Both had gray covers and the child was confused as to which was the "storybook." Holding up both books, the teacher asked the group how one might tell them apart. Clarise said, "One's bigger'n the other." Sue noted that one book was thicker and longer than the other. "That's fine help from both of you," praised the teacher. "Does anyone see any other way to pick one or the other?" "The book you read to us yesterday had [a picture of] two boys on it. It's that one!" said Steve, pointing.

Through the brief discussion, as well as by means of observing the children's facial expressions, the teacher gained insight into her pupils' maturity of understanding. Comparison of size and dimensions, recognition of distinguishing symbols, and differentiating between "one" and "two" were the particular abilities appraised.

Celebrating his birthday, Tom brought a box of candy bars for his fellow fifth-graders. The teacher asked how they would divide the bars. Archie suggested counting the bars of candy and the number of people. (Thought the teacher: "His understanding hasn't developed beyond the 'one-to-one relationship' in concepts of application. Yet he works textbook problems in division and fractions. I must make a note of that, and see that Archie has more opportunity to develop functional meanings of principles and processes.") Mae objected that "double-counting" would take too long. ("She doesn't really understand division, or she's too eager to get at the candy to think," the teacher noted.) "Can anyone think of another way?" the teacher asked. Jack thought they could weigh the box of candy. Everyone agreed that was a good idea. It weighed four pounds and five ounces. "Divide that by the number of people in the room," said Naomi. "What about the box?" asked Polly. "It weighs something. We'd have to subtract that." Emptied, the box was found to weigh five ounces. "That leaves four pounds of candy. Let's find how much of a pound each person ought to get," Lew suggested. Dividing 64 ounces by (among) 24 people, they found each share should be $2\frac{2}{3}$ ounces. "We've got to find out what one candy bar weighs," Joan observed. ("That's the first time Joan has contributed effectively in mathematics—must make a record of it," noted the teacher). Fortunately, the bars weighed about 1⅓ oz. each. "Goody, we can all have two whole bars!" Zoe exclaimed. ("That's the first time Zoe has ever thought through a fraction problem on her own," the teacher observed to herself.)

LISTENING AND OBSERVATION

On a rainy day the first-grade group was enjoying a free-choice period of quiet indoor recreation. One group of three boys was playing with rook cards. Tom complained to Carl, "You have too many red cards. Give me some of 'em!" Carl proceeded to count from one to five as he picked out red cards. Then he said, "That's all you can have, 'cause I'll only have one left." Eric, who had also picked out his red cards, then observed, "I got eight red ones. How many ought I give you?" "Four," Tom declared, reaching for them. "No," objected Carl. "Then you'd have almost all the red ones." After some argument as to how many red cards there were, Carl proposed, "Let's put 'em all together. Then give 'em out to each of us, one at a time."

Through listening to the above conversation between the three boys, the teacher obtained accurate evaluative data on their understanding of one-to-one matching relationships, counting, comparing, and dividing. The episode reported below gave evidence on a slow learner's understanding of money and comparative values.

Gloria was looking through a comic book during the fourth grade's free-reading period. The teacher maintained genuine "free reading," permitting the children to read whatever they wished. The "retarded readers," of whom Gloria was one, were encouraged in using simple materials to gain speed and broaden basic vocabulary. Gloria read a story of a girl who searched for bubble gum. Following the picture-story, the girl in the story dug and found oil, dug again and found a chest of gold, but continued to search for bubble gum. "That's silly," observed Gloria, "I'd sell the oil and gold. Then I'd buy gum an' anything else I wanted."

CONFERENCES WITH CHILDREN

The first grade was to prepare and present a play, as part of the culminating activity for a broad unit. The teacher was having conferences with individual children to arrange parts in the cast. "I don't want a very big part," said Gary, "'cause I'm 'fraid I'll get mixed up." When asked what he thought a "big" part was, Gary replied, "It's when you have to say something lots of times —more'n five!"

The group assigned parts, with teacher guidance, and Gary had a "small" part, as he had wished. The play was developed, rehearsed, and presented. During a conference to evaluate the performance, Gary observed wistfully, "I wish I'd taken a big part, now. 'Cause I think I'd have gotten along all right. Asked again what he thought a "big" part was, Gary answered, "Oh, it's when you have ten or twelve times to say somethin'." The teacher noted and recorded Gary's growth in perspective on "big" and sensitive use of numbers.

A committee had been appointed by the fourth grade to paint a harvest-scene mural. Their teacher agreed to sit with them in a planning conference on how large to make it and where to put it. They decided to place their mural on the bulletin board facing the door. That decision reached, several children volunteered to go for the paper. Another child objected, "How do you know how much paper to get?" The children looked blankly at each other for a moment, then several hands shot up. "We've got to measure the space," said one child. "Yes, how high and how wide," added another. "How wide is the paper?" inquired a third. "What difference does that make?" asked another child.

For evaluation, it is important that the teacher remember whose hands were raised, and the nature of each child's contribution. For example, the third child has evidenced a mature level of comprehension of square measure and measurement relationships or equivalence. The last child quoted doesn't understand the principle of division very well. The conscientious teacher makes notes of such matters and follows through in providing individual guidance.

REPORTS FROM PARENTS

Illustrative of the evaluative data on mathematical understandings which can be provided by parents are the following accounts. Perhaps even more important than their use in evaluation is the co-operation between home and school. As parents and teachers work together in studying children's problems and progress, many benefits accrue. A few examples of the benefits are: improved understanding by parents of the school program and their children's problems of learning, better provision for individual differences in ability and progress, more comprehensive bases for evaluation. The illustrations accompanying, and others like them, are useful in PTA meetings and parent conferences as means of showing parents how they can help their children and the teacher by identifying, recording, and reporting significant episodes.

The Cub Scout den mother was briefing the third- and fourth-grade boys in the den for their duties in the "Scout-o-rama." Tickets were to be issued for hourly drawings of their hand-crafted objects as prizes. "Now, be careful to give tickets only to adults!" she cautioned. "There are 2000 tickets in this roll, and 15,000 people are expected."

"Which is more?" asked Steve.

"Fifteen thousand is a lot more," said Bill. "More'n seven times as many."

"Aw, 'tain't so. How'd you know, anyway?" argued Alex.

"Gee, that's easy. Two times seven is fourteen. Two into fifteen would go seven an'a half times. So, 15,000 is seven an'a half times as much as 2000. But—I don't know zackly what a thousand is!"

Returning from the barber shop, to which he had unwillingly gone, a twelve-year-old commented argumentatively, "I saw a man in the barber shop who didn't need a haircut anymore than I did. He could have waited another week—saved a whole dollar and a quarter! Just like I could have!"

"Well, yes, the man could have saved some money by letting his hair grow another week. So could you," the father answered, "But neither of you would have saved a great deal."

"Sure we could!" the twelve-year-old argued. "Haircuts are a dollar and a quarter. We could have saved that."

"But only for a week," it was explained. "It has been a month since you got a haircut. You paid $1.25 at the end of four weeks, that's $31\frac{1}{4}$ cents per week. Suppose you waited until next Saturday. You would then pay $1.25 at the end of five weeks. That would be how many cents per week for your haircut?"

Thinking for a moment, the boy answered, "Twenty-five cents."

"Then it costs 31¼ cents a week for haircuts, if you get one each four weeks, and 25 cents if you get one each five weeks. So, how much would you save by waiting another week?"

"Oh, I see," said the boy. "I wouldn't save the whole dollar and a quarter. I'd just spread it out. Guess I'd save a quarter."

CASE HISTORY AND BEHAVIOR JOURNAL

With data accurately and specifically recorded, and kept up to date, the individual case history provides a valuable means of evaluating achievement and maturity over long periods of time. For brevity, family background data, as well as entries relating to subjects other than mathematics, have been omitted from the following sample.

Name: Jimmy X   *Physical Measurements:*(omitted)
Family Background: (omitted)   *Health Data:* (omitted)
Personality: (Descriptive comments) High-strung, tense, jittery. Exerts strong self-control much of the time, to give adequate attention and effort to work. Friendly and co-operative. Responds willingly; particularly responsive to praise. Spontaneous and active in group concerns. Works consistently and tries to do well. Very interested in mechanics and has much manual dexterity. Nearsighted.
    Very weak in arithmetic—needs individual help.
Test Data: California Test of Mental Maturity, IQ, 130. Stanford-Binet, IQ 133. Metropolitan Reading Readiness Test, 39th percentile. (Other test data omitted.)
Behavior Samples: (Entries not related to mathematics have been omitted.)
Oct. 3—Helped him with counting and adding. Can't seem to grasp idea of numbers representing quantities. Doesn't see relationships.
Oct. 25—Can't add or multiply numbers over 2. Doesn't understand the process. "Gee! I wish I could do it. Everybody else can! What's the matter with me?" Worries because he doesn't understand.
Nov. 19—"Miss P——, I can get done with my numbers fast enough now. But I don't get the right answers!" Is now resorting to visual memorizing of form.
Dec. 6—The sixth grade has eggs in incubator, to learn how chicks hatch, to study development of chickens, and to measure feed and growth. Jimmy wanted group to visit sixth grade; said, "It would be good for us to see what the eggs *have achieved.*" (Is this a sign of feeling too much pressure?)

Jan. 18—Commented, when we were choosing helpers, "Gee, I never get to count the milk money!"

Feb. 20—Had been chosen as one of two people to count milk money for the week. We had just finished the order when Jimmy said, "I like my job. I never got to count money before. All I ever got was old seats an' books an' stuff like that!" Is beginning to get clear understanding of counting, adding, and subtracting.

March 8—Has gained rapidly in understanding and skill with addition and subtraction. New difficulty with multiplication—writes many numbers backward; i.e., 625 for 526, 3 $\times$ 10 = 03. When asked, said, "Miss P——, I'm right-handed and the numbers just want to go that way. There's nothing I can do about it!" (Is he giving up? Confused by the difficulty? How can success experiences be provided in multiplication?")

April 22—Group discussing story of airplanes. Picture in reader of 2-engine plane. Someone said plane used a gallon of gas every three miles. Jimmy said, "It has two engines. Does the whole plane use a gallon, or each engine?" Quantitative thinking much improved, especially in reference to *real* things and problems.

May 17—Multiplication clearing up. Picnic preparation—used pennies to illustrate costs. He saw multiplication as short cut for addition, understood that reversing figures changed value. *Thinks* more now, as he figures.

THE CONCEPT-SKILL INVENTORY

As teachers broaden the base of evaluation, utilizing functional situations in various subjects and activities, it is increasingly necessary to check the subject matter coverage. The most systematic and effective means of insuring balance in instruction and evaluation is an inventory of concepts and skills, listed by topics. The following is an example of a twenty-three topic breakdown for elementary mathematics (12).

1. *Approximation or Estimation*—Physical Education. Placing the foul-line in laying out a basketball court. (Grades 5–8)

2. *Average*—Language Arts. Finding average number of words per page, in planning school news. (Grades 4–8)

3. *Counting and Ranking*—Taking attendance, checking supplies, etc. (Grades 1–5). Rating various foods on calorie value, vitamin content, cost, etc. (Grades 4–8)

4. *Formulas and Algebraic Symbolization*—Discussing and comparing the "axle-mile" and "ton-mile" formulas for taxing or measuring economy runs. (Grades 5–8)

5. *Fractions, Common*—Finding fractional and multiple parts of recipes for group parties. (Grades 3–8)

6. *Fractions, Decimal*—Comparing costs and figuring savings for puppetry making, school bazaar, school banking, etc. (Grades 5–8)

7. *Geometric Forms*—Shuffleboard court, designing pottery, baskets, etc. (Grades 4–8)

8. *Graphic Representation*—Keeping weather charts, reading population maps, etc. (Grades 3–8)

9. *Grouping and Number Combinations*—"This team has more children (seven) than that team (five)." (Grades 1–5)

10. *Identification: Meaning of Number Symbols*—"The '19' is in red, 'cause it's Sunday." (Grades 1–3)

11. *Measurement: Linear, Quantity, Temperature, Time*—"Is that enough paper to cover the bulletin board?" (Grades 1–4). "How many cups of water do I need for a quart?" (Grades 1–4). "Is it cold enough outside to wear coats?" (Grades 1–5). "We've been in school an hour, already. It's ten o'clock!" (Grades 1–3)

12. *Money*—"How much will I owe the library on this overdue book?" (Grades 1–8)

13. *Number System: Organization, Serial Idea, Decimal Nature*—"Why is it so easy to count on our fingers?" (Grades 1–5). "If ten 100's are called a 'thousand,' why aren't ten 1000's called a 'million'?" (Grade 4)

14. *Operations: Addition, Subtraction, Multiplication, Division*—"We need two more (or less) to have a team of nine!" (Grades 1–6) "Keeping books" on Halloween party, etc. (Grades 4–8)

15. *Percentage*—"The aquarium is half full? Fifty per cent of the job is done!" (Grades 2–4). "This 20 per cent sale has basketballs at $4. What was the cost before?" (Grades 5–8)

16. *Place Value and Face Value*—"Eleven boys present. We write two 1's side by side to make 11, because the 1 on the left represents one ten." (Grades 1–3, taking attendance, etc.)

17. *Problem-Solving*—"If we are going to make a square box this long (any length decided on), the other sides would have to be the same length—wouldn't they? How can we tell?" (Grades 2–4)

18. *Proof and Generalization*—"If Dick steps it off (distance for dart throwing, etc.), we'll have to throw farther than if Mary steps it off. His legs are longer!" (Grades 2–4)

19. *Quantitative Thinking: Mathematical Judgment*—"Do we get more for our money when we buy double-dip cones?" (Grades 2–5)

20. *Ratio and Relationship*—"The wider the skin is, the bigger drumhead we can make." (Grades 3–6)

21. *Reading and Writing of Number Ideas*—"Tom should have read 'Two hundred and twenty-five miles' instead of 'two two five,' because . . ." (Grades 3–5)

22. *Vocabulary of Number and Quantity*—"Are the *big* brushes in the *top*, *middle*, or *lower* drawer?" (Grades 1–3). "It's really 213 miles to Chicago, but we say 'about 200 miles.' Round off the number and put two zeros for the 13." (Grades 5–7)

23. *Zero Representation*—"Zero is where we start before we have even one to count!" (Grades 1–2). "It's really 213 miles to Chicago, but we say 'about 200 miles.' Round off the number and put two zeros for the 13." (Grades 5–7)

Examples of Tests for the Evaluation of Geometrical Learning[6]

Donovan Johnson

MULTIPLE CHOICE

The following items are based on illustrations of the use of circles in practical situations. Read each description carefully and then answer the items about it by marking out the letter of your choice on the answer sheet.

When a ray of sunshine enters a raindrop, the light is refracted (bent) and reflected within the drop as shown by the drawing. Since the colors of light are refracted and reflected unequally, a rainbow is produced.

61. The ray of light from the sun passing through a raindrop is an example of (a) a secant, (b) a tangent, (c) a chord, (d) a diameter, (e) an arc.

62. When a ray of light is reflected inside a raindrop, the

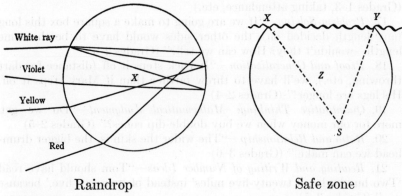

Raindrop   Safe zone

---

[6] The items are numbered **according** to the original excerpt furnished by Donovan Johnson.

angle formed is (a) a central angle, (b) an interior angle, (c) an inscribed angle (d) an angle between a chord and secant, (e) an angle between intersecting chords.

63. The angle formed by the rays of violet light *inside* the raindrop compared to the angle formed by the rays of red light inside the drop is (a) the same, (b) smaller, (c) larger, (d) dependent on the size of the raindrop, (e) impossible to determine.

In the drawing above X and Y are harbor lights on a shore. Outside the circle it is dangerous sailing. Major arc XY is 300° and the distance from X to Y is 100 rods.

64. In order for the ship S to stay within the safe zone, $\angle XSY$ *must* be (a) more than 60°, (b) more than 120°, (c) less than 30°, (d) more than 30°, (e) none of these.

65. If the points X and Y, as viewed from the ship, subtend an arc of 60° then the ship *must* be (a) on the circle, (b) at the center of the circle, (c) on the perpendicular bisector of XY, (d) within the circle, (e) outside the circle.

66. In order for a submarine to stay outside the circle, points X and Y as viewed from the submarine, *must* subtend an arc (a) more than 60°, (b) more than 120°, (c) less than 60°, (d) less than 30°, (e) none of these.

A piece of a round pottery plate of 150° of arc, similar to the drawing below, is found in an Indian grave. In order to reconstruct the original plate, it is necessary to know the diameter. The length XY is 4 inches.

67. The diameter of the pottery plate is (a) 4 inches, (b) 8 inches, (c) 12 inches, (d) 4π inches, (e) none of these.

68. Which one of the following methods can be used to determine the diameter of this plate? (a) Draw a perpendicular to a tangent to the arc at the point of tangency. (b) Draw the perpendicular bisector of the longest chord of the available arc. (c) Draw the perpendicular bisectors of any two chords. (d) Draw the perpendicular bisector of one chord and the perpendicular to a tangent. (e) Measure the number of degrees of arc and the

longest chord. The ratio of the measured arc to 180° will be the same as the ratio of the chord to the diameter.

A piston, Z, is attached to a crank, XY, which describes a circle as it turns on the axle, X. XY is 5-inches long and the connecting rod, YZ, is 12-inches long. As the crank turns, the piston moves backward and forward.

69. The number of positions where the crank XY will be perpendicular to the connecting rod YZ during one revolution is (a) four, (b) two, (c) one, (d) none, (e) any number.

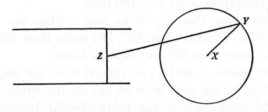

70. The number of positions where YZ is a secant to circle X during one revolution is (a) none, (b) one, (c) two, (d) four, (e) any number.

71. In one revolution of the crank the piston will move a total distance, backward and forward of (a) 5 inches, (b) 10 inches, (c) 12 inches, (d) 31.14 inches, (e) 20 inches.

72. The angle between YZ and XY as the crank turns is *always* (a) an inscribed angle, (b) an acute angle, (c) an angle between a chord and radius, (d) measured by one-half the intercepted arc, (e) none of these.

73. If the crank makes one revolution in 12 seconds, the number of degrees it turns per second is (a) 360, (b) 120, (c) 30, (d) 12, (e) unknown.

The gable of a quonset hut is an arc of a circle with a radius of 10 feet. The arc of this gable is 180°.

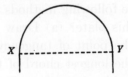

74. The width XY of the foundation for a quonset hut must be (a) 10 feet, (b) 15 feet, (c) 20 feet, (d) 30 feet, (e) none of these.

75. The end of the hut is an example of (a) major arc, (b) sector, (c) semicircle, (d) segment, (e) none of these.

76. The height of the gable above the foundation XY will be (a) 5 feet, (b) 10 feet, (c) 15 feet, (d) 20 feet, (e) none of these.

77. The length of the gable arc XY will be (a) 20 feet, (b) 30 feet, (c) 15 feet, (d) 10π feet, (e) none of these.

The cross section of cells of a bee's honeycomb is a regular six-sided figure. This is an example of remarkable engineering skill because mathematicians have proved that such a form requires the least amount of wax to hold a certain amount of honey.

78. Groups of bee's cells occupy less space than circular cells because (a) the cells are regular polygons, (b) hexagonal cells are tangent in more points than circular cells, (c) the vertices of six hexagonal cells will just fit around a point without overlapping, (d) the area of a hexagonal cell is less than that of the inscribing circle.

79. If the cross section of a bee's cell is inscribed in a circle, which of the following is true? (a) Each side is a tangent. (b) Each intercepted arc is equal to 72°. (c) Each side is equal to the radius. (d) Each side is a secant. (e) The distance from the center of the circle to the midpoint of each side is equal to the radius.

80. Each interior angle of a bee's cell is (a) 30°, (b) 60°, (c) 120°, (d) 150°, (e) unknown.

A target for a dart game is made up of rings with scoring values as shown in the drawing. The width of each ring is two inches and the radius of the inner circle is two inches.

81. This target is an illustration of (a) concentric circles, (b) parallel circles, (c) overlapping circles, (d) circles tangent internally, (e) circles with common diameters.

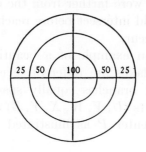

82. The area of the 50-point ring is, (a) the same as the area of the 100-point circle, (b) the same as the area of the 25-point ring, (c) twice the area of the 100-point circle, (d) half the area of the 25-point ring, (e) none of these.

83. The straight lines divide the target circles into (a) twelve equal arcs, (b) major arcs, (c) semi-circles, (d) segments, (e) twelve arcs of equal arc degrees.

TRUE-FALSE

Answer the following items by marking out on the answer sheet the "T" if it is true and "F" if it is false.

An eclipse of the sun occurs when the moon is between the earth and the sun as shown in the accompanying drawing. The total eclipse is visible in the area of the moon's shadow on the earth. Light rays travel in straight lines as indicated in the drawing.

84. The rays of light in the drawing are examples of common internal tangents of the sun and moon.

85. The length of the ray between the points of tangency, X and Y, is equal to the distance between the centers of the sun and moon.

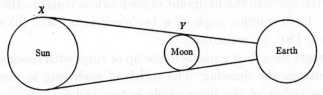

86. As the moon and the earth move, they will attain a position where it is possible for a ray of sunlight to be tangent to all three heavenly bodies.

87. If the moon were farther from the earth so that the tangent light rays would intersect before reaching the earth, a total eclipse would not occur.

A snowflake is an example of a beautiful geometric design. Although all snowflakes are different, every snowflake is symmetric and has six branches equally spaced about its center. Each of the six points (U, V, W, X, Y, Z) of a snowflake is equidistant from the center P as illustrated in the accompanying figure.

88. The distance between adjacent points, for example, XY, is equal to half the distance WY.

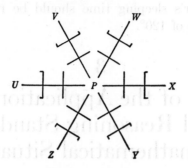

89. The distance XY is equal to the distance PZ.

90. Snowflakes are congruent figures.

91. The $\angle XPW$ is equal to 30°.

92. A snowflake design can be inscribed in a circle.

The great circle route between two cities is the shortest route on the earth's surface between the two cities. This circle route is the minor arc of a great circle on the earth's surface. The center of this great circle is the center of the earth and its radius is equal to the radius of the earth. Which of the following statements are correct?

93. The great circle route between two cities can be measured in degrees of arc as well as in miles.

94. The shortest route between two cities for an airplane to fly is the chord of the great circle passing through the two cities.

95. The circumference of the great circle passing through Minneapolis and New York City is approximately equal to the circumference of the earth at the equator.

96. The great circle arc from Minneapolis to the equator is 45°. The central angle subtended by this arc is 90°.

Two circle graphs are drawn to show the distribution of time of a father and his son in different daily activities. The graphs show 8 hours of sleep per day for the father and 10 hours for the son.

97. The amount of time spent in different activities should be represented by sectors of the circles.

98. The parts of the circle representing sleeping time should have central angles of 8° and 10°.

99. The son's sleeping time should be represented by a segment with an inscribed angle of 150°.

100. The father's sleeping time should be represented by a sector with an arc of 120°.

3

Evaluation of the Application of Mathematical Reasoning Standards to Nonmathematical Situations

Illustrations and Analyses

BJARNE R. ULLSVIK

HARRY LEWIS

BJARNE R. ULLSVIK (28) selected a description of 10 *behaviors* given by L. W. Grever (11) and listed a test item for each. When rearranged slightly the material takes this form:

1. Recognize and define key words and phrases which need definition.
2. Detect unstated assumptions.
3. Analyze if-then arguments in terms of basic assumptions and conclusions which logically follow.
4. Distinguish between evidence that is relevant and evidence that is irrelevant to the problem in question.
5. Judge evidence in terms of its potency of argument.
6. Detect a change in definition during the course of an argument.
7. Recognize that opposing courses of action are based on different assumptions.
8. Distinguish between conclusions which do and conclusions which do not follow logically from a given set of assumptions.
9. Recognize inadequate sampling in generalizations which do not justify a conclusion.
10. Recognize unwarranted analogies in arguments.

The test items which are designed to call forth respectively Behaviors 1–10 are items 11–20 respectively listed under Problem II, which follows:

PROBLEM II

Jack and his older brother are Boy Scouts and their younger brother Billy wants to become a Boy Scout. The rules state that a boy must be at least 11 years of age before he can become a Boy Scout, and before he can wear the official uniform he must: (a) know the scout oath and law, motto, sign, salute, and significance of the badge and uniform; (b) know the composition and history of the flag of the United States and the customary forms of respect due it; (c) be able to tie the square knot and other knots including the bowline.

Questions

11. As given above, before a boy can wear the official uniform of the Boy Scouts, he must know the composition and history of the flag of the United States and the customary forms of respect due it. The term which is most in need of definition in this requirement is (a) official uniform, (b) United States, (c) customary forms of respect, (d) composition and history.

12. Billy was heard to say, "Jack is a Boy Scout, therefore he does good deeds." In making this statement, Billy is assuming that (a) not all Boy Scouts do good deeds, (b) most Boy Scouts do good deeds, (c) some Boy Scouts do not do good deeds, (d) all Boy Scouts do good deeds.

13. If Jack is 17 years old, then one can conclude that his younger brother Billy is (a) at least 11 years old, (b) younger than 11 years old, (c) more than 11 years old, (d) younger than 17 years old.

14. Which one of the following statements is not related to the argument that Billy may or may not join the Boy Scouts? (a) Billy's brother Jack is not a good Boy Scout. (b) Billy does not know how to tie the square knot. (c) Billy does not know how to tie the bowline knot. (d) Billy does not know the scout oath.

15. Which one of the following statements most strongly leads one to believe that Billy cannot join the Boy Scouts? (a) Billy is not yet 11 years old. (b) Billy does not as yet know the scout oath. (c) Billy does not know how to tie a slip knot. (d) Billy does not like to go camping.

16. Mr. Green believes that the customary forms of respect due the United States flag include proper folding when not in use and burning a flag to be discarded. Mr. White believes that burning a flag to be discarded is not a customary respect, but that proper folding is a customary respect to the flag. While taking down a United States flag, Jack did not fold it properly. In doing so, he did not observe the customary forms of respect as explained above by (a) Mr. Green, (b) Mr. White, (c) both Mr. Green and Mr. White, (d) neither Mr. Green nor Mr. White.

17. When the United States flag of a Boy Scout troop was worn out, it was sold to a local rag dealer. In doing so, the troop did not observe the cutomary forms of respect as explained in question 16 by (a) Mr.

Green, (b) Mr. White, (c) both Mr. Green and Mr. White, (d) neither Mr. Green nor Mr. White.

18. If all Boy Scouts do good deeds, then: (a) all boys who do good deeds are Boy Scouts; (b) some boys who do good deeds are Boy Scouts; (c) some Boy Scouts do not perform good deeds; (d) Jack, a Boy Scout, does good deeds.

19. Because more than half of the boys of Jack's home town between the ages of 11 and 21 are Boy Scouts, Jack concludes that at least half of the boys in Illinois between the ages of 11 and 21 are Boy Scouts. Jack's conclusion: (a) must be accepted, (b) must be rejected, (c) is not necessarily true.

20. The Boy Scout rule book states that after one has ceased to be a scout or has left the scout movement, he should no longer wear the official scout uniform. Jack's friend Mike is no longer a Boy Scout, but still wears his scout uniform on certain occasions. He argues that he can do so since some discharged servicemen wear their uniforms on special occasions. Mike's argument cannot be supported because (a) not all discharged servicemen were Boy Scouts, (b) some servicemen were given dishonorable discharges, (c) the Boy Scouts are in no way connected with the Armed Services, (d) some leading military men were Boy Scouts at one time.

Two of the procedures used by Harry Lewis (15) in evaluating the development of critical thinking through the teaching of plane demonstrative geometry were: (a) an analysis of monthly reports of his students, and (b) a study of questionnaire responses given at the end of the course. Excerpts from Lewis' description of the use of these procedures follow:

On the first day of each month during the year that the study was being conducted, each student . . . was asked to submit a paper on any topic which he felt was in some way related to the material discussed in class. . . . Although the students were constantly exposed to nonmathematical problems designed by the instructor, there is a marked difference between the ability to analyze these, and the ability to detect similar situations for themselves while reading a newspaper or listening to a political address. . . .

Lewis compared early and later reports written by each student. . . . Although this comparison would seem to be highly subjective, he felt that the improvement in ability to analyze critically pertinent issues was so apparent that the gains might be said to be obvious. Two sets of these "before and after" studies follow, accompanied by the investigator's analysis of their comparative merits.

No effort was made to select these reports for their literary value but rather as an indication of the diversity of areas to which the training received by the students "transferred."

Early Report of First Student

TEST FOR FOOLPROOF AUTHORITY

What is logic? To some it may mean a rash study on human thought. To others it is no more than the thinking with which every normal person is born. Both are misleading concepts of the word in question as it really is an everyman's art. To Funk and Wagnall's it means "the science of reasoning, and of thinking accurately." However, according to A. E. Mander's book (16), *Clearer Thinking*, around which I intend to build my composition, it is not true to say that we, at least those of us of normal mind, are naturally endowed with this ability to think clearly without taking on any practice or learning. To quote Mander, "People with untrained minds should no more expect to think clearly and logically than people who have never learned and never practiced can expect to find themselves good carpenters, golfers, bridge-players, or pianists."

One of the most interesting phases of Mander's writing tells how we may judge recognized expert authority. The outline to be followed in this case is to note these qualities of the authorities: identification, recognition, whether the person is living, the lack of bias.

For the sake of analysis we shall take a Wonderfield cigarette ad in a current magazine, having for authority, Joan Fairfield, famous Hollywood actress of motion pictures. She states that in her home guests always insist on Wonderfields because they're so mild. First of all, is the person *identified*? Definitely! Secondly, is she *recognized* on this particular subject? No! In fact, we find that she doesn't smoke, according to her words. She states that her guests always insist on Wonderfields. Is Joan Fairfield *living*? (Or is she dead, and has it been so long that her opinion might have been altered by facts that have since come to light?) She is living as of today. Is she unbiased? That we do not know. The mere fact that she may have been paid a large sum of money to appear for Wonderfield may have cast aside all her prejudices. Possibly she even has disliked cigarettes or Wonderfields particularly. In my opinion, as in Mander's, this is quite a difficult test to consider.

When a prominent manufacturer of cigarettes says that 113,597 doctors smoke for pleasure one does not know who the doctors are, whether they are throat specialists or horse doctors. Their recognition is not known; that is, whether they are prominent horse doctors or failure horse doctors. Are they all dead, half dead, all alive, or what? Their reasons are not apparent. According to logic, such advertising is definitely breaking all the rules.

Now comes the judgment of someone in whom we, personally, have confidence. For example, if we have a friend from whom we would like to obtain some desired information we must ask ourselves: (a) Do we have confidence in his knowledge of the subject, and in his ability, honesty, and impartiality? (b) Do we know him so that we can believe him? (c) Our confidence must be sufficient to make us feel that we should be equally prepared to accept his judgment—even if it were the opposite of what it is. If these three conditions are fulfilled we are justified in accepting a belief on the judgment of another (he not being a recognized expert authority). . . .

Later Report of First Student

COMMENTS ON "ORIGIN OF SPECIES" BY DARWIN
CHAPTER I. VARIATION UNDER DOMESTICATION

It is to this work that I have chosen to apply the study of analysis. For, in the first chapter of this book, there are many words and reasoning methods used by Darwin (6) which have appeared both illogical and invalid. However, we should keep in mind that the author himself takes these possibilities into consideration, as he writes in the introduction to the *Origin of Species*: "For I am well aware that scarcely a single point is discussed in this volume on which facts cannot be deduced, often apparently leading to conclusions directly opposite to those at which I have arrived." We must also keep in mind that it was Charles Darwin who after many centuries revolutionized the many correlated fields of science.

A particular instance of a fallacy is found in the section of the first chapter, "Effects of Habit and of the Use or Disuse of Parts; Correlated Variation; Inheritance." Here Darwin, attempting to convince the reader of the vast importance and breeding profit of the survival of organisms, writes on the superior and inferior traits of some animals; in this case, the pig. He states that color and physical appearance are linked together with survival and illustrates by a letter written to him by a friend, in which the writer states that pigs which always survived after eating a certain plant, paintroot, were not of the white type but rather the black members of the litter. These white pigs became victims of the plant which caused their hoofs to degenerate. Therefore, he concludes that it is better to select the black members of the litter, for "they alone have a good chance of living."

Being unharmed by the eating of a single plant does not necessarily mean that black pigs are endowed with a "good chance of living." As far as we know, the white members of the litter may well be able to survive every other plant under the sun, save the "paintroot" variety, or these may also be of greater resistance to contaminated food infection than are the black pigs. Of the two groups, these may live the longer making them the better on a farm that is not infested with "paintroot." In other words, survival of the *one* thing should not imply superiority.

More important factors and a greater quantity of obstacles survived generally make up a superior group. To clarify the word, "superior," I mean the ability for the animal class to produce a stronger, more adaptive offspring as well as possessing these qualities themselves; Darwin's concept probably does not differ since he goes on to give the reader a pretty good idea of the word.

The author's use of "colored" words is extensive also. He refers to animals and plants as better, good, worse, and bad without giving us any idea of his concepts as he might have as in the case of *superiority*. For example, quoting from different parts in the first chapter, we find: "The inheritance of *good* and *bad* qualities is so obvious"; "perseverance of the *best* individuals"; "hardly anyone is so careless as to breed the worse." In such an instance he describes the pear of early Roman times as worse than that of today, basing his conclusions on the observations of the poet Virgil. The fruit was smaller and less plump, therefore Darwin said they were worse. Worse for whom? Breeders or farmers who are dependent on their crops for the prices the plump ones will bring? Or worse for the pear itself, which through centuries and constant alteration to a plump variety became comparatively less resistant and made to struggle harder for existence?

"What English breeders have actually effected," writes Darwin in another section of the first chapter "Principles of Selection Anciently Followed, and Their Effects" "is proven by the enormous prices given for animals with a good pedigree . . . ." Here the teaching of logic can again be applied for it is here that Charles Darwin (6) concludes that high prices offered for the new animals produced by the breeders makes them good pedigree (whatever that may mean). That is, to say, that a perfume is of excellent quality on account of the fifteen dollar price tag tied to it. In other words, the high prices paid for a certain pedigreed dog (as Darwin goes on to say) "does not definitely reflect the accomplishments of the English breeders—or any breeders for that matter!"

ANALYSIS BY DR. LEWIS OF THE ABOVE REPORTS

For his first report the boy selected two chapters from a book which had been listed on a bibliography recommended by the teacher as interesting reading material. Other than quoting extensively from this source, he applied the tests of recognition of "expert authority" as suggested by Mander to only two different advertisements. There is very little in this report which would show any originality of thinking for he merely asked himself each of the questions found in *Clearer Thinking*, (16) then answered them in terms of the advertisements he had chosen.

On the other hand, in the later report the book he analyzed was one of his own choice having no apparent connection with geometry or "logic for the layman." At no time was Darwin's *Origin of Species* (6) discussed in class; its selection and analysis grew out of the boy's own experience and did not follow a set pattern of rules that he may have gleaned from some source as had the earlier report. The boy showed that he had a wide understanding of the nature of proof by his ability to:

1. Point out assumptions made by Darwin in the following statement: "high prices paid for a new variety of animals produced by breeders make them of good pedigree."

2. Show how Darwin made use of ambiguous and "colored" terms. such as "good," "bad," "worse."

3. Illustrate wherein Darwin had used incomplete induction to "prove" that superior pigs on one farm would be superior on every farm, in addition to making use, rather poorly, of the indirect proof by listing only one factor that may produce superiority rather than all factors.

The student did not merely compile a list of statements showing evidence of inconclusive reasoning by the author, he pointed out why such reasoning was poor and suggested how it may have been improved by suggesting other conclusions that were equally plausible. It is evident, however, that the student himself could have tempered his own observations to a greater degree than he did. Considered *in toto*, the end result is a decided improvement over his early efforts.

Early Report of Second Student

SEARCH FOR TRUTH BY ERIC TEMPLE BELL

In his book, *Search for Truth*, Eric Temple Bell (1) traces the history of deductive reasoning through the ages. He uses Pilate's question, "What is truth?" to introduce the first chapter; then goes on to say that in the 19 centuries since Pilate first asked that misleading question thousands of answers, no two alike, have been given by theologians, philosophers, metaphysicians, cranks, and visionaries. It is noted as the story of these replies leads to the present there is an ever-accelerating speed in the piling up of new guesses. But, we are told:

"Our greater productivity is due partly to the fact that scores of hundreds of workers dig like demons side by side in a single narrow field which only a century ago, was abandoned to one cogitating, dyspeptic hermit and the crows. This, by definition, is progress. Put a lot of goldfish in a bathtub, give them all they can eat, and naturally they will breed."

In attempting to show that difficulty is encountered in this search for truth because some problems are so seemingly simple that they are harder to handle than more complex ones, the author cites the example of Mr. Z. This mathematician was conducting experiments where anyone could watch him. Someone in the audience suggested that he examine a seemingly trivial subject that everyone in the room had known about since his first year in high school. Mr. Z proceeded to set down all the assumptions from which the subject is developed in the schoolbooks. Having spent four days at this task, Z decided to slightly alter the simplest of his assumptions; then by the laws of common logic he developed the consequences of this slightly modified set of assumptions. The new road he traveled was almost like the old one but gradually the slight divergence led to new unconquered land that looked not at all like the drab region from which he had set out. The moral: "To make a radical advance one must tamper with the roots, not with the branches of the tree of knowledge"; and these roots are simply assumptions (1).

Thus the author states that the difficulties in the way of advances in clear thinking are our inability to discard traditional patterns of reasoning which were acquired during hard work in school, and the natural difficulty of taking hold of something that is so simple that there is nothing to take hold of.

Then in the course of the next few pages, Mr. Bell goes on the first of his many rampages through territory that is way, way, way above my head. After reading one or two chapters, Dad tells me that Mr. Bell is just having a good time sarcastically showing what is wrong with certain theories in mathematics, but the thing is, you have to understand a lot more than we do to find out what he is attacking. Like a good little girl I merrily struggled on to the end of the book and gave a sigh of relief when I finished the last page. However, looking back now, I am overjoyed to find that I do understand some parts. What a wonderful word is "assumption," for when it is mentioned I usually understand what Mr. Bell is talking about!

I did get from the book a very definite realization that the history of deductive reasoning certainly shows some amazing ups and downs. Mr. Bell emphasizes four periods as being important landmarks. First came the Egyptians with their truncated pyramids sliced into infinity (?), then Greece bringing both good and bad, and then advances of 1826 and 1930. What happened in Greece is especially important. At this time the logic of such men as Plato, Aristotle, and Euclid was accepted as eternal, superhuman, Absolute Truth and it was accepted until such men as Pythagoras, Lobachevsky, Lucasiewicz, and Tarski dared to question and find the loopholes. In Mr. Bell's words:

"Thus logic—cold reasoning—was the ultimate reality, higher even than the God they (the Greeks) worshipped, and it alone was the arbiter of fate and the body and soul of Truth. It has taken us long enough, God knows, to escape from this stupid nightmare, but at last we are free. The experiences of our race in Europe from 300 to 1500 A.D. should make us reluctant ever to discover another Absolute Truth."

There was another discussion which I definitely understood. It concerns just what we have been doing in class—examining the assumptions behind the conclusions and considering their validity. Mr. Bell dwells on the fact that our conclusions can hold no more truth than do the assumptions they are based upon. In the mill of clear thinking, then, we get no more out than we put in.

"If our assumptions conceal spectacular impossibilities, our mathematically induced theories will fairly scintillate with dazzling plausibilities."

In conclusion Mr. Bell's advice is: "Pick the assumptions to pieces till the stuff they are made of is exposed to plain view—this is the cardinal rule for understanding the basis for our beliefs." This is just the method by which the reasoning of Aristotle was picked to pieces.

So with these excerpts and other sections that I understood in mind, I would like to say the gist of *Search for Truth* is that we must keep open minds at all times—not being hasty to condemn or accept, and certainly aware of the mistake that was made when the logic of Aristotle was dubbed the Absolute Truth. Pilate's question remains unanswered and Mr. Bell suggests that it is really just a lot of meaningless noises. Mr. Bell's advice is, "Common sense is not what you need if you are going to find out anything worth knowing; it is uncommon sense."

Now I find that I am glad that I read *Search for Truth*. Even though many parts were far from being easy or even understandable reading, I think I gained something from the book.

Excerpts from Later Report of Second Student

THE RIGHT—COSMIC OR SOCIAL

The idea of the "right" as presented in Statement 1 would place the right out of the hands of men and represent it as existing whether man thinks about it or not. In this case, when a disagreement arises all we can do is rely on its being settled sometime by what is referred to as "an absolute just tribunal." What comes to mind is, what is that "absolute just tribunal" going to be composed of. If it is going to be every man for himself in deciding what judge he is going to use or even if all men would agree on one thing, if that thing would be some other man-made code of laws or tradition, I don't see just how far that would work. This also means to suggest that it is of little use to try to set certain goals as leading to any kind of a worthwhile life, because the right would exist above and beyond our thoughts and may be so prearranged that we are not supposed to have any idea about it. If it is understood that that "absolute just tribunal" will not appear on earth then each man can go his own way and recognize no social demands on himself, in his belief that his conception of the best way to live will meet the approval of whatever he may think of as "absolute just truth" (23).

Statement 3 seems to be a more practical view, but on consideration it seems to lead to the same problem or even worse. If the right is represented as the demands that others make on us of which some account should be taken, the question is how much account and of whom. If a child is placed among thieves, "the right" would demand his following their lead as they would induce him to think and desire. In this case the right could hardly lead to any conception of what the "good life" may be. If every one fulfills part of the social obligations that his neighbors place on him, each person will have different forces influencing him according to his surroundings and if these surroundings are those that thieves would provide, I don't see how the world would get ahead much. If the Lord put men to earth to follow the commands of other men, why should he have given a conscience, etc. to each when a few could very easily rule.

In this case, as in Statement 1 the only hope would lie in the enlightenment of the people in general so that through education that "absolute just tribunal," if it must be established would be halfway reasonable to depend on, and in the second case, the demands wrought by society would be such that they would not hinder the individual but help him reach the "good."

REFLECTIVE VS. CUSTOMARY MORALS

In the same manner that people living together would have to decide about the "right" the question of "morals" comes. Two remedies would be suggested for today's situation—reflective morals or customary morals. I think that a strict code of morals would have the same effect on civilization today as Aristotle had on geometry. How can a code be made up by one man or any group of men in one age be adaptable to other men in the following generations? This is a changing world if not because of changing ideas, then at least because of changing personalities. To tie each generation down to the code of their fathers is just as silly as allowing the dishwasher to stand aside and to wash dishes as your mother did just because she did.

Without saying that the two situations would be analogous, just consider what happened in geometry because men accepted absolute truth and were afraid to question it. This should be warning enough. As far as "super-this" or "super-that" truths are concerned, I think that there are very few if any and very few would be necessary. Why accept anything without question because of mere tradition when tradition may be more harmful than helpful today. I don't think that one code of morals could possibly hold effective for very long with all the changes that go on. When we can use our own minds and reach an original decision once in a while, perhaps the world may get somewhere. Not that there should be no restraint or that every code of morals should be thrown out periodically but rather that man should use his intelligence and impartially consider the situations from the standpoint of all concerned, guided both by the useful opinion of his elders as presented in their code of morals and by education designed to give some idea of solutions to general problems but not laying down an ironbound catechism. Then this standard can serve as a guide to be alternately relied upon or modified as changing situations arise.

ANALYSIS OF THE SECOND STUDENT'S REPORTS BY DR. LEWIS

It is quite apparent from the two reports that the girl who wrote them was an exceedingly able student. Unfortunately, she chose to read Bell's

Search for Truth (1) at a time when her understanding of both the nature of proof and geometry were not sufficiently developed. Though she did gain something from the reading as her humorous account of it indicated, it was very little more than a superficial grasp of the essence of the content of the book.

The pupil's analysis of "The Right" and "Morals" shows a depth of comprehension that is rarely found among college students. This is not intended to imply that the year's course in geometry had raised the level of her thinking by six or seven years. It is felt that through the course she had developed an ability to evaluate critically material that previously she had been able to read only on a juvenile level. Her later writing shows evidence that she was constantly aware of the hypothetical nature of the statements that both she, and the sources she quoted, were making.

The teacher had given the girl a copy of Sayer's *Introduction to Philosophy of Education* (23) and suggested that she might enjoy Part IV, Sections C and D. No discussion had ever occurred in class concerning the material found in these sections. Her later report was simply the application of the principles developed during the year to these philosophical issues. Whether one agrees with her views is not important to this study. What is of consequence, is the fact that the girl showed a marked improvement in reflective thinking through this writing in comparison with her work at the beginning of the experiment.

Another procedure used by Lewis involved an analysis of the replies to a questionnaire. One week prior to the close of the school year each student received a questionnaire which he was asked to answer within the following four days. The distribution of these forms was handled entirely by two students in the group. These two clarified any inquiries that were raised by the others. The unsigned, sealed questionnaires were returned to the two students who held them until the very last day of school at which time it would have been too late to alter any grades.

It was hoped that these precautions would remove any doubt that may have existed in their minds concerning the possibility of their replies affecting their marks. In turn this may have increased the likelihood that the answers were truly representative of their reactions to the course. The fact that they were returned unsigned may have resulted, however, in very rapid and haphazard circling of numbers merely to fulfill an unpleasant obligation. This seemed evident in but a small number of cases. Moreover, the variations in their ratings would suggest that they had deliberated over them before selecting the category that most closely represented their attitude.

Excerpts from this questionnaire appear below.

I. To begin with we are interested in learning to what extent you may have spoken to other people concerning the content of this course.

Scale of values:

1. Frequently 2. Occasionally 3. Never.

Circle the number which, in your judgment, most closely approximates the frequency with which you have talked to the following people with reference to the material of this subject.

a. Other students	1 2 3
b. Brothers and sisters	1 2 3
c. Mother	1 2 3
d. Father	1 2 3
e. Other relatives	1 2 3
f. Storekeepers	1 2 3
g. People in other schools	1 2 3
h. Teachers	1 2 3
i. Friends	1 2 3

Perhaps the classes of people listed above are not complete. Add any you may care to in the space provided immediately below.

II. Through this group of items we would like to determine the places or sources wherein you may have noticed yourself making use of the material that arose in the course.

a. Material appearing in the newspaper such as: . . .
b. Things heard over the radio: . . .
c. In purchasing articles at stores
d At the movies
e. Conversation at home
f. In athletics.

Topics "a" and "b" were divided into subtopics as was the greater part of the remainder of the questionnaire. As in I and throughout the questionnaire the students were provided with a scale of values from which to make a choice.

III. Under this heading we are anxious to find out if any of the concepts of the course had any applications for you to any of the following topics:

a. Civil rights problems
b. Housing problems
c. Problems of law
d. Problems of taxation.

IV. As you see it, has the work in "critical thinking" been of use to you in some of the other work in school?

a. English
b. Biology
c. Latin.

V. To what extent has this course aided your judgment in each of the following areas?

    a. Judging the intelligence of people
    b. Judging the character of people
    c. Understanding the causes of arguments between people
    d. Understanding the causes of racial prejudices.

VI. Will you indicate briefly your reactions to each of the following questions? Please write more than just a "Yes" or "No" answer.

    a. Do you feel that this course has had any effect upon raising your own standards?
    b. Has it enabled you to see more clearly how to "size things up?"
    c. Has the course given you more confidence in your own thinking?

In order that he might evaluate the nature of the replies to the questionnaire, the investigator formulated a set of tables of which the accompaning would be typical.

TABLE 1

FREQUENCY WITH WHICH THE STUDENTS CIRCLED THE NUMBERS 1 AND 2 IN THE QUESTIONNAIRE

Times Circled	Per Cent of Students Circling Individual Numbers											
	I^1 1	I 2	II^1 1	II 2	III^2 1	III 2	IV^2 Homework 1	IV Homework 2	IV Classwork 1	IV Classwork 2	V^2 1	V 2
One or more......	73	100	86	100	68	91	18	73	36	73	73	73
Two or more.....	59	96	77	96	50	82	5	59	9	55	55	46
Three or more....	41	77	59	86	46	77	0	32	5	18	36	18

    [1] Key for I and II: 1. Frequently, 2. Occasionally, 3. Never.
    [2] Key for III, IV and V: 1. Great Help, 2. Some Help, 3. No Help, 4. Confused.

This table points up the frequency with which the numbers 1 and 2 were circled in the questionnaire. It should be interpreted as follows:

Seventy-three per cent of the students circled the number 1 one or more times in Part I, 59 per cent circled the number 1 two or more times while 41 per cent circled the number 1 three or more times. Similarly, 100 per cent circled the number 2 one or more times, 96 per cent the number 2 two or more times and 77 per cent the number 2 three or more times, and similarly in the other numbers.

The evidence presented here would indicate that by far the great majority of students had discussed the contents of the course "frequently" with at least one or more people while 100 per cent of them had done this "occasionally." Similarly, almost all of them expressed the opinion that they had made use of the class material "frequently" in at least one of the items appearing in Part II and everyone had used it "occasionally." In Part III where an effort had been made to determine the extent to which the course aided the child in clarifying his thinking concerning controversial issues, it was learned that 68 per cent believed the work to be a "great help" in one or more situations; 91 per cent felt that it was at least some help. Although only 18 per cent indicated that the material they learned had been a "great help" to them in their other school subjects, 73 per cent did find it some help.

Notwithstanding the fact that there are a number of apparent weaknesses in the use of the questionnaire, its value cannot be overstressed. Awkward wording of questions, hurried thoughtless replies by the pupils, fear of reprisals, plus other causes all lead to lowering the stature that this means might take in ascertaining the outcomes of educational research. Secondly, voluminous statistical interpretations applied to these data do not necessarily lend validity to the replies. It must be emphasized, however, that this information taken in conjunction with other evidence may indicate that probable conclusions are warranted.

4

Evaluation of Attitudes and Appreciations

Techniques Used by Teachers for Evaluating or Testing of Attitudes and Appreciations in Mathematics

J. WAYNE WRIGHTSTONE

A major objective in the learning of mathematics is development of attitudes toward and appreciations of mathematics. Attitudes are general or specific. The general attitude toward mathematics may be defined in terms of behavior that reveals the degree to which the pupil likes or dislikes the subject. The specific attitudes may be defined in terms of behavior that reveals the degree of pupil acceptance and adjustment in dealing with specific processes and concepts in mathematics. Do the pupil's learning experiences lead him to regard addition or subtraction in arithmetic as fun or as a bore? Does he enjoy engaging in activities in which mathematics plays an integral role?

Appreciations, like attitudes, are related to the content and the use of mathematics. These appreciations include, among other items: (a) an understanding of the development of the number system; (b) the role that mathematics plays in business or industry; (c) the social significance of mathematics in the activities of daily life, such as the cost of mailing a letter or package, the past and present ways of telling time, how money has developed, or how weather is measured; (d) a tendency to sense mathematics as a part of normal experience, as in making a dress or costume, planning a party or keeping score at a baseball game.

In order to determine the techniques that teachers and supervisors use to evaluate mathematical attitudes and appreciations, a survey was made among representative teachers and supervisors in the New York City elementary, junior high, and senior high schools. From the examples which are given in the next section of this report, it will be noted that three major types of evaluation or testing techniques are used. These include: (a) teacher-made test exercises and questionnaires; (b) teacher observation and anecdotal records of children's activities; (c) reports and projects by pupils.

In general, the evaluation of attitudes and appreciations was not conducted as systematically as the testing of skills, information and understandings of mathematical concepts and processes. It is encouraging to note, however, that sincere efforts are made and that a variety of techniques are used by teachers and supervisors in their formal and informal evaluation of mathematical attitudes and appreciations.

Examples of Evaluation Techniques

TEACHER-MADE TEST EXERCISES

Elementary School

1. New York is called the largest city in the nation because (a) it has most money, (b) it has most land, (c) it has most people.

2. Which size of packaged potatoes would probably cost lowest per pound? (a) 1 pound, (b) 5 pounds, (c) 10 pounds, (d) 25 pounds.

3. Our present number system is based on that invented by the (a) Romans, (b) Greeks, (c) Arabs, (d) Egyptians.

Junior High School

1. A person or persons to whom money is paid by the insurance company in case of death is called the _____.

2. Money paid for the use of money is called _____.

3. Whenever the cost is more than the selling price, we can say that there was a _____ in the sale.

Senior High School

1. Which of the following activities use mathematics? __ (a) making a map, __ (b) deciding how to vote, __ (c) playing football, __ (d) repairing a toaster, __ (e) running a business.

2. Mark T for "true" and F for "false." __ (a) Mathematics began before there were cities. __ (b) There have been great mathematicians in all countries. __ (c) Many great discoveries in mathematics were made by accident.

3. Write the name of a great mathematician on each line. (a) from Greece or from India _____ (b) from France or from Norway _____.

TEACHER OBSERVATION AND ANECDOTAL RECORDS

Elementary School

1. A sixth-grade class was discussing the size and speed of the new *S. S. United States*. The terms "nautical mile" and "knots" were used. A committee of pupils looked in the *World Almanac* and found that a nautical mile was 15 per cent longer than a land mile.

2. Children in a fifth-grade class kept temperature records for a week and used the figures to compute temperature ranges. Others kept records of the changes in the length of day and night for a month.

3. On a class trip to the Museum of Natural History, pupil committees found the total cost of the bus and cost per child, purchase of the lunch and cost per child, collection of money and necessary change. The teacher checked the committee records.

4. Lillian, a fourth-grader, said, "It's fun since I learned about halves, fourths, and eighths. My mother lets me measure the ingredients when she bakes or cooks."

Junior High School

1. A record and evaluation is made of individual or committee original work in arithmetic, and these are exhibited on special bulletin boards in the classroom and the hall.

2. In a class of ninth-grade slow-learners, committees investigated and reported on the size and area of the playing fields in baseball, basketball, football, tennis, and boxing.

3. A class wrote and presented for an assembly program an original play, *Mathematics in Our Daily Life*.

Senior High School

1. In one school, a part of the evaluation of pupil interest in mathematics is made from the record of the pupil on such items as: membership in the mathematics club, membership on a mathematics team, extra-school mathematical activities, and contribution of original problems.

2. In another school, a record was kept of book reports by pupils from a list of mathematics books posted on the bulletin board at the beginning of the term.

REPORTS AND PROJECTS BY PUPILS

Elementary School

1. In one class, each pupil keeps a mathematics notebook, which the teacher evaluates periodically. Among the reports in the notebook are such assigned topics as follows: (a) Report on weight and cost of articles sold in boxes and cans; (b) Study of time, including sunrise, sunset, time belts, records of hours of sleep, and like activities related to time.

2. In one class, children kept detailed accounts for one week of the

part arithmetic played in their daily lives. They interviewed their parents on the arithmetic involved in their adult activities in the home or on the job.

3. Individual reports are submitted by pupils on such topics as: "How Gas and Electricity Are Measured and Sold," "Arithmetic Used in Cooking and Baking," and "Arithmetic I Use with My Chemistry Set." These reports are evaluated in terms of appreciations that pupils have gained about the use of mathematics.

Junior High School

1. One class collected newspaper articles illustrating the use of per cent as applied to commission, discount, and similar operations.

2. Another class made scrapbooks of current event items pertaining to mathematics, on such topics as science, business world, sports, and other subjects.

3. Construction of original "math project" such as: (a) Geometric city—geometry of future cities, (b) Erector set models of bridge types, (c) Charts comparing various thermometers, (d) Construction to scale of typical neighborhood streets, stores, and houses.

4. Collection and classification of graphs of all types found in newspapers and magazines and construction of graphs by the pupil based on ststistics gathered by him.

Senior High School

1. Mathematical problems, puzzles, and projects contributed by pupils. Examples: report on the Development of Precision and Standardization in Measures; report on Early Number Systems of Other Peoples.

2. Reports by pupils on such books as: (a) *Short History of Mathematics* by Sanford, (b) *The Teaching of Arithmetic* by Klapper, (c) Chapter in *Mathematics for the Million* by Hogben.

Teaching and Measurement of Appreciations of Mathematics

Howard F. Fehr

WHAT IS APPRECIATION

Much has been said and written concerning the value of an *appreciation of mathematics*, but very little has been written about the behavioristic nature of this appreciation, and there has been no reported research in this area of learning. All reports and most leaders subscribe to its value; none, however, indicates how it is achieved or how it is measured. This article is a pioneering essay to identify the nature of, characteristics of, and developmental procedures for creating appreciation of mathematics.

The point of view taken here is that appreciation is a mental process and is to be explained in terms of human behavior. It depends upon the ability of the person to follow, mentally, a series of adjustments. To this extent it does not depend entirely upon one's ability as a performer in the field of mathematics, but rather upon one's ability as a recipient, an auditor, visualizer, feeler, analyzer, or other participator. This implies that one who is appreciating is at the time giving the attention of his whole self to the stimuli under consideration. There can be no distraction. Under these provisions we recognize *appreciation* as a form of *discriminating reaction*.

For this discrimination, we must admit to knowledge and skill in production in mathematics. The greater the knowledge and skill, the higher the ability to discriminate. It is the prevalence of individual differences that accounts for different reactions to the same stimulus, one of mere passive acceptance, the other an emotional reaction of appreciation. As one learns mathematics, he frequently is led to certain unexpected but striking and significant relations. The *awareness* of the relation excites a pleasurable emotion which is frequently exhibited by locomotor or audible expression. Thereafter, when the relation occurs, there is always the recognition and the accompanying pleasure which we call appreciation.

The emerging concept of a linear function may be used to illustrate the foregoing point of view. We first consider relation-

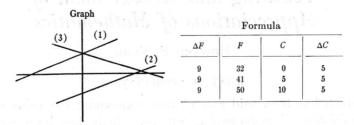

Graph		Formula			
		ΔF	F	C	ΔC
		9	32	0	5
		9	41	5	5
		9	50	10	5

ships between two variables, like the following: $C = \frac{5}{9}(F - 32)$ (temperature); $W = 1.5D + .125$ (bolthead); $r = -0.5t + 12.5$

(stair riser), and other similar relationships, all taken from our environment. We draw the graphs of these functions and note their linearity; we make a table of values and note their relationship in the table; we finally recognize all these functions in the form $y = mx + b$ where m is the rate of increase or decrease.

The mathematics students then investigate data, seeking those that have linear relationship. The relationship of Fahrenheit temperature and the number of chirps made by a grasshopper in one second is a striking example of an unexpected linear relationship. It is the recognition of this linear form and the search for the form that leads to appreciation. When, while working with quantitative data, the statistician, the scientist, or the mathematician come upon an explanation that results in the form $y = mx + b$ they have had a type of discriminating reaction that gives appreciation.

The concept of "form" is basic to appreciation. According to Gardner Murphy (17), "Form is a value perceived, felt, and thought." When thus recognized, form in music, in art, in algebra, in geometry, or in logic gives appreciation. It is not the circle, or its properties, nor the triangle, nor any geometric figure in itself, but it is the repetitive recognition of the form that gives appreciation. An individual develops *"a feeling for mathematical form that he wants"* and the occurrence of the form gives appreciation. Hence as an esthetic sense, we define: *appreciation is the satisfaction (emotional pleasure) derived from a successful quest for mathematical form.* The word, "form," is here used in its broadest philosophical sense.

CHARACTERISTICS THAT MEASURE APPRECIATION

The degree to which appreciation can be developed depends upon the imperiousness of this quest for form. This quest shows high individual differences and is a function of the inherited or developed capacities for the area of life that is to be organized, for example the numerical, spatial, or logical. Form perception and the capacity to *respond* and to *use* form appear to develop in a direction partly determined by the individual's idiosyncrasy. These capacities are recognized in his

1. Attitude or recognition of the value of form
2. Gratification accompanying the application of discrimination
3. Stimulus for activities beyond the work-a-day mathematics
4. Esteem for the concepts and skills perceived
5. Acquisition of quantitative procedures for use in philosophical inquiries.

It is in the detection of these capacities and their degree of development that measurement of appreciation must take place.

Appreciation can thus come only as a result of growth in *mathematical responsiveness*. We must teach for this end, and attempt to develop attitudes favorable toward the subject, if we are to develop an appreciation. Responsiveness involves a number of areas of learning that are more or less specific, and for which tests might be devised to measure their degree of presence. The most important are:

1. Growth in mathematical *awareness*, recognition, or apprehension. By this is meant the recognition of mathematics in all phenomena surrounding us—the parabolas in lenses, the hyperbolas in map projections, the loci of moving objects, the arithmetic in the newspapers, the functional relations in physical and social situations, and other common phenomena. For appreciation we must *see* mathematics wherever it occurs.

2. Growth in mathematical *application*, practice, or initiative. This is the sort of inner drive or compulsion that makes a person want to use mathematics to solve his problems. There is a genuine desire to find the interest rate on any loan; to express a quantitative problem in terms of variables, functions, and equations; to seek the geometric relations in planning or designing. For *appreciation*, there is the *urge to use* mathematics.

3. Growth in mathematical *abstraction* and discrimination. This is a search for the best and the proper mathematical explanation. Algebra is used where arithmetic would be complex and inelegant. Trigonometry is used to explain periodic phenomena; the binomial theorem suggests a path to the exploration of higher dimensionality. For appreciation there must be a *selection* of elegant mathematical exposition.

4. Growth in mathematical *skill* or ability. More and more

the ability to use the algorithms, the propositions, and mathematical procedures is developed and applied to the attack of new problems. The power of these skills is sensed as we solve new problems. We give our almost total attention to the discovery of new relationships, to the search of new mathematical forms, because the skills function almost automatically. For appreciation *cleverness* in mathematics is essential.

5. Growth in mathematical *insight*. The examination of a problem is accompanied by a sudden revelation of a mathematical pattern. A sea shell is examined and presently the spiral and the mathematical properties of growth, leap to the fore. A debate is heard and in good time the logical structure of deductive proof displays the truth or falsity of the argument; a new problem in analysis confronts an individual, and after awhile, the organization of past algebraic and geometric patterns shows the path to the solution. For appreciation a *reorganization* of past knowledge within a new situation is of tremendous importance.

All these phases mean not only a continuous accumulation of mathematical knowledge, but also a change in intellectual behavior. It is suggested that these phases can be measured by confronting the students with situations involving quantitative problems and noting their responses. The degree to which students can show meaning, generalization, abstraction, discovery, and creation will give indication of their ability to search for form, and hence to have appreciation for mathematics.

EXAMPLE OF FORM AND APPRECIATION

The British Report on *The Teaching of Algebra* (3) says, "The joys of pure mathematics, the study of algebraic form, the appreciation of an 'elegant' method are for the pure mathematician, and not the average boy." Whether this be true or not, the mere juggling of x's, y's, propositions, and equations has no merit, unless the boy can see something deeper and more lasting in all he is doing. It is suggested that teaching so as to create a search for form, can, even at the high-school level, result in the appreciation as we have defined it.

As one illustration, appreciation resulting from a search for symmetry as a mathematical form can be pursued in all the branches of mathematics. It occurs in arithmetic in the addition tables and the multiplication tables. Take out these tables now and study them, search for symmetric relations and you may be surprised at how much you have missed. Now make similar tables for numbers to the bases 5, 6, and 7, and note again the symmetric relations. See if this search does not give you emotional satisfaction, and note in the future how you will search a new table for symmetric relations. Children can gain the same appreciation if they are led to this type of study.

This is not the only phase of arithmetic that contains symmetry. Consider Pascal's number triangle and all its delightful relations, the various sequences of numbers, the application of number sequences to geometric drawing, and symmetry in certain addition and multiplication examples. In algebra, symmetric functions can be introduced very early. The expansion of $(x + y)^n$ for n integral and the factoring of symmetric polynomials of the type $2x^2 + 5xy + y^2$ into symmetric factors lead to a general search for symmetric forms.

In the study of geometry, the study of congruence leads immediately to symmetric figures. This can be extended to a study of inversion and reflection and their relationship to symmetry. The study of homothetic figures and locus abounds in relations that lead to repeating form and dynamic symmetry. It is the search for symmetry in the study of locus that leads frequently to discovery, to thrills, and to appreciation. But even more important, the symmetry of logical form as suggested by the accompanying diagram can lead to appreciation of necessary and sufficient conditions, and to the search for these forms in all areas of knowledge where propositional functions may be used.

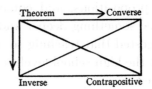

The extension of symmetry as a mathematical form for which the successful search gives appreciation should be evident now. The reader can gain greater insight in seeing the application of all these forms to the interpretation of the world around us as revealed in books by Ghyka (9), Bragdon (2), Schillinger (24), Thompson (27), and Weyl (31). It is the measurement of the degree to which students recognize, that is, are aware, select, apply, and cleverly discriminate these forms, that he has appreciation for mathematical symmetry.

Of course, symmetry is only one type of form leading to appreciation. Some other forms are: *extensional* as revealed in building the number systems, theory of exponents, and higher dimensional geometry; *logical* as revealed in the postulational system, the forms of an implicative proposition, the laws of logic, the types of proofs, and the power of symbolic logic; *generalization and abstraction*, as revealed in non-Euclidean geometries, topology, groups, rings, determinants, and matrices. We can also seek appreciation by leading students to search for historical forms, service forms, philosophical forms, and relational forms within the bounds of quantitative and mathematical study.

SUGGESTIONS FOR TEACHING AND MEASURING APPRECIATION

As yet there are no devices for measuring mathematical appreciation. This is an area wide open for research and investigation. An interested worker might well seek the nature and definitions of appreciations in the fine arts, music, English literature, and poetry, and the attempts to measure appreciations in these areas. At present the mathematics teacher must measure by observation as he looks for the attributes listed above, or for those characteristics which he in his own thinking associates with appreciation.

More and more, as general or well-rounded education becomes a dominant phase of high-school and college education, teachers of mathematics must make appreciation a prominent goal of mathematics instruction. Teaching for appreciation is an emerging practice in mathematics education. The following suggestions seem to have value in helping teachers attain some success in developing mathematical appreciation.

1. The teacher, himself, must have or gain this sense of appreciation and the discovery of form. He must have imagination and be sincere in his attitude.

2. The teacher must be a continued student of mathematics; always seeking evidence of its power and its use.

3. The classroom atmosphere must reflect enthusiasm, interest, mental activity, and delight in learning.

4. Recognize the value of mathematical recreations. These can frequently lead directly to the search for mathematical explanations thus creating a deep and sustaining interest in the subject.

5. Service to mankind is a "form." Constantly showing or leading the student to discover the power of applied mathematics in its service to mankind aids students to search for such appreciation.

6. Mere pleasure is not necessarily appreciation. The emotional reaction must be one that accompanies a deepening concept, a clearer configuration, and a stronger desire to have more mathematics.

7. Mystic awe, clever manipulation, magical tricks in themselves do not lead to higher values. To be appreciated, mathematics must be understood.

8. The dignity of every pupil must be continually honored. The teacher must sense things that are significant to the pupil and show the mathematics therein. Catching the student's interest may help the pupil catch the teacher's enthusiasm and lead to the development of an appreciation of mathematics.

5
Reporting to Parents
Pupil Progress

ALICE M. HACH
DONOVAN JOHNSON

EVALUATION OF THE MASTERY OF FRACTIONAL EQUIVALENTS

Many teachers are seeking improved procedures for reporting pupil progress. Practices of two such procedures follow. J. J. K.

Satisfactory work reports:

1. Inform parents when a child has mastered the fractional equivalents.

2. Inform parents regarding the length of time required.

Unsatisfactory work reports:

1. Explain to parents how they can help child.

2. Point out the need of this skill for future progress.

3. Give parents the actual skills that are to be mastered.

4. Indicate teacher interest rather than teacher criticism.

I am glad to report that _____ has passed the *Fractional Equivalent Test*. This knowledge will be very helpful to your child in working percentage problems.

The record [page 396] enclosed will show you the results for each test taken. Passing the test, two times in succession, assures a mastery of fractional equivalents.

It is always a pleasure to report good work to you.

(TEACHER'S SIGNATURE)

_____ needs to study the 15 fractional equivalents below. Each child has made a set of flash cards to use for practice work. Will you please encourage your child to study these flash cards? It might be advisable to allow 20 minutes each evening for studying these fractional equivalents. Your child has had a number of weeks to learn these. It is for this reason I am suggesting more homework on this material.

If this work is mastered and the fractions can be given accurately and quickly, the next unit dealing with percentage will be much easier for your child.

I know you will appreciate this information and will encourage your child to study this material. I want your child to succeed and that is the reason I am notifying you.

Sincerely yours,
(TEACHER'S SIGNATURE)

$\frac{1}{2} = .50$	$\frac{1}{5} = .20$	$\frac{5}{6} = .83\frac{1}{3}$
$\frac{1}{3} = .33\frac{1}{3}$	$\frac{2}{5} = .40$	$\frac{1}{8} = .12\frac{1}{2}$
$\frac{2}{3} = .66\frac{2}{3}$	$\frac{3}{5} = .60$	$\frac{3}{8} = .37\frac{1}{2}$
$\frac{1}{4} = .25$	$\frac{4}{5} = .80$	$\frac{5}{8} = .62\frac{1}{2}$
$\frac{3}{4} = .75$	$\frac{1}{6} = .16\frac{2}{3}$	$\frac{7}{8} = .87\frac{1}{2}$

NAME ————————————

FRACTION DECIMAL EQUIVALENTS

DATE → FRACTION	FEB 1 1953	FEB 8 1953	FEB 15 1953	FEB 22 1953	APR 1 1953						
$\frac{1}{2}$											
$\frac{1}{3}$											
$\frac{2}{3}$											
$\frac{1}{4}$											
$\frac{3}{4}$											
$\frac{1}{5}$											
$\frac{2}{5}$				*passed*	*passed*						
$\frac{3}{5}$											
$\frac{4}{5}$											
$\frac{1}{6}$											
$\frac{5}{6}$	X	X	X								
$\frac{1}{8}$											
$\frac{3}{8}$	X										
$\frac{5}{8}$	X										
$\frac{7}{8}$				X							

LETTERS TO PARENTS WRITTEN BY PUPILS

1. Each child writes a letter to his parents at the middle of the grading period and evaluates his progress.

2. Letters are folded as business letters, addressed on the outside, and turned in to teacher.
3. Teacher reads letters and writes additional comments at the end of letters.
4. Letters are given back to the children who take them to parents for signature.
5. Letters are finally returned to teacher.

ADVANTAGES OF PUPIL LETTERS

1. It creates good public relations since all parents receive a letter rather than only the parents of failing children.
2. A child is unusually fair and honest when evaluating unsatisfactory work.
3. Parents are more willing to accept a child's self-criticism rather than the criticism by a teacher.
4. It is usually unnecessary for a teacher to write a detailed explanation for unsatisfactory work after a child has made an analysis of his work.
5. It forces a child to evaluate his progress early in the semester.

EVALUATION OF WORK HABITS

1. The class, with the guidance of the teacher, decides on the habits that they feel should be established.
2. A record is then made and each child receives a copy to file in his notebook.
3. Twenty per cent may be earned each day for each habit. Thus it is possible for a child to earn 100 per cent at the end of the week for each work habit listed.

ADVANTAGES OF THE PLAN

1. The child is forced to think of the work habits that are important as he helps compile the original list.
2. The child has a part in the evaluation.
3. The child is constantly made aware of work habits.
4. The child earns a specific grade in work habits, and this evaluation is not the subjective opinion of a teacher.
5. It forces a child to evaluate his progress early in the semester.

Nancy Holt
9^2 Algebra
December 17, 1953

Dear Mom and Dad,

I am writing another letter to you like the last one, telling you my average on my tests. The marks and average are as follows:

94%	$94\frac{1}{4} = 94\%$
86%	4 ⟌ 377
97%	36
100%	17
377%	16
	1

I have three per cent more this time than on my last average. I like algebra even more!

We are now studying about dividing a polynomial by a polynomial. (If you know what that means!)

I hope I do even better on my test average next time. I'll try to surprise you and do just that!

Love,

Nancy

I am sure you will be most happy to receive this letter showing the excellent work Nancy is doing in Algebra— Christmas Greetings[4]

Alice Jones

---

[4]Teacher's comment originally appeared in red.

EXAMPLE OF PARENT'S REPLY

I did enjoy the letter — it is an excellent idea. I can see by Mary Ellen's last sentence that she realizes that she could be more careful in her work.

Mary Hays

October 31, 1953

EXAMPLE OF TEACHER'S REPORT

This is to report that your child did not have the following assignment completed for today:

Page _____ Examples _____.

This will make the next assignment more difficult for him.

I know you will appreciate being notified as this will enable you to help and guide your child in home study. Often your interest and your encouragement will do a great deal toward helping your child complete homework.

Home study is required in greater amounts as a child progresses in his education. Therefore anything you can do to help your child establish good habits of home study will be of great value to him.

Sincerely yours,

(TEACHER'S SIGNATURE)

VARIOUS KINDS OF SPECIAL REPORTS

This type of report gives the parents information: (a) regarding a specific deficiency, (b) regarding ways to help a child, (c) Regarding the need for building a particular work habit, (d) Regarding the teacher's interest in helping both the parents and the child.

SUGGESTION FOR JUNIOR HIGH SCHOOL USE

In junior high school it is effective to permit one or two incomplete assignments without questioning the child or reporting the incident to the parents. At times emergencies arise that make it difficult for a child to do home study. This special consideration gives a pupil a feeling of security and also a feeling that the teacher understands his problems.

The abuse of this privilege is rare. Children recognize that at times there are justifiable reasons for not being able to do home

MY WORK HABIT RECORD

Date   Name

I had a complete assignment for today.

	1	2	3	4	5	6	7	8	9
Monday									
Tuesday									
Wednesday									
Thursday									
Friday									

I remembered to bring my homework to class.

Monday									
Tuesday									
Wednesday									
Thursday									
Friday									

I had my pencil sharpened. (Two pencils sharpened during homeroom avoids taking time in class.)

Monday									
Tuesday									
Wednesday									
Thursday									
Friday									

I remembered the school rule not to chew gum in class and abided by it.

Monday								
Tuesday								
Wednesday								
Thursday								
Friday								

work. Therefore they hesitate to take advantage of this privilege. Children, when losing a daily paper, have been known to say, "Can't I make this up? I don't want to use up my privileges because I may *really* need to use them some day."

CHILDREN'S EVALUATION OF NEATNESS

The child evaluates his work on the basis of the following points:
1. The examples are well-spaced.
2. The examples are carefully numbered.
3. The digits are written on the lines.
4. Each digit is carefully made.
5. The digits are large enough to be easily read.
6. The numbers are dark and clear.

ONE PLAN FOR CHILD'S EVALUATION OF NEATNESS

1. Each child provides a notebook for his daily papers which is to be kept in the mathematics classroom.
2. The child evaluates his daily papers on the basis of the foregoing six points.
3. If the paper is evaluated as a neat paper, the child files it in the front of his notebook; otherwise the paper is filed toward the back of the notebook.
4. At the end of the semester the child counts the number of neat papers and the number of papers that did not qualify for neatness.
5. The child then evaluates his work in neatness for the semester by comparing the number of papers accumulated in each group.

A SECOND PLAN FOR CHILD'S EVALUATION OF NEATNESS

1. The pupil turns in daily papers at the end of the period.
2. Two wire baskets are used for this purpose; one for the neat papers and the other for papers which do not have the necessary qualifications for neatness.
3. The child evaluates his paper on the basis of the foregoing six points.
4. As the child leaves the classroom he deposits the paper in the proper basket according to the evaluation that he has made.

5. The neat papers are saved by the teacher and given back at the end of the semester.

6. The child then makes an evaluation for the semester based on the number of neat papers accumulated.

The neat papers accumulated by either of the plans can be made into booklets. Each child designs a cover for his booklet. In this booklet he places the evaluation with all the neat papers accumulated for the semester. The booklet is then given to the parents.

TEACHER'S REPORT ON NEATNESS

This is a report of your child's work in neatness when doing mathematics. Since neatness, careful number formation, proper spacing, often result in accuracy, it is important that your child form habits of neatness.

You can help your child by encouragement and giving your approval or disapproval on homework. If your child seems to have difficulty in number formation it might be worthwhile for him to write numbers 1 to 10 a few times each evening. Do not become discouraged if your child has not turned in a number of neat papers in the past few weeks. Often forming the habit of neatness takes considerable time and encouragement.

Your child does neat work regularly _____.

Your child usually does neat work _____.

Your child does neat work at times _____.

Your child seldom does neat work _____.

Your child has not turned in a really neat paper this period and needs considerable help _____.

_____   _____
Date   (Teacher's Name)

EVALUATION OF CLASS PROCEDURE FOR END OF SEMESTER

The pupil's evaluation which follows was written at the end of the semester. The class was asked to write three things: (a) their choice of a secretary, (b) the things they liked about the class and would want continued, (c) the things they wanted changed or suggestions they might have for improving the class. The class was told that they did not have to sign their names on the evaluation. It was explained that the only purpose of this evaluation was to build the kind of a class pupils like and the kind that would be most helpful to them. They were also told that all procedures that had been used in the class were the results of pupil evaluation from year to year.

EXAMPLE OF PUPIL'S EVALUATION

Mary Alt

9² Algebra

January 21, 1954

Algebra Class

I think that Jane Mann would make a good secretary.

What I like and feel should be continued —

1. I like the assignment sheet because I won't ever have a chance of losing or forgetting assignments. I know, I have experienced that!

2. Putting the answers for daily papers on the blackboard in case you didn't hear them.

3. I especially like and think that weekly tests are important.

4. And I have always liked the way you explain difficult problems and help us with them.

What I would liked changed — I know you would probably want suggestions for having changes, but I don't have any. I just think that if you just keep on doing the same things that you have been doing, everything will be almost perfect.

EXAMPLE OF A HIGH-SCHOOL SELF-APPRAISAL FORM

Student Self-Appraisal Check list in Mathematics

Math I, II, III, IV, V, VI, VII   Mark last quarter_____

This check list is intended to help you discover your strengths and how you can improve. Check each statement truthfully and thoughtfully so that the best kind of activities can be planned for you. Use the code below in describing how you think, feel, or act with respect to the statement given.

Always 5   Usually 4   Sometimes 3   Seldom 2   Never 1

_____ 1. I complete the required assignments on time.
_____ 2. I complete the optional assignments.
_____ 3. I complete my assignments independently.
_____ 4. I check my work to find my errors.
_____ 5. I understand the processes I use to solve problems.
_____ 6. I understand the mathematical words used in my textbook.
_____ 7. I understand the mathematical words used by my instructor.
_____ 8. I add, subtract, multiply, and divide accurately.
_____ 9. I can use mathematical words to express myself in writing.
_____10. I can use mathematical words to express myself in discussions.
_____11. I bring applications of mathematics to class.
_____12. I can interpret graphs which I find in newspapers and magazines.
_____13. I can read tables of data which I find in newspapers and magazines.
_____14. I find mathematics used in the newspapers, books, or magazines which I read outside of class.
_____15. I use the mathematical facts I learn in this class in my other classes.
_____16. I use the mathematical facts I learn in this class at home, in recreations, or at work.
_____17. I discover principles and generalizations before I read them or hear them stated by my instructor or fellow students.
_____18. I use materials other than my textbook to learn mathematics that is not required in this course.
_____19. I listen carefully to the explanations of my instructor.
_____20. I do original, creative work in drawing designs, giving reports, or completing projects rather than repeating what someone else has said or done.
_____21. I keep a list of important ideas or rules studied.
_____22. I understand the explanation of my instructor.
_____23. I use the methods of analysis I learn in this class in other classes.
_____24. I use the methods of analysis I learn in this class at home, in recreation, or at work.
_____25. I learn to reduce my errors by checking my work.
_____26. I use the statements of the textbook or instructor rather than my own words when I recite.
_____27. I participate in classroom discussions.
_____28. I look for assumptions behind controversial statements which my classmates make.
_____29. I can locate useless or unimportant material in a problem or in an argument.

_____30. I can translate relationships expressed in words or sentences into equations.

_____31. I can visualize statements or descriptions of stated problems so that they become realistic.

_____32. I can measure accurately with simple measuring instruments such as a ruler, protractor, scale.

_____33. I can multiply and divide with a slide rule.

_____34. I can use a compass and ruler to draw accurately.

_____35. I can represent a three-dimensional figure on a plane surface.

_____36. I use short cuts such as "transpose" or "cancel" without knowing the reason the short-cut works.

_____37. I solve practice exercises (such as equations) mentally rather than writing down steps in the solution.

_____38. Drawings in the text, by the instructor or by myself, help me find the solutions to problems.

_____39. I can memorize rules better than I can understand how the rule is to be used.

_____40. I can read my textbook with understanding.

_____41. I can learn how to work exercises by going over the textbook illustrations.

_____42. I know how to get information about a mathematical topic in the library.

_____43. I ask questions about classwork I don't understand.

_____44. I label and organize my work so that someone else looking at it can closely see what I have done.

_____45. I get most help in understanding my work from my friends.

_____46. I get most help in understanding my work from my parents.

_____47. I could learn much more mathematics if I tried harder.

_____48. I review the important ideas even when I am not preparing for a particular test.

_____49. I look up or ask about words when I am not sure of their meaning.

_____50. Most of my errors are due to lack of understanding of the process to use.

EXAMPLE OF A HIGH-SCHOOL PROGRESS CHART

HIGH SCHOOL MATHEMATICS PROGRESS CHART

Mathematics I, II, III, IV, V, VI, VII

Code: Excellent (5) Above average (4) Average (3) Below average (2) Unsatisfactory (1)									
Classroom Performance									
Completes Required Assignments									
Completes Optional Assignments									
Organizes Work Effectively									
Works Problems Independently									
Solves Problems With Understanding Rather Than Mechanically									
Solves Problems Completely									
Checks Work to Discover Errors									
Brings Applications of Math to Class									
Shows Insight and Understanding of Processes									
Computes Accurately									
Does Creative, Original Work									
Discovers Principles and Generalizations									
Uses Supplementary Material to Extend Knowledge									
Uses Time Effectively									
Listens Attentively									

MATHEMATICS DEPARTMENT PROGRESS REPORT

Name _____ Quarter F W S Year 19__

Subject—Mathematics I, II, III, IV, V, VI

ACHIEVEMENT RATINGS	Above Average	Average	Below Average	Basis of Rating
Knowledge of facts				Achievement compared with the achievement of all members of the class as measured by tests, projects, class work, assignments, and such.
Skill in computation				
Analysis of problem situations.				

ACTIVITY RATINGS	Good	Acceptable	Poor	Basis of Rating
Achievement compared with apparent ability to achieve				Standardized test scores, previous achievement, and such
Work habits.				Independent and extra work, promptness, completeness and accuracy
Classroom co-operation				Co-operation, courtesy, dependability, attention, attitudes, and such

Mark for Quarter____   Mark for Year____

Comments: Background in Mathematics: _____

Remedial Instruction Needed: _____

Improvement: _____

Special Projects: _____

Recommendation for Future Training: _____

Other: _____

_____

Instructor

Student Inventory of Mathematics

Mathematics I, II, III, IV, V, VI, VII   Grade Last Quarter____

This check list is intended to help us discover what you think about this mathematics course. Check each statement truthfully and thoughtfully so that the best kind of course can be planned for you and for those who follow you. You need not sign your name. Use the following code in describing your thinking with respect to the item.

Agree A   Undecided U   Strongly disagree D

1. Mathematics is my most difficult course.
2. Mathematics is my easiest course this year.
3. I am taking this course because I like mathematics.
4. The only reason I am taking this course is that it is required for college entrance.
5. I learn mathematics best by working things out for myself.
6. I'd rather have my teacher make specific assignments than to plan my own work.
7. Most projects in mathematics are of little value.
8. Mathematics is as important a part of our culture as music or art.
9. I get more out of solving stated problems than out of practice exercises.
10. I don't have enough time to do my best in this class.
11. I think students are foolish to spend a lot of time doing neat work.
12. I think it is more important to do a lot of things than to do a few things well.
13. It is easy to get a good grade in this class.
14. This course is the most valuable course I am taking this year.
15. This course is the least valuable course I am taking this year.
16. The only reason I enjoy this course is that I like the instructor.
17. One of the things I like best about mathematics is its logic and precision.
18. I get a lot of satisfaction out of doing my work in an orderly, neat way.
19. There is too much homework in mathematics.
20. This class gives me a chance to do lots of independent projects.
21. This course will help me to become the kind of person I want to be.
22. I am getting experiences in this class that will be valuable all my life.
23. My work in this course is teaching me how to discover facts.
24. I would like to have time to do still more work in this course.
25. I have advised my friends to take this course.
26. This course is about problems and ideas that interest me.
27. One of the things I like about mathematics is that it is challenging.

28. I think training in mathematics is necessary for most vocations.
29. Mathematics courses give me a chance to do creative, original work.
30. I would like school better if I didn't take mathematics.
31. I need more help with arithmetic than with the mathematics in this class.
32. I wish mathematics was more concrete than the mathematics of this class.
33. I have learned how to express myself more concisely in this class.
34. This course has made me curious about many new ideas.
35. This course has shown me how to buy things wisely.
36. I am trying my best to improve my achievement in this class.
37. I waste a lot of time in this class.
38. I would be learning more if I were in a different class.
39. Most of my work in this class is done to get a good grade rather than to learn something worthwhile.
40. I waste most of my time in this class talking to my friends.
41. I have lost interest in this class because I am not successful.
42. I need help outside of class in order to keep up with my friend.
43. This course doesn't help me learn how to study.
44. I would like to have more courses like this one.
45. This course has shown me the value of mathematics in our society.

PART SIX

Bibliography of "What is Going on in Your School?"—1950-53

A Department of *The Mathematics Teacher*

J. A. BROWN
J. R. MAYOR

CURRICULUM

HESS, ADRIEN L. "Adjusting First-Year College Mathematics for Special Interest Groups." *Mathematics Teacher* 46: 360–63; May 1953.

This is a plan used at Montana State College to meet the needs of freshman students in special areas. The courses are planned for students in home economics, nursery, agriculture, applied science, botany and bacteriology, zoology, entomology, and commercial science. The regular introductory college mathematics is designed primarily for those interested in engineering, mathematics, physics, and chemistry. A type of homogeneous grouping is attempted on a limited scale with this latter group.

HYMAN, HUGH H. "A Faculty Looks at Mathematics for General Education." *Mathematics Teacher* 45: 307–309; April 1952.

The faculty of Florida State University voted to give more time to the study of mathematics in the general education program. The faculty felt that students need an understanding of mathematics to make progress in many fields of study. In the course, emphasis is placed on the language of mathematics, ratio and proportion, variation, and the use of algebra.

INDIANA MATHEMATICS TEACHER. "Special Classes and a Dual Mathematics Club in Shortridge High School, Indianapolis." *Mathematics Teacher* 45: 132–36; February 1952.

Three articles of special interest, originally published in the official journal of the *Indiana Council of Teachers of Mathematics*, are given. The first describes an experimental four-year program of mathematics, with special emphasis on integration with science, for students planning to enter technical vocations. Algebra IV (Special), reviewed in the second article, is a course designed for students who wish to take the College Board Examinations. The third article describes the Shortridge Hi-Pi Club which is open to all students and is generally composed of freshmen, and the regular Mathematics Club, in continuous existence since 1918, which has a restrictive membership and is for upper classmen.

411

JAEGER, JANE, and MERWIN, JACK. *The Illinois Council of Teachers of Mathematics News Letter.* "Curriculum Revision at Moline." *Mathematics Teacher* 45: 534–36; November 1952.

This report describes an attempt to encourage mathematics teachers to do something about improving the curriculum. Help was secured from out-of-school experts in mathematics education. In process of organization during the past five years, the program has been presented to the PTA, to business and industry, and to the Board of Education.

KACKLEY, GERALD. "Mathematics at Hammond Technical Vocational High School." *Mathematics Teacher* 46: 104–105; February 1953.

The mathematics curriculum in the vocational high school includes the city-wide college preparatory courses, boys shop mathematics, and girls shop mathematics. In the vocational courses, five semesters of shop mathematics are required of the boys and three semesters of applied mathematics are required of the girls. Reference is made to topics included, reasons for their selection, required standards of accuracy in calculation, and provisions for individual instruction.

MOCK, GORDON. "A Mathematics Curriculum for a Small High School." *Mathematics Teacher* 45: 589, 593; December 1952.

This is a description of a mathematics curriculum in a small four-year high school. The courses for each grade are described briefly. Lists of topics for the eleventh and twelfth grade courses, which are planned to be given in alternate years, are included.

PRATT, VIRGINIA LEE. "Mathematics at Central High School, Omaha, Nebraska." *Mathematics Teacher* 45: 131–32; February 1952.

The four-year mathematics program of a large city high school is briefly, but carefully, outlined. Reference is also made to the testing program, the annual school exhibit, equipment for mathematics, use of bulletin boards, and other special projects.

WILSON, HORTENSE. *The Illinois Council of Teachers of Mathematics.* May 1952. "Mathematics Curriculum Study at Elgin." *Mathematics Teacher* 45: 588–89; December 1952.

At Elgin, Illinois, a committee of 19 members has been organized to study curriculum problems, starting with the kindergarten and extending through Grade XIV. The article lists objectives and recommendations of the committee and makes special reference to teaching aids for the various grade levels.

ELEMENTARY AND JUNIOR HIGH SCHOOL MATHEMATICS

GIBB, E. GLENADINE. "Mathematics in Baseball." *Mathematics Teacher* 45: 35–36; January 1952.

Twenty-six fifth- and sixth-grade children, attending a summer laboratory school, found a common interest in baseball and organized the mathematics class around baseball projects. Some of the projects included were (a) making scale models of ball fields, (b) laying out a softball field, (c) studying the origin of standard units of measure, (d) studying standard units of time, and (e) computing batting averages.

GRIME, HERSCHEL E. "Mental Arithmetic in the Junior High Schools of Cleveland." *Mathematics Teacher* 45: 228–31; March 1952.

This is a description of a plan used in Cleveland to teach mental arithmetic in the seventh and eighth grades. Each semester eight lessons are broadcast by radio. These lessons, one of which is included in the article, illustrate problems in mental arithmetic which occur in everyday living. As a part of the plan, mimeographed sheets of problems to be solved mentally are distributed to the class. The article reports favorable results for the program.

HACH, ALICE M. "A Project Giving Practice in Reading and in Writing Roman Numerals." *Mathematics Teacher* 45: 460–61; October 1952.

This is a description of a project for teaching Roman numerals at the junior high-school level. Several of the stories written by pupils, in which all quantities are expressed as Roman numerals, are included.

HAWKINS, ESTHER L. "A School Bank." *Mathematics Teacher* 46: 359; May 1953.

An eighth-grade mathematics class organized a school bank or "Corner Junior Bank." The group deposited money and loans were made to any student in school. Officers, elected by the class, kept complete records of the bank's business proceedings. Interest was computed at the end of the year and paid to the depositors.

MASON, HAZEL L. "Special Topics for Eighth Grade Arithmetic"; *Mathematics Teacher* 46: 195–96; March 1953.

Illustrations are given of exercises in symbols of grouping, exponents, infinite series, factorials, and averages, which can be introduced to eighth-graders. The exercises are intended to arouse the curiosity of the gifted and to enlighten the slower students.

STOCKTON, RAY H. "An Experiment in the Acceleration of Seventh Grade Mathematics Pupils." *Mathematics Teacher* 45: 304–306; April 1952.

In the school at Owatanna, Minnesota, the problem of individual differences is met by resorting to individualized instruction, whereby the bright student could progress as fast as his ability permitted, and the slower pupil could also work at his own rate. Materials used are (a) a workbook with drill exercises, (b) the Strathmore Plan which includes exercises covering mathematical ideas taught in arithmetic, and (c) a textbook used for reference work. There was some use of ability grouping by classes.

ULLRICH, ANNA M. "Report of the Investigation Concerning the Marking of Answers to Problems in Elementary School Arithmetic." *Mathematics Teacher* 46: 292–93; April 1953.

A summary is given of 275 replies to a questionnaire on practices in labeling answers to problems in arithmetic involving concrete numbers. The questionnaire was sent to teachers, school administrators, and textbook authors. A few illustrations of practices in specific problem situations are included.

FAIRS, EXHIBITS, AND CONTESTS

BEGNAUD, LURNICE. "A Mathematics Exhibit." *Mathematics Teacher* 46: 196–97; March 1953.

A variety of student-prepared materials were exhibited in the school library for the high-school students and staff, and later for the Parent Teachers Association. Mathematics students served as guides to explain the exhibits.

CURREY, MURIEL G. " 'M' Day in Gilmer County." *Mathematics Teacher* 46: 294–95; April 1953.

The mathematics classes of Glenville High School, Glenville, West Virginia served as hosts to mathematics students, teachers, school board members, and other citizens of Gilmer County. The afternoon's program included a display of materials prepared in mathematics classes, and exposition of selected topics in mathematics by high-school students with emphasis on applications and mathematical recreations.

GOLD, BEN K. "Los Angeles City College Mathematics Prize Competition." *Mathematics Teacher* 45: 34–35; January; 536, 542; November 1952.

Each year Los Angeles City College has a William B. Orange Mathematics Prize Competition for high-school students of Los Angeles. These reports include two sample sets of questions and a description of awards.

GOUSS, HAROLD A. "Newark Secondary Schools Sponsor Mathematics Fair." *Mathematics Teacher* 44: 582–84; December 1951.

The Newark (New Jersey) Council of Teachers of Mathematics sponsored a Fair at Arts High School. Decorations, exhibits, pamphlets containing mathematical puzzles, talks by students and faculty members, and a contest were features of the event. The Executive Council declared the event a success particularly in terms of mathematical interest created in all administrative, teacher, student, and parent groups.

HENDRIX, GERTRUDE. "Mathematics Conference for High School Students." *Mathematics Teacher* 45: 303–304; April 1952.

Approximately 80 students from eight high schools attended Eastern State High School's second annual mathematics conference for high-school students at Eastern Illinois State College, Charleston, Illinois. The principal part of the program consisted of favorite problems presented by individual students. In the afternoon there was a mathematical treasure hunt, followed in the evening, by a dinner.

THE INDIANA MATHEMATICS TEACHER. "Mathematics In School and Out." *Mathematics Teacher* 45: 136; February 1952.

The Mathematics Club of Indianapolis Crispus Attucks High School carried out several projects to "sell" the value of the practical applications of mathematics both in school and out. Projects included preparation of charts showing "tie-up" of mathematics with other courses in high school and college, demonstration of mathematical tools, display of pictures of successful graduates who had found mathematics particularly useful, and an auditorium program.

KNUPPEL, HERMAN D. "Career Panel Discusses Engineering." *Mathematics Teacher* 45: 388–89; May 1952.

Four experienced engineers participated in a panel discussion on engineering in an auditorium program in Belleville, New Jersey. Both students and parents attended and took part in the question period. Engineering materials were simultaneously on display in the library and a special information sheet was distributed to students at the close of the meeting.

LAWLER, MYRTLE. "The Bulletin Board Demonstration." *Mathematics Teacher* 46: 103–104; February 1953.

An outline of suggestions on bulletin board use is developed under the following major topics: Physical Aspects, Purposes, and Outcomes and Attitudes Developed. A helpful bibliography is included.

MATHEMATICS TEACHER. "Science Talent Search." *Mathematics Teacher* 45: 130–31; February 1952.

This is a brief report on participation of mathematics students in the Westinghouse Electric Corporation and Science Service Annual Science Talent Search, with special reference to the Eleventh (1950–51) Science Talent Search including topics in mathematics chosen by winners.

GEOMETRY

ALLEN, FRANK B. "The Multi-Converse Concept in Geometry." *Mathematics Teacher* 45: 582–84; December 1952.

The author gives various examples illustrating the adaptation of the multi-converse concept in plane geometry. The multi-converse concept is applied to theorems concerning parallel lines, quadrilaterals, and perpendicular lines intersecting on a circle. Some advantages of the method which are listed are: training in English, opportunity for discovery and creation of exercises, and emphasis on the fact that a converse is not necessarily true.

DRAKE, ODESSA. "Geometry Football." *Mathematics Teacher* 46: 461, 470; October 1952.

The class and teacher do creative planning in the development of a game of "football" adapted to a geometry class. A set of rules and suggestions for the game are given. This appears to be an excellent method of review.

KAASA, CLARICE. "A Project in Indirect Measurement." *Mathematics Teacher* 45: 304; April 1952.

A geometry class uses angle mirrors, a hypsometer, sextants, two home-made transits, and other instruments, made by students in indirect measurement in a park near the school. Each student does his own measuring and the next day in class the solutions are discussed.

SUMRALL, MARGARET. "Light Locus." *Mathematics Teacher* 45: 586–88; December 1952.

This article describes experiments designed to illustrate locus by photographing light beams. A flashlight suspended and swinging like a pendulum produces interesting paths of lights. Several photographs illustrate the effects that can be obtained.

MATHEMATICS OF THE JUNIOR AND SENIOR YEARS

AUERBACH, MAMIE L. "The Students of Senior Arithmetic Class Talk It Over." *Mathematics Teacher* 46: 197–98; March 1953.

This is a dialogue on some of the topics studied in the course with special reference to understanding of the topics and their applications in Richmond business and industry.

BLACKWELL, ROSA W. "Mapping the School District." *Mathematics Teacher* 45: 226–28; March 1952.

The trigonometry class of Ensley High School carried on a special project in mapping the school district as part of a school project called "Appreciation of Our Environment". Material was obtained from various sources including the City Engineer's office, the Jefferson County Engineering Department, the Tennessee Coal and Iron Company, and the Birmingham Electric Company. Two maps appear in the article.

HALLEY, ROBERT R. "The Trigonometry Class, First Assignment." *Mathematics Teacher* 46: 295–96; April 1953.

As a first assignment students are asked to make two cardboard triangles which have five parts of one triangle equal to five parts of the other, but the sixth parts unequal. The discovery approach is used to good advantage to introduce trigonometry and provide a review of geometry.

KRAFT, ONA. "Fourth Term Algebra." *Mathematics Teacher* 46: 582; December 1951.

Those attending a discussion group on the topic "What Belongs in Fourth Term Algebra" at the Northfield, Minnesota National Council meeting reported on the topics they include in the fourth semester algebra course. It was recognized that differences were in considerable part due to the year in which the course is taught and the accepted purpose of the course.

MAYOR, J. R. "Solid Analytic Geometry for Seniors." *Mathematics Teacher* 46: 105–106; February 1953.

An experimental three weeks unit on solid analytic geometry in a senior class is reported. Equations of the plane, the line, and the sphere were studied. Advantages of the unit as seen by the author, are outlined.

MATHEMATICS CLUBS

BOYD, JAMES R. "A Mathematics Club for the Able." *Mathematics Teacher* 46: 43–45; January 1953.

The Mathematics Club at San Marcos High School, San Marcos, Texas develops many research projects in which the students prepare original papers. Among topics included are: An Exception to Euclid's Fifth Common Notions, concerning the Moebius Band, An Introduction to the Theory of Groups, and Hilbert's Approach to Congruence.

NEWSLETTER OF THE INDIANA COUNCIL OF TEACHERS OF MATHEMATICS. "Industrial Survey." *Mathematics Teacher* 45: 460; October 1952.

The Mathematics and Science Clubs of Bedford High School conducted a survey of industries in and around Bedford. Statements made by key-men in the various industries indicating the importance of mathematics in their fields are given.

KELLY, INEZ. "Garfield Mathematics Club." *Mathematics Teacher* 45: 37–38; January 1952.

The Mathematics Club at Garfield High School, Terre Haute, Indiana organized its program around student reports which required quite a bit of research. Reports given included: The Global Concept, The Theory of Relativity, The Fourth Dimension, The Mathematics of Probability and Gambling, Topology, and Non-Euclidean Geometry. On the recreational side, puzzles, brain teasers, paradoxes, and fallacies are used for program materials.

OWEN, EVELYN L. "A High School Mathematics Club." *Mathematics Teacher* 45: 457–60; October 1952.

A beginning teacher describes her experiences in sponsoring a Mathematics Club. Included is a description of the organization and examples of problems and puzzles, types of games, and interesting topics that have been presented at various meetings. One of the most popular topics was "Mathematics From A to Z," in which it was shown how mathematics is applied to various subjects from Astronomy to Zoology. *See also:* "Special Classes and a Dual Mathematics Club in Shortridge High School, Indianapolis," page 411.

SPECIAL CLASSROOM PROCEDURES AND TEACHING AIDS

BAKST, ELOISE B. "Honor Work in Secondary School Mathematics." *Mathematics Teacher* 45: 306–307; April 1952.

In Jamaica High School, New York City, honor students are selected according to (a) IQ; (b) arithmetic records in eight-year elementary schools; (c) reading ability; (d) general achievement; and (e) personality. The group selected travel as a special "Core Group" in the school. In general, the pupils are guided so that the mathematics course is largely self-developed. This contribution includes descriptions of special classroom methods to be used with gifted students.

BARTHOLOMEW, RUTH E., and GOERZ, LYDIA R. "Daily Assignments." *Mathematics Teacher* 45: 36; January 1952.

This article describes how two teachers met the problem of students failing to do homework. In one case, special forms were given to students to sign when they did not do their assignments. After four missed homework assignments, the parents were notified. The other teacher tells about the adaptation of the over-all school plan for homework to mathematics classes and also the use of superior students to assist slower ones.

BUTLER, CHARLES H. "Homemade Problems for Algebra." *Mathematics Teacher* 45: 584–86; December 1952.

This is a list of 20 verbal problems prepared by a class of juniors and seniors at Western Michigan College of Education to be used in Algebra. The questions present unusual problems not found in most textbooks, which may arouse interest and develop understanding. It is suggested that an algebra class may make its own set of problems.

GOERZ, LYDIA R. "An Experiment with Students Failing in General Mathematics." *Mathematics Teacher* 46: 360; May 1953.

A class of tenth-graders, with IQ's ranging from 73 to 96 received remedial work for one semester. After trying to change the pupils' attitudes toward mathematics a plan for remedial instruction began with emphasis on meaning and simple but practical examples. The pupils showed a marked improvement in their computational skills.

MEYER, HENRY. "Evansville Teacher Invents Gradoscope." *Mathematics Teacher* 45: 389–90; May 1952.

Leroy W. Schrode of Central High School, Evansville, Indiana has invented a "gradoscope" for simplifying and speeding up the process of marking papers. The device, methods of using it, and advantages are given in some detail.

NEWSLETTER OF THE OHIO COUNCIL OF TEACHERS OF MATHEMATICS. "Mathematics Teachers Help Students Read Better." *Mathematics Teacher* 46: 106; February 1953.

A list of suggestions prepared by Cleveland high-school teachers for improvement of the reading of students in mathematics classes is given. This list was prepared as a part of a schoolwide effort to help students improve in six special areas.

WENAAS, SIGURD B. "Exploratory Development of Mathematics Kits." *Mathematics Teacher* 46: 42–43; January 1953.

Anyone interested in the laboratory method of teaching mathematics may find helpful suggestions in this article. The contents of the kits, the concepts to be taught, and suggested activities for using the kits are described. Kit No. 1 consists of a wooden box containing various plane figures made from one-eighth inch Masonite; Kit No. 2 will be used as an aid in teaching concepts of volume and solid measure; and Kit No. 3 will contain 150 recreations in mathematics printed on 3 x 5 cards.

STATISTICAL STUDIES

BROWN, J. A.; MAYOR, J. R.; and WEISEL, P. M. "What Is Going on in Your School?" *Mathematics Teacher* 43: 373; November 1950. 44: 151, February; 268–69, April; 326, May; 494–95, 501, November; 1951. 45: 130, February; 385–88, May 1952.

Five questions on mathematics enrollments through Grades IX–XII are given in November 1950 and five questions on school offerings in general mathematics are given in February 1951. The title of the study and the plan followed were used by Raleigh Schorling for the Commission on Post-War Plans. Readers are invited to submit answers for their schools. In April 1951 a tabulation of 15 replies to questions on mathematics enrollments are tabulated. The May number presents five questions on third-year mathematics including reference to course organization, ability grouping, mathematics clubs, use of films, and the library.

In November 1951, lists of questions on mathematics enrollments, general mathematics, and third-year mathematics are repeated and a summary is made of additional replies to questions on mathematics enrollments. Special reference is made to the fact that most schools reporting had not changed mathematics requirements in 10 years. It is observed that the schools reporting show a considerably higher than average per cent of graduates entering college.

A preliminary report on replies to questions on general mathematics and third-year mathematics was made in February 1952. Replies on per cent enrollments in general mathematics in Grade IX ranged from 8 per cent to 100 per cent, although more than half reported fewer than 50 per cent in general mathematics. Early replies on third-year mathematics show it to be almost equally popular: a semester of algebra and a semester of solid geometry, a semester of algebra and a semester of trigonometry, a second year of algebra, and a year of plane geometry.

A final report on answers to all three sets of questions is given in May 1952. One hundred twenty-one schools in 31 states and Canada participated in the study. More than half of the schools reported had an enrollment over 500. The reports from more than half of the schools showed that more than 30 per cent of their graduates completed three years of mathematics in Grades IX through XII. In summary it is observed that while the sample is too small to be conclusive and that schools reporting evidence special characteristics, the data should be of at least limited value to those seeking clues to current trends in secondary-school mathematics.

MAYOR, J. R. "What Is Going on in Your School?" *Mathematics Teacher* 44: 413–14; October 1951.

A brief selection of statistics relating to mathematics enrollments is taken from the Federal Security Agency, Office of Education Statistical Circular, No. 294, National Summary of Offerings and Enrollments in High School Subjects, 1948–49. Mathematics courses from the Grade IX through calculus are included, and there are some references to other subjects such as English, social studies, and science for purpose of comparison. Comparisons of enrollments for 1948–49 with those for 1933–34 are an important part of the study.

Selected References

PART ONE

1. ARBUCKLE, DUGALD S. *Teacher Counseling*. Cambridge, Mass.: Addison-Wesley Press, 1950. 111 p.
2. BAUMGARTNER, R. A. "A Mathematics Curriculum for the Gifted." *School Science and Mathematics* 53: 207–13; March 1953.
3. BETZ, WILLIAM. *Everyday Algebra*. New York: Ginn and Co., 1949.
4. BETZ, WILLIAM. "Five Decades of Mathematical Reform—Evaluation and Challenge." *Mathematics Teacher* 43: 377–87; December 1950.
5. BRAVERMAN, B. "Mathematics in the Senior High School Differentiated According to Needs." *Mathematics Teacher* 38: 264–68; October 1945.
6. BRUECKNER, L. J. "The Social Phase of Arithmetic Instruction." *Arithmetic in General Education*. Sixteenth Yearbook. National Council of Teachers of Mathematics. 1941. p. 140–56.
7. CARPENTER, D. "Planning a Secondary Mathematics Curriculum To Meet the Needs of All Students." *Mathematics Teacher* 42: 41–48; January 1949.
8. COMMISSION ON POST-WAR PLANS. "Second Report on the Commission on Post-War Plans." *Mathematics Teacher* 38: 205–206; May 1945.
9. COMMISSION ON POST-WAR PLANS. "Guidance Report of the Commission on Post-War Plans." *Mathematics Teacher* 40: 315–39; November 1947.
10. COMMISSION ON POST-WAR PLANS. "The First Report of the Commission on Post-War Plans." *Mathematics Teacher* 37: 226–32; May 1944.
11. COMMISSION ON POST-WAR PLANS. "The Second Report of the Commission on Post-War Plans." *Mathematics Teacher* 38: 195–221; May 1945.
12. DEPARTMENT OF PUBLIC INSTRUCTION. "General Mathematics in the High School." *Mathematics Bulletin* No. 2, *Curriculum Bulletin* No. 17. Madison, Wis.: the Department, 1950.
13. EALES, JOHN R. "A Job Survey as Class Motivation in General Mathematics." *Mathematics Teacher* 43: 318–20; 1950.
14. FAWCETT, H. P. *The Nature of Proof*. Thirteenth Yearbook. Washington, D. C.: National Council of Mathematics, a department of the National Education Association, 1938.
15. GAGER, W. A. "A Functional Program for Secondary Mathematics." *Mathematics Teacher* 42: 381–85; December 1949.
16. GAGER, W. A. "A Functional Mathematics—Grade Seven Through Twelve." *Mathematics Teacher* 44: 297–301; May 1951.

17. GENERAL ELECTRIC CO. *Why Study Math?* Schenectady, N. Y.: the Company, Department of Public Relations.
18. GENERAL MOTORS CORP. *Can I Be an Engineer?* Detroit, Mich.: the Corporation, Education Section, Department of Public Relations.
19. GENERAL MOTORS CORP. *Can I Be a Craftsman?* Detroit, Mich.: the Corporation, Education Section, Department of Public Relations.
20. GRAMBS, JEAN D., and IVERSON, WILLIAM J. "Learning Activities: Community Resources." *Modern Methods in Secondary Education.* New York: William Sloan Associates, 1952.
21. HAWKINS, G. E. "Adjusting the Program in Mathematics to the Needs of Pupils." *Mathematics Teacher* 22: 38–48; January 1929.
22. HICKS, VERNON. "The Butcher, the Baker, the Candlestick Maker." *NEA Journal* 41: 397–98; October 1952.
23. HURBURT, A. S., and HOLTON, S. M. "Can Citizens Really Help in Solving Educational Problems?" *Nation Schools* 51: 73–75; 1953.
24. KENDALL, G., and OTHERS. "Community a Curriculum Resource." *Vision for Elementary School Administration.* Twenty-Fourth Yearbook. California School Administrators Association, 1952. p. 59–77.
25. KILPATRICK, W. H. "The Next Step in Methods." *Mathematics Teacher* 15: 16–25; 1922.
26. LANGFORD, F. G., and CLARK, JOHN R. *Basic Ideas in Mathematics.* New York: World Book Co., 1950.
27. LUFKIN RULE CO. *The Amazing Story of Measurement.* Saginaw, Mich.: the Company.
28. MATHEMATICS SERIES OF THE IOWA SECONDARY SCHOOL. *Co-operative Curriculum Program* 19: 12; 1949.
29. MATHEMATICS TEACHER. Entire issue of January 1953.
30. MENSENKAMP, L. E. "Ability Classification in Ninth Grade Algebra." *Mathematics Teacher* 22: 38–48; January 1929.
31. METROPOLITAN SCHOOL STUDY COUNCIL. *Fifty Teachers to a Classroom.* New York: Macmillan Co., 1950.
32. NATIONAL COUNCIL OF TEACHERS OF MATHEMATICS. *The Learning of Mathematics; Its Theory and Practice.* Twenty-First Yearbook. Washington, D. C.: the Council, a department of the National Education Association, 1953.
33. NATIONAL SCHOOL PUBLIC RELATIONS ASSOCIATION. *It Starts in the Classroom.* Washington, D. C.: the Association, a department of the National Education Association, 1952.
34. NATIONAL SOCIETY FOR THE STUDY OF EDUCATION. *The Community School.* Fifty-Second Yearbook, Part II. Chicago: the Society, 1941. p. 140–56.
35. NEW YORK STATE EDUCATION DEPARTMENT. *Mathematics for All*

High School Youth; A Report of Basic Skills Conferences in Mathematics. Albany: the Department, 1953.

36. PRICE, H. VERNON. "An Experiment in Fusing Plane and Solid Geometry." *School Science and Mathematics* 49: 199–203; March 1949.

37. REEVE, WILLIAM D. "The Place of Mathematics in Secondary Education." *School Science and Mathematics* 53: 273–85, April; 375–86, May 1953.

38. SCHLOERB, LESTER. *School Subjects and Jobs.* Chicago: Science Research Associates, 1951.

39. SIMS, WELDON, and OLIVER, ALBERT. "The Laboratory Approach to Mathematics." *School Science and Mathematics* 50: 621–27; November 1950.

40. STANDING COMMITTEE ON MATHEMATICS OF NEW YORK CITY. "Concerning the Teaching of Second-Track Mathematics." *Mathematics Teacher* 44: 537–49; December 1951.

41. UNITED STATES STEEL CORP. *Joe—The Genie of Steel.* Kansas City, Kans.: the Corporation, Director of Public Relations.

42. WELCHONS, ALVIN M., and KRICHENBERGER, W. R. *Algebra, Book Two.* New York: Ginn and Co., 1949.

43. WICHITA PUBLIC SCHOOLS. *A Look Around Wichita at the Use of Mathematics in Homes, Business, and Industry.* Wichita, Kans.: compiled by students of Wichita secondary schools, 1951.

44. WITTICH, W. A. "School and Community Look at the Content of Consumer Mathematics." *Mathematics Teacher* 36: 106–108; 1943.

PART TWO

1. ABBOTT, WALDO. *Handbook of Broadcasting.* Third edition. New York: McGraw-Hill Book Co., 1950.

2. ADAMS, R. G. and CO. *Development of Radio Education Policies in American Public School Systems.* Edinboro, Pa.: Edinboro Educational Press, 1939.

3. ANDERSON, GEORGE R. "Teaching the Slide Rule via Television." *Mathematics Teacher* 43: 272–74; October 1950.

4. ASSOCIATION OF TEACHERS OF MATHEMATICS OF NEW YORK CITY. *Radio Talks on Mathematics.* the Association, Publications Committee, 1941.

5. ATKINSON, CARROLL. *Development of Radio Education Policies in American Public School Systems.* Edinboro, Pa.: Edinboro Educational Press, 1939.

6. AYRE, H. G. "Our Mathematical Universe." *Mathematics Teacher* 32: 356–59; June 1939.

7. BELL, KATE. "The Making and Using of Slides for the Teaching of Mathematics." *Multi-Sensory Aids in the Teaching of Mathematics.*

Eighteenth Yearbook. Washington, D. C.: National Council of Teachers of Mathematics, a department of the National Education Association, 1945, p. 289–93.

8. BRODERICK, GERTRUDE. *Radio and Television Bibliography.* Bulletins 1952, Nos. 18, 204. U. S. Office of Education, Federal Security Agency, Washington, D. C.: Superintendent of Documents, Government Printing Office. 20¢.

9. BROWN, C. H. *The Teaching of Secondary Mathematics.* New York: Harper and Brothers, 1953. p. 310–11.

10. DALE, EDGAR. *Audio-Visual Methods in Teaching.* New York: The Dryden Press, 1946. p. 219–301.

11. DENT, ELLSWORTH. *The Audio-Visual Handbook.* Sixth edition. Chicago: Society for Visual Education, 1949. p. 49–101.

12. ENGLE, T. L. "Some Suggestions for Using Amateur Photography in Mathematics Courses." *School Science and Mathematics* 33: 506–10; May 1933.

13. HAMILTON, G. E. *How to Make Handmade Lantern Slides.* Meadville, Pa.: The Keystone View Co., 1952. 24 p.

14. HARRELL, FRIEDA S. "Inexpensive Slides for Daylight Projection." *Multi-Sensory Aids in the Teaching of Mathematics.* Eighteenth Yearbook. Washington, D. C.: National Council of Teachers of Mathematics, a department of the National Education Association, 1945. p. 294–303.

15. HOBAN, C. F.; HOBAN, C. F., JR.; and ZISMAN, S. B. *Visualizing the Curriculum.* New York: The Dryden Press, 1946. p. 157–91.

16. INFELD, LEOPOLD. "The Fourth Dimension and Relativity." *Scripta Mathematica* 7: 79–85: May 1938.

17. JANES, W. C. "On the Measurement of Angles." *Mathematics Teacher* 40: 30–32; January 1947.

18. KINNEY, L. B., and PURDY, C. R. *Teaching Mathematics in the Secondary School.* New York: Rinehart and Co., 1952. p. 290–303.

19. LEVENSON, WILLIAM B., and STASHEFF, EDWARD. *Teaching Through Radio.* New York: Farrar and Rinehart, 1945. 61 p.

20. MCKOWN, H. C., and ROBERTS, A. B. *Audio-Visual Aids to Instruction.* Revised edition. New York: McGraw-Hill Book Co., 1949. p. 159–94.

21. NATIONAL SOCIETY FOR STUDY OF EDUCATION. *The Teaching of Arithmetic.* The Fiftieth Yearbook, Part II, Chapter 9. Chicago: University of Chicago Press, 1951.

22. PAULU, BURTON. *Radio-Television Bibliography.* Urbana, Ill. National Association of Educational Broadcasters. $2.

23. POOLE, LYNN. *Science via Television.* Baltimore: Johns Hopkins University Press, 1950.

24. WEAVER, G. G., and BOLLINGER, E. W. *Visual Aids, Their Construction and Use.* D. Van Nostrand Co., 1949. p. 179–206.

25. WITTICH, W. A., and SCHULLER, C. F. *Audio-Visual Materials, Their Nature and Use.* New York: Harper and Brothers, 1953. p. 330–48.

RADIO

26. ANDERSON, H. A. "Efforts To Harness the New Media." *School Review* 58: 315–17; September 1950.
27. ANDERSON, RONALD L. "New Audio Aid to Education." *Audio-Visual Guide* 18: 7–10; January 1952.
28. BENDER, WILLIAM JR. "Educational Radio: An Uphill Fight." *Adult Education Journal* 9: 23–26; January 1950.
29. BRODERICK, GERTRUDE G. *Radio Script Catalogue.* U. S. Office of Education, Federal Security Agency, Washington, D. C.: Superintendent of Documents, Government Printing Office. (List of more than 1300 radio scripts available for free loan.)
30. CLEVELAND PUBLIC SCHOOLS. "Classroom Teachers Guide for Radio Lessons." Arithmetic Packet V, Item 5; September 1951.
31. CORWITH, DORIS. "Radio as an Educational Medium." *Educational Record* 33: 24–29; January 1952.
32. DAY, M. M. "Small Schools Can Now Afford To Operate Radio Stations." *Nations Schools* 48: 80–86; September 1951.
33. FISHER, STERLING W. "Credit Courses on the Air." *Education* 70: 225–27; December 1949.
34. FOSTER, EUGENE S. "Empire State FM School of the Air; Progress Report." *New York State Education* 36: 576–78; April 1949.
35. GRIME, H. E. "Mathematics by Radio: Teaching Aid for Cleveland Classrooms." *Clearing House* 25: 137–39; November 1950.
36. HILLS, L., and SULLIVAN, T. *Facsimile.* New York: McGraw-Hill Book Co., 1949.
37. LATHAM, G. "Radio Brings the School Closer to the Community." *California Journal of Elementary Education* 19: 212–20; May 1951.
38. MALANSON, W. "FM: Low Power, Low Cost; New 10-Mile Voice for the Schools." *Scholastic Teacher Monthly* 56: 13T, 23T; February 1950.
39. MCGILVREY, M. J. "Radio and the Schools, Achievement and Challenge." *Association for Education by Radio Journal.* February 1949.
40. NOVOTNY, LILLIAN E. "Education and the Mass Media of Communication—Radio." *Elementary English* 27: 240–46; April 1950.
41. SCOTT, J. A. "Twelve Guides for School Radio Programs." *Clearing House* 23: 367–68; February 1949.
42. SWICK, W. A. JR. "Empire State FM School of the Air." *Educational Screen* 29: 158–60; April 1950.
43. TEMPLE, W. J. "Our 121 Educational Stations." *Scholastic Teacher Monthly* 58: 22T; May 1951.
44. ZWEMER, R. L. "New Device for Document Transmission." *Library Journal.* February 1951.

TELEVISION

45. ANDERSON, G. R. "Teaching the Slide Rule via Television." *Mathematics* 43: 272–74; October 1950.

46. ANONYMOUS. *Educational Television.* Washington, D. C.: National Citizens Committee for Educational Television, Ring Building.

47. ANONYMOUS. "Credit Courses by Television." *Higher Education* 8: 33–34; October 1951.

48. BARTLETT, KENNETH G. "Television at Syracuse University." *Education on the Air.* Twenty-First Yearbook. Columbus: Institute for Education by Radio and Television, Ohio State University, 1951.

49. BORDONARO, J. F. "Teaching Science Through Television." *School Science and Mathematics* 52: 344; May 1952.

50. DAVIS, S. W. "Adult Education Telecasts in Baltimore." *Adult Education* 2: 24; October 1951.

51. DUNHAM, FRANKLIN. "Education Prepares to Use Television." *School and Society* 76: 374–76; December 13, 1952.

52. GABLE, MARTHA A. "Philadelphia's Classroom Television." *Journal of Education* 134: 50–52; February 1951.

53. GABLE, MARTHA A. "Television in the Philadelphia Schools." *Instructor* 61: 41; September 1951.

54. HOYER, LOUIS P. "Television in the Schools." *Education on the Air.* Twentieth Yearbook. Columbus: Institute for Education by Radio and Television, Ohio State University, 1950.

55. HULL, RICHARD B. "First Educational Television Station Service the Community." *Higher Education* 7: 180–81; April 1951.

56. LEVENSON, W. B. and STASHEFF, E. *Teaching Through Radio and Television.* New York: Rinehart and Co., 1952.

57. NEWSOM, CARROLL V. *A Television Policy for Education.* Washington, D. C.: American Council on Education, 1952.

58. PATRIDGE, HELEN F. "Schools at Work on Television." *New York State Education* 39: 510–13; April 1952.

59. PITTSBURGH BOARD OF PUBLIC EDUCATION. *Television and Education.* Pittsburgh: the Board, Division of Curriculum Development and Research, 1951.

60. PROBST, GEORGE E. "1953: The Year of Decision in Educational Television." Reprinted from the *University of Chicago Magazine* by the Joint Committee on Educational Television, Washington D. C.: the Committee, 1953.

61. ROCK, R. T.; DUVA, J. S.; and MURRAY, J. E. "Training by Television— The Comparative Effectiveness of Instruction by Television, Television Recordings, and Conventional Classroom Procedures." Office of Naval Research, SDC Report 476–02–2, Special Devices Center, Port Washington, New York.

62. ROCK, R. T.; DUVA, J. S.; and MURRAY, J. E. "Training by Television—

a Study in Learning and Retention." Office of Naval Research, SDC Report 476–02–3, Special Devices Center, Port Washington, New York.

63. SOOP, E. J. "University of Michigan Television Hour." *Adult Education* 2: 113–16; Fall 1952.

64. STEDLER, DICK. "Education and Television Team-up in Buffalo." *School Executive* 71: 54–56; November 1951.

65. TAYLOR, TELFORD. "Television as an Educational Medium." *Educational Record* 33: 30–34; January 1952.

66. U.S. OFFICE OF EDUCATION, FEDERAL SECURITY AGENCY. "Teaching with Radio, Audio Recording, and Television." Joint Committee of the U.S. Office of Education and the Radio Manufacturers Association. Washington, D.C.: Superintendent of Documents, Government Printing Office.

67. U.S. OFFICE OF EDUCATION, FEDERAL SECURITY AGENCY. "Television in Our Schools." Bulletin 1952, No. 16. Washington, D.C.: Superintendent of Documents, Government Printing Office. 15¢.

PART THREE

1. AMERICAN ASSOCIATION OF TEACHERS COLLEGES. *School and Community Laboratory Experiences in Teacher Education.* Oneonta, New York: American Association of Teachers Colleges, 1948. 7 p.

2. BADANES, SAUL. *New Foundations for the More Efficient Learning and Teaching Primary Number.* New York: Continental Printing Co., 1935. 30 p. Out of print.

3. BADANES, SAUL. *The Falsity of the Grube Method of Teaching Primary Arithmetic.* New York: New York University, 1895. 47 p. (Doctor's thesis, New York University, 1895.)

4. BARTH, MARK. *Remedial Arithmetic: Manual for Teachers of Classes and Groups.* New York: Board of Education, New York City, 1940.

5. BARTH, MARK. *Practice Units and Special Diagnostic Tests for Units 1–94 in Remedial Arithmetic.* New York: Board of Education, New York City, 1940.

6. BELL, ERIC TEMPLE. *Mathematics, Queen and Servant of Science.* Toronto: McGraw-Hill Book Co. of Canada, 1951. 437 p.

7. BOARD OF EDUCATION OF THE CITY OF NEW YORK. *New York Inventory of Mathematical Concepts.* New York: Bureau of Educational Research.

8. BOYER, LEE EMERSON. "Improve the Performance of all in Mathematics." *Teacher Education Journal* 6: 101–103+; December 1944.

9. BOYER, LEE EMERSON. *College General Mathematics for Prospective Secondary School Teachers.* State College, Pa.: School of Education, 1939.

10. BRESLICH, E. R. "Curriculum Trends in High School Mathematics." *Mathematics Teacher* 41: 63; February 1948.
11. CURRICULUM SERIES. *Curriculum Development in the Elementary Schools.* Curriculum Bulletin No. 1, 1945–46. 219 p.
12. CURRICULUM SERIES. *Arithmetic: Kindergarten–Grade Three.* Curriculum Bulletin No. 2, 1947–48. 74 p.
13. CURRICULUM SERIES. *Course of Study in Mathematics.* Grades K–VI. Curriculum Bulletin, 1951.
14. DEPARTMENT OF PUBLIC INSTRUCTION. *A Course of Study in Mathematics for Secondary Schools.* Harrisburg, Pa.: Commonwealth of Pennsylvania, Department of Public Instruction, 1952.
15. FAWCETT, H. P. "The Training of Mathematics Teachers." *Educational Research Bulletin* 26: 85–95; April 16, 1947.
16. FEHR, HOWARD F. "The Place of Multi-sensory Aids in the Teacher Training Program." *Mathematics Teacher* 40: 212–16; May 1947.
17. GROSSNICKLE, FOSTER E. "The Training of Teachers of Arithmetic." *The Teaching of Arithmetic.* Fiftieth Yearbook, Part II. Chapter XI. Chicago: Society for the Study of Education, University of Chicago Press, 1951. 209 p.
18. HARDGROVE, CLARENCE ETHEL. "Exploring the Use of Professional Laboratory Experiences in a Special Methods Course in the Professional Education of Mathematics Teachers." Ohio State University, 1950. (Unpublished doctoral dissertation. Ohio State University 1950.)
19. KEPPERS, GEORGE L., and CHAPDELAINE, PERRY A. "The Slide Rule Made Meaningful." *Mathematics Teacher* 44: 392–94; October 1951.
20. LAZAR, MAY. *Diagnostic and Remedial Work in Arithmetic Fundamentals for Intermediate Grades.* Publication No. 21. New York: Bureau of Reference, Research, and Statistics. Board of Education, New York City, 1928. 203 p.
21. NEWSOM, CARROLL V. "Mathematical Background Needed by Teachers of Arithmetic." *Teaching of Arithmetic.* Fiftieth Yearbook, Part II. Chicago: University of Chicago Press, 1951. p. 232–50.
22. TRIMBLE H. C.; BOLSER, F. C.; and WADE, T. L. JR. *Basic Mathematics for General Education.* New York: Prentice-Hall, 1950.
23. TRIMBLE, H. C.; BOLSER, F. C.; and WADE, T. L. JR. *An Introduction to Mathematics for Teachers.* New York: Henry Holt and Co., 1950.

PART FOUR

1. BANK OF AMERICA. *Basic Facts About the Market Served by the Bank of America.* San Francisco, Calif.
2. BAKST, A. *Approximate Computation.* Twelfth Yearbook. Washington, D. C.: National Council of Teachers of Mathematics, a department of the National Education Association, 1937.

3. BEATLEY, RALPH. "Third Report of the Committee on Geometry." *Mathematics Teacher* 28: 329–79, 401–50; March 1935.

4. BETZ, WILLIAM. *The Teaching of Direct Measurement in the Junior High School.* Third Yearbook. Chapter XI. Washington, D. C.: National Council of Teachers of Mathematics, a department of the National Education Association, 1928.

5. BETZ, WILLIAM. "The Present Situation in Secondary Mathematics with Particular Reference to the New National Reports on the Place of Mathematics in Education." *Mathematics Teacher* 33: 339–60; December 1940.

6. BETZ, WILLIAM. "The Transfer of Training with Particular Emphasis to Geometry." Fifth Yearbook. *Teaching of Geometry.* Washington, D. C.: National Council of Teachers of Mathematics, a department of the National Education Association, 1930. p. 167.

7. BOND, E. A. "Significant Digits in Computation with Approximate Numbers." *Mathematics Teacher* 24: 208–12; April 1931.

8. BOYCE, G. A., and BEATTY, W. W. "Six Issues in Secondary Mathematics." *Clearing House* 11: 102–107; October 1936.

9. BOYER, LEE EMERSON. "Elementary Approximate Computation." *Mathematics Teacher* 32: 249–53; October 1939.

10. BRESLICH, E. R. "Some Proposals Regarding the Preparation for Teaching High School Mathematics." *Mathematics Teacher* 39: 200–203; May 1946.

11. BRUECKNER, L. J., and GROSSNICKLE, F. E. *How To Make Arithmetic Meaningful.* Philadelphia: John C. Winston Co., 1947.

12. BUTLER, C. H., and WREN, F. L. *The Meaning of Secondary Mathematics.* New York: McGraw-Hill Book Co., 1951. p. 279–89.

13. COMMITTEE ON THE FUNCTION OF MATHEMATICS. "A Report of its Committee on the Function of Mathematics in General Education for the Commission on Secondary School Curriculum of the Progressive Education Association." New York: Appleton-Century-Crofts, 1940. p. xiv, 423.

14. CULLMORE, O. R. *The Use of the Slide Rule.* Hoboken, N. J.: Keuffel and Esser Co., 1925.

15. DODGE, H. F., and ROMIG, H. G. *Sampling Inspection Tables; Single and Double Sampling.* New York: John Wiley and Sons, 1944. 106 p.

16. DOUGLASS, HARL R. "Two Important Deliberative Reports Concerned with Mathematics in the Schools." *Mathematics Teacher* 33: 361–66; December 1940.

17. FAWCETT, H. P. *The Nature of Proof.* Thirteenth Yearbook. Washington, D. C.: National Council of Teachers of Mathematics, a department of the National Education Association, 1938.

18. FISHER, R. A. *Design of Experiments.* New York: Clarke-Irwin, 1949.

19. FREEMAN, FRANK N. "Teaching Mathematics for the Million." *California Journal of Secondary Education* 19: 246–54; May 1944.

20. GADSKE, RICHARD EDWARD. "Demonstrative Geometry as a Means for Improving Critical Thinking." 1940. (Unpublished doctor's thesis, Northwestern University.)
21. GAGER, WILLIAM A. "Computations with Approximate Numbers." *School Science and Mathematics* 47: 424–41; May 1947.
22. GRANT, EUGENE LODEWICK. *Statistical Quality Control.* New York: McGraw-Hill Book Co., 1946. 563 p.
23. HUNT, HEROLD. "Mathematics—Its Role Today." *Mathematics Teacher* 43: 313–17; November 1950.
24. JUDD, CHARLES H. "The Relation of Special Training to General Intelligence." *Educational Review* 36: 28–42; 1908.
25. JUDD, CHARLES H. *Psychology of Secondary Education.* Boston: Ginn and Co., 1927.
26. KINNEY, LUCIEN B. "The Reorganization of Mathematics for the Emergency." *Mathematics Teacher* 36: 3–10; January 1943.
27. KOKOMOOR, F. W. *Mathematics in Human Affairs.* New York: Prentice-Hall, 1949. p. 54–59.
28. KRAMER, E. E. *Mainstream of Mathematics.* Chapter VIII. Toronto: Oxford University Press, 1951.
29. MCCORMICK, CLARENCE. *The Teaching of General Mathematics in the Secondary Schools of the United States,* Contributions to Education, No. 386. New York: Bureau of Publications, Teachers College, Columbia University, 1929.
30. MOORE, ELIAKIM HASTINGS. "On the Foundations of Mathematics." *Science* 17: 401–16; March 1903. Reprinted in *A General Survey of Progress in the Last Twenty-Five Years.* First Yearbook. Washington, D. C.: National Council of Teachers of Mathematics, a department of the National Education Association, 1926.
31. NATIONAL COMMITTEE ON MATHEMATICAL REQUIREMENTS. "Reorganization of Mathematics in Secondary Education." A report by the National Committee on Mathematical Requirements of Mathematical Association of America, the Association, 1923. p. x, 652.
32. NATIONAL COMMITTEE ON MATHEMATICAL REQUIREMENTS. "Reorganization of Mathematics in Secondary Education." A Report by the National Committee on Mathematical Requirements of Mathematical Association of America, the Association, 1923. p. 95.
33. NATIONAL COUNCIL OF TEACHERS OF MATHEMATICS. *Place of Mathematics in Secondary Education.* Fifteenth Yearbook. Washington, D. C.: National Council of Teachers of Mathematics, a department of the National Education Association, 1940. p. vi, 253.
34. NATIONAL EDUCATION ASSOCIATION. "Junior High School Mathematics." *Junior High School Curriculum.* Fifth Yearbook. Washington, D. C.: Department of Superintendents, 1927.

35. NATIONAL EDUCATION ASSOCIATION. *Report of the Committee of Ten on Secondary School Studies.* New York: American Book Co., 1894. p. xii, 249.

36. NATIONAL EDUCATION ASSOCIATION RESEARCH DIVISION. "Population Trends and Their Educational Implications." *Research Bulletin* 16: 5–58; January 1938.

37. NATIONAL EDUCATION ASSOCIATION RESEARCH DIVISION. "Schools and the 1940 Census." *Research Bulletin* 19: 205–31; November 1941.

38. NEYMANN, JERZY. *First Course in Probability and Statistics.* Chapter I. New York: Henry Holt and Co., 1950. 350 p.

39. PEASE, E. M. J., and WADSWORTH, C. P. *Engineering Trigonometry.* Scranton, Pa.; International Textbook Co., 1946. p. 214–255.

40. PERRY, JOHN, editor. *Discussion on the Teaching of Mathematics.* New York: The Macmillan Co., 1901. p. ix, 101. (A report of a meeting of the British Association at Glasgow.)

41. REEVE, WILLIAM DAVID. "The Case for General Mathematics." *Mathematics Teacher* 15: 381–91; November 1922.

42. REEVE, WILLIAM DAVID. "Attacks on Mathematics and How To Meet Them." *Mathematics in Modern Life.* Eleventh Yearbook. Washington, D. C.: National Council of Teachers of Mathematics, a department of the National Education Association, 1936.

43. REICHENBACH, HANS. *Experience and Prediction; An Analysis of the Foundations and Structure of Knowledge.* Chicago: University of Chicago Press, 1938. 410 p.

44. REPORT OF COMMISSION ON POST-WAR PLANS. "Guidance Report of the Commission on Post-War Plans." *Mathematics Teacher* 40: 315–19; November 1947.

45. ROSSKOPF, M. F.; ATEN, H. D.; and REEVE, W. D. *Mathematics, A Second Course.* New York: McGraw-Hill Book Co., 1951.

46. ROSSKOPF, MYRON F. "Transfer of Training." *The Learning of Mathematics, Its Theory and Practice.* Twenty-First Yearbook. Washington 6, D. C.: National Council of Mathematics, a department of the National Education Association, 1953. p. 205–27.

47. SCHORLING, R. "The Place of Mathematics in General Education." *School Science and Mathematics* 15: 14–26; January 1940.

48. SHUSTER, CARL N. "Computation with Approximate Data." *Metric System of Weights and Measures.* Twentieth Yearbook. Washington, D. C.: National Council of Teachers of Mathematics, a department of the National Education Association, 1952. p. 238–259.

49. SMITH, DAVID EUGENE. *A General Survey of Progress of Mathematics in our High Schools in the Last Twenty-Five Years.* First Yearbook. Washington, D. C.: National Council of Teachers of Mathematics, a department of the National Education Association, 1926. p. 1–31.

50. SMITH, D. E., and REEVE, WILLIAM DAVID. *Teaching of Junior High School Mathematics*. New York: Ginn and Co., 1927. p. 99.
51. TATE, M. W. "Notes on Approximate Computation." *School Science and Mathematics* 44: 425–30; May 1944.
52. THORNDIKE, E. L., and WOODWORTH, R. S. "Influence of Improvement in One Mental Function upon the Efficiency of Other Functions." *Psychological Review* 8: 247–61; June 1901.
53. ULMER, GILBERT. "Teaching Geometry To Cultivate Reflective Thinking: An Experimental Study with 1239 High School Pupils." *Journal of Experimental Education* 8: 18–25; September 1939.
54. ULMER, GILBERT. *Some Suggestions for Teaching Geometry To Develop Clear Thinking*. Kansas Studies in Education, Vol. 2, No. 7. Lawrence: University of Kansas Publications, 1942. p. 1–42.
55. UPTON, CLIFFORD BREWSTER. *The Use of Indirect Proof in Geometry and in Life*. Fifth Yearbook. Washington, D. C.: National Council of Teachers of Mathematics, a department of the National Education Association, 1930, p. 131.
56. UPTON, CLIFFORD BREWSTER. "The Influence of Standard Tests on the Curriculum in Arithmetic." *Mathematics Teacher* 18: 191–208; April 1925.
57. WALKER, HELEN M. *Elementary Statistical Methods*. New York: Henry Holt and Co., 1943. p. 11–21.
58. WHEELER, R. H. "The New Psychology of Learning." *Teaching of Arithmetic*. Tenth Yearbook. Washington, D. C.: National Council of Teachers of Mathematics, a department of the National Education Association, 1935. 239 p.
59. WILLIAMS, DONALD C. *Ground of Induction*. Cambridge, Mass.: Harvard University Press, 1947. 213 p.

PART FIVE

1. BELL, ERIC TEMPLE. *Search for Truth*. Baltimore: Williams and Wilkins Publishing Co., 1934.
2. BRAGDON, CLAUDE. *The Frozen Fountain*. New York: Alfred A. Knopf, 1932.
3. BRITISH REPORT. *The Teaching of Algebra*. New York: Alfred A. Knopf, 1932.
4. BROWNELL, W. A., and GROSSNICKLE, FOSTER E. "The Interpretation of Research." *Arithmetic in General Education*. Sixteenth Yearbook. Washington, D. C.: National Council of Teachers of Mathematics, a department of the National Education Association, 1941.
5. BROWNELL, W. A. "How Children Learn Information, Concepts, and Generalization." *Learning and Instruction*. Forty-Ninth Yearbook, Part I. Chicago: National Society for the Study of Education. University of Chicago Press, 1950. p. 92–128.
6. DARWIN, CHARLES. *Origin of Species*. New York: Appleton-Century-Crofts, 1926.

7. FAWCETT, HAROLD P. *The Nature of Proof.* Thirteenth Yearbook. Washington, D. C.: National Council of Teachers of Mathematics, a department of the National Education Association, 1941.

8. GADSKE, RICHARD EDWARD. *Demonstrative Geometry as a Means for Improving Critical Thinking,* 1940. (Unpublished Doctor's Thesis, Northwestern University.)

9. GHYKA, MATILA. *The Geometry of Art and Life.* New York: Sheed and Ward, 1946.

10. GLENNON, VINCENT J. "Testing Meanings in Arithmetic." *Arithmetic 1949.* Supplementary Educational Monograph, No. 70. Chicago: University of Chicago Press. November 1949. p. 64–74.

11. GREVER, L. W. *Evaluating Critical Thinking.* Normal, Ill.: Illinois State Normal University, 1952. (Unpublished master's thesis, Illinois State Normal University, 1952.)

12. HARDING, LOWRY W. *Functional Arithmetic: Photographic Interpretations.* Dubuque, Iowa: William C. Brown Co., 1952.

13. HENDRIX, GERTRUDE. "Prerequisite to Meaning." *Mathematics Teacher* 43: 334–39; November 1950.

14. INGE, WILLIAM RALPH. *God and the Astronomers.* London: Longmans, Green and Co., 1933.

15. LEWIS, HARRY. *An Experiment in Developing Critical Thinking Through the Teaching of Plane Demonstrative Geometry.* New York: New York University, 1950. (Doctor's dissertation.)

16. MANDER, A. E. *Clearer Thinking: Logic for Everyman.* New York: Franklin Watts, 1936.

17. MURPHY, GARDNER. *Personality—A Biosocial Approach to Origins and Structure.* New York: Harper and Brothers, 1948.

18. NATIONAL COUNCIL OF TEACHERS OF MATHEMATICS. *Mathematics in Modern Education.* Eleventh Yearbook. Washington, D. C.: National Council of Teachers of Mathematics, a department of the National Education Association, 1936.

19. NATIONAL SOCIETY FOR THE STUDY OF EDUCATION. *The Measurement of Understanding.* Forty-Fifth Yearbook, Part I. Chicago: National Society for the Study of Education, 1946. p. 138–57.

20. NUNN, T. P. *The Teaching of Algebra (Including Trigonometry).* New York: Longmans, Green and Co., 1914.

21. PROGRESSIVE EDUCATION ASSOCIATION. "Aspects of Thinking." *Appraising and Recording Student Progress.* Chapter II. New York: Harper and Brothers, 1942.

22. ROSSKOPF, M. F. "The Present State of Evaluation of Critical Thinking in Algebra and Geometry." *Mathematics Teacher* 43: 143–48; April 1950.

23. SAYERS, E. V. *An Introduction to Philosophy of Education.* New York: Henry Holt and Co., 1952.

24. SCHILLINGER, JOSEPH. *The Mathematical Basis of the Arts.* New York: Philosophical Library, 1948.

25. SPITZER, HERBERT F. "Testing Instruments and Practices in Relation to Present Concepts of Teaching Arithmetic." *The Teaching of Arithmetic.* Fiftieth Yearbook, Part II. National Society for the Study of Education, 1951. p. 186–202.
26. SUELTZ, BEN. "The Measurement of Understanding and Judgments in Elementary Mathematics." *Mathematics Teacher* 40: 279; October 1947.
27. THOMPSON, D'ARCY. *Growth and Form.* New York: Cambridge University Press, 1952.
28. ULLSVIK, BJARNE R. "An Attempt to Measure Critical Judgment." *School Science and Mathematics* 59: 445–52; June 1949.
29. ULMER, GILBERT. "Teaching Geometry To Cultivate Reflective Thinking." *Journal of Experimental Education* 8: 18–25; September 1939.
30. VAN ENGEN, HENRY. "The Formation of Concepts." *The Learning of Mathematics.* Twenty-First Yearbook. Washington, D.C.: National Council of Teachers of Mathematics, a department of the National Education Association, 1953. p. 70–77.
31. WEYL, HERMAN. *Symmetry.* Princeton, N. J.: Princeton University Press, 1953.